Signpost

SELECTED PREMIER HOTELS
and ACCOMMODATION
in Great Britain and Ireland

1999

PRIOR
PUBLICATIONS LT

D1413741

ISBN **1 871985 28 5**

Publisher: Malcolm Orr-Ewing; **Cartographer**: Neil ffrench-Blake
© Priory Publications Ltd 1998

Printed by Ebenezer Baylis & Son Ltd, London Road, Worcester WR5 2JH.
Published by Priory Publications Ltd, Syresham, Brackley, Northants NN13 5HH.
Tel: 01280 850603; Fax: 01280 850576

Trade distribution in UK by W Foulsham & Co Ltd
The Publishing House, Bennetts Close.
Cippenham, Berks SL1 5AP
Telephone: 01753 526769; Fax: 01753 535003

Signpost is published in the USA under the title *Premier Hotels of Great Britain & Ireland*

Signpost, with on-line booking service, is now available electronically
on the Internet under the web site:
http://www.SIGNPOST.co.uk

Front Cover: Fawsley Hall Hotel, Nr Daventry, Northamptonshire;
Title Page: Old Government House, St Peter Port,Guernsey, Channel Islands;
Rear Cover (top): Hotel Europe, Killarney, Ireland.

ii

Contents

The regions

KERRY

Map of the regions

1. CITY OF DUNDEE
2. CLACKMANNANSHIRE
3. FALKIRK
4. EAST DUNBARTONSHIRE
5. WEST DUNBARTONSHIRE
6. INVERCLYDE
7. RENFREWSHIRE
8. CITY OF GLASGOW
9. NORTH LANARKSHIRE
10. WEST LOTHIAN
11. CITY OF EDINBURGH
12. MIDLOTHIAN
13. EAST RENFREWSHIRE
14. STOCKTON-ON-TEES
15. MIDDLESBROUGH
16. HARTLEPOOL
17. REDCAR & CLEVELAND
18. NORTH LINCOLNSHIRE
19. CITY OF KINGSTON UPON HULL
20. NORTH EAST LINCOLNSHIRE
21. ABERCONWY & COLWYN
22. DENBIGHSHIRE
23. FLINTSHIRE
24. WREXHAM
25. CITY OF STOKE-ON-TRENT
26. CITY OF DERBY
27. CITY OF LEICESTER
28. LUTON
29. SWANSEA
30. NEATH & PORT TALBOT
31. RHONDDA CYNON TAFF
32. MERTHYR TYDFIL
33. BLAENAU GWENT
34. TORFAEN
35. MONMOUTHSHIRE
36. BRIDGEND
37. VALE OF GLAMORGAN
38. CARDIFF
39. CAERPHILLY
40. NEWPORT
41. NORTH WEST SOMERSET
42. CITY OF BRISTOL
43. SOUTH GLOUCESTERSHIRE
44. BATH & NORTH EAST SOMERSET
45. SWINDON
46. POOLE
47. BOURNEMOUTH
48. SOUTHAMPTON
49. PORTSMOUTH
50. BRIGHTON & HOVE

Welcome to the 60th edition of **Signpost** - *the definitive guide to 220 of the finest hotels in Great Britain and Ireland.*

Our inspectors have checked every single hotel personally, and we believe our standards are second to none. Motoring conditions may have changed since the founder of *Signpost* first took to the road, but inspectors' standards are still the same: individual style, value for money, friendly service and a personal welcome.

Signpost founder, Gordon 'Mac' McMinnies, late grandfather of the present publisher, leaving Sheffield for the English Six Days Hill Climb in March 1913.

The Signpost sign. Your guarantee of a top quality hotel.

So whether you're looking for a quiet weekend away, or a two-week family holiday, *Signpost* has a wide variety of hotels to choose from - magnificent country hotels set in beautiful grounds, small hotels with log fires and cosy bedrooms deep in the heart of quiet country villages, as well as modern city hotels with full leisure and business facilities.

London Inspector Alistair Hankey with Valerie Gilliatt outside the Pembridge Court Hotel, London W2.

Scottish Inspector Bill Smith (right) with James Lerche of Macdonald Hotels.

Somerset Inspector Bill Wright (right) with David Ireland, Manager, outside Dukes Hotel, Bath.

Signpost -*The first edition in 1935*

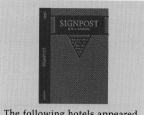

Reproduced from original 1930's drawings by the founder of Signpost,
W.G. McMinnies A.F.C. B.A. Oxon.

So what else was going on in 1935?

There was a drought lasting 22 days and for the fourth consecutive year, the maximum temperature exceeded 90°. Quite a contrast with 1998!

It was the year of King George V's Silver Jubilee. The bank rate stood at 2% and the Archbishops' Commission on the Ministry of Women declared that there was no place for women in the priesthood.

It was announced that London's first television station was to be built at Alexandra Palace and a committee was set up to study the problems raised by television. There was a cinema seat for one out of every twelve people in the UK and attendance was nearly 22 visits a a year for every man, woman and child in the country.

80% of cinema -goers paid less that five pence to see two full length movies.

1935 saw the opening of Imperial Airways (the forerunner of British Airways) regular service to Australia. In those days the journey took 12 days.!

Britain prospered in the field of sport. Fred Perry retained his Wimbledon tennis title and Great Britain retained the Davis Cup; Golden Miller won the Cheltenham Gold Cup for the fourth time and Sir Malcolm Campbell broke the world land speed record at 301 miles an hour.

England made the best motorcycles in 1935 and Norton won both the 500cc and 350cc events at the European Motorcycling Championships.

In colouring, furnishing and general treatment this room achieves a rare distinction.

185

The Three Swans, Market Harborough

Mr Hore-Belisha, of zebra-crossings fame, announced in 1935 a new five-year Road Plan. This included the introduction of dual carriageways, the removal of all blind corners as well as the replacement of dangerous crossroads by *roundabouts* and *flyovers*. In that year 350,000 cars were produced in the UK and British vehicles enjoyed 94% of the home market. There were no fewer than 74 different makes of private car to choose from.

It became law on 17th November 1935 that it was prohibited to drive a motor vehicle at more than 30 mph on any road in a built-up area. Secondly the secretary of the Automobile Association was reported as saying that roads would be incapable of accommodating traffic in the near future unless road construction and modernisation were speeded up. *Plus ça change…*

A glimpse of the hall, noted for its bright colouring and comfort.

Silver End Hotel, Witham, Essex.

And what of hotels in 1935? Mr McMinnies wrote in the first edition: *"Proprietors agree that good beds and good food play the most important part in an hotel's success. With good beds go woolly blankets, soft sheets and a hot bottle; a light over the bed… running water with the hotel's own special tablet of soap and a tube of toothpaste, tea and a paper in the morning, plenty of cupboard room, a ramp on which to lay your suitcase and even a footrest to help you when removing your shoes and a light over the washbasin for shaving."*

Some may disagree with the original publisher, who described his profession on his income tax return in 1935 as a 'hotel tester' and his descriptions on this page, but his conclusion then still holds good today. He wrote: *"The most successful places are those run by people with the biggest share of common sense, a passion for attention to detail and a love of continuous hard work."*

Oatlands Park Hotel, Weybridge, Surrey.

20 Miles from London, 14 miles from Guildford and 13 miles from Bagshot.
(For position see map on page 9, square C.5).

A magnificent mansion appealing to those in search of comfort, rest or recreation—Value-for-money terms include first class facilities for golf, swimming, squash rackets, tennis, dancing, boating and badminton—Grounds and gardens of great beauty and historic interest.

I AM not surprised that this splendid place, although unlicensed, is proving a tremendous success. After all it only means that you pay for your drink when ordering it, and if you're living there you have your own supply just as at home. And Oatlands is essentially a home, but a home with a variety, completeness and appeal that are unique.

If young and active the sunny swimming-pool, 9-hole golf course, squash and hard tennis courts will attract you. Near by you will find a perfect paradise for children, fitted with all kinds of games and amusements, and every now and then you'll glimpse the lake where you can laze away an idle afternoon. Inside a magnificent ballroom which can be converted into a theatre, a badminton court and a most impressive lounge hall, reminiscent of the sort of thing you meet at the famous touring hotels on the Continent, add to the varied attractions of the place.

I stayed the night at Oatlands and dined with a friend from whom I learned the things that only a resident can tell, among them the high standard, variety and tastiness of the food, the willingness and courtesy of the staff and last but not least, the value-for-money terms which include all sports.

137

Hare and Hounds, Nr. Tetbury, Glos.

ON THE TETBURY TO BATH AND BRISTOL ROAD

3 Miles from Tetbury, 19 miles from Bath, 22 miles from Bristol.
(For position see maps on pages 13, square I.8, 17, square J.2 and 18, square A.4).

A charmingly furnished and restored grey stone Cotswold house adjoining the famous Westonbirt Arboretum and Beaufort Polo Club's grounds—Squash, badminton and grass tennis courts—Six acres of pleasant grounds and gardens—A place with a welcome.

IT seems almost a pity to call this place an hotel for it's much more like the country home of a rich man with a love of luxury, sport and culture. You see these things reflected in the soft yet colourful style of furniture and pictures satisfying both mind and body. Bed and bathrooms are in their own way just as outstanding and perfectly contrived as are the downstairs rooms and of course they're equipped with every modern aid to comfort. You see them too in the provision of squash, badminton and tennis courts, in the fine recreation room and ballroom, in the perfectly kept lawns, flowerbeds and borders. And most of all in the good plain fare and hospitable atmosphere of the place which might well be run by some invisible friend of yours anxious that your stay should be pleasant and your parting a regret. From which you will gather that the Hare and Hounds is a model of what a country hotel should be. A few years ago it was an ordinary inn but since then money and brains have been lavished on it with the above result. Bed and breakfast from 9/6, lunch 3/6, dinner 5/-.

A Cotswold stone wall protects the approach to the hotel.

The original logo adopted by the founder of Signpost 60 years ago - WG 'Mac' McMinnies

Our standards

Today our inspectors still set the highest standards and expect every hotel to live up to them. We demand fine cuisine, using the best fresh produce. Bedrooms should be furnished with style and have all the comforts you

West Midlands Inspector, Tricia Doyle, (centre) with proprietors Colin and Rosemary Vaughan at the Swan Hotel, Hay-on-Wye.

need away from home. The hotel should be located in an interesting area, with plenty of opportunity for sport and leisure. Above all hotels should be welcoming, places you want to return to again and again.

Devon Inspector Olof White (right) with Ian Davies, owner of the Osborne Hotel, Torquay.

Bonus

Once again this year the majority of our approved establishments have agreed to an *extra bonus* for Signpost readers. By presenting one of the vouchers at the back of this book,

Signposters are entitled to a £5 reduction off the cost of their stay - at least the equivalent of a free bottle of wine!

Competition

In 1999 we again have a FREE weekend for two to be won. The prize is two nights bed and breakfast at a Country House Hotel. See page 291 for full details.

How to use the guide. The guide is divided into 11 regional sections.

There is a map of the regions at the beginning of the guide. If you want to look up the hotels in a particular region, simply turn to the relevant regional colour-coded section. Alternatively, turn to the colour maps starting on page 295. The numbers on the maps refer to the pages in this guide on which **Signpost** approved hotels are described

The guide is divided into 11 regions. Each region has its own selection of hotels as well as an FactFile of useful information.

Fact File

Each regional section is prefaced by an illustrated guide to places of interest, walks, and historic houses and museums in the area together with a unique diary of events that take place. All designed to give you a feel for the area.

The factfile shows you places to go, gardens open, and a diary of events that take place in the area.

Hotel entry   The hotel entries for each region follow and most hotels have a page to themselves. There is a large colour photograph of each hotel and a detailed description of all the features of the hotel -

number of bedrooms standards of comfort, cuisine, leisure and sport facilities etc. There is also a description of the location and general ambience of the hotel to give you an idea of its character. **Signpost** member hotels make an annual contribution towards the costs of our inspections and a range of member services we provide.

Each hotel has a page to itself, with a large colour photograph and full details of rooms.

Room rates

Room rates are clearly shown as well as details of any special offers for weekend breaks etc.

Single room including breakfast from £31.00
Double room including breakfast from £62.00
Leisure Breaks:
2 day breaks or longer from
£36.00 pp per night b & b;
£46.00 p.p including dinner.

Room and room rates are clearly marked as well as full details of special rates for weekend breaks etc.

How to get there

To help you find the hotel, there is an area map which shows the hotel location and the surrounding roads and motorways.

A location map shows the position of each hotel.

Listings and Maps

Page 272 Sporting and conference facilities

Page 282 Hotels listed by county

Page 293 Hotels listed alphabetically

Page 297 Map section
Maps showing the whole of the British Isles, and London street plan with locations of Signpost Selected Premier Hotels.

Internet

Reservations and enquiries can now be made directly via our INTERNET site on **http://www.signpost.co.uk.** Watch this site also for special offers from individual hotels throughout the year.

The West Country

Historical Sites & Museums

Bath & North-East Somerset
Museum of Costumes, Bath
Pump Room, Bath
Roman Baths Museum, Bath

Bristol
Bristol City Museum & Art Gallery
Harveys Wine Museum, Bristol

Cornwall
Launceston Castle
Restormel Castle, Lothwithiel
St. Catherine's Castle, Fowey
St. Mawes Castle
St. Michael's Mount, Marazion
Tintagel Castle

Devon
Buckfast Abbey, Buckfastleigh
Buckland Abbey, Yelverton
Castle Drogo, Drewsteignton, Exeter
Compton Castle, Marldon, Paignton
Dartmouth Castle
Okehampton Castle
Powderham Castle, Kenton, Nr.
 Exeter
Royal Albert Memorial Museum,
 Exeter
Watermouth Castle, Berrynarbor,
 llfracombe

Dorset
Corfe Castle
Dorset County Museum, Dorchester
Maiden Castle, Dorchester
Portland Castle
Sherborne Castle

Somerset
Cleeve Abbey, Washford, Watchet
Dunster Castle
Glastonbury Abbey
Nunney Castle
Taunton Cider Mill
Wells Cathedral

Wiltshire
Avebury Stone Circles, Nr.
 Marlborough
Great Western Railway Museum,
 Swindon
Longleat House, Warminster
Museum & Art Gallery, Swindon

Old Wardour Castle, Tisbury,
 Salisbury
Salisbury Cathedral
Stonehenge, Amesbury, Salisbury

Entertainment Venues

Bristol
Bristol Zoological Gardens

Cornwall
Cornish Seal Sanctuary, Gweek,
 Helston
Flambards Victoria Village Theme
 Park, Helston
Land's End, Penzance
Newquay Zoo
Paradise Park, Hayle
World in Miniature, Truro

Devon
City Museum & Art Gallery,
 Plymouth
Combe Martin Wildlife & Dinosaur
 Park
Dartmoor Wild Life Park & West
 Country Falconry Centre,
 Sparkwell, Plymouth
Kents Cavern Showcaves, Torquay
Paignton & Dartmouth Steam Rail
 way, Paignton
Paignton Zoological & Botanical
 Gardens
Plymouth Dome, Plymouth
Riviera Centre, Torquay
Torquay Museum

Dorset
Brownsea Island, Poole
Lyme Regis Marine Aquarium
Weymouth Sea Lite Park, Lodmoor
 Country Park, Weymouth

Somerset
Cheddar Showcaves, Cheddar
 Gorge
Haynes Motor Museum Sparkford,
 Yeovil
The Tropical Bird Gardens, Rode
West Somerset Railway, Minehead
Wookey Hole Caves & Papermill

Wiltshire
Lions of Longleat Safari Park,
 Warminster

For further information contact:

TOURIST BOARDS

**The West Country Tourist
Board.** 60 St. Davids Hill,
Exeter, Devon EX4 4SY
Tel: (01392) 76351

Southern Tourist Board
40 Chamberlayne Rd,
Eastleigh, Hampshire SO50
5JH. Tel: (01703) 620006

DIARY OF EVENTS

February

26-Mar 6. **Bath International
Literature Festival.**
Various venues, Bath

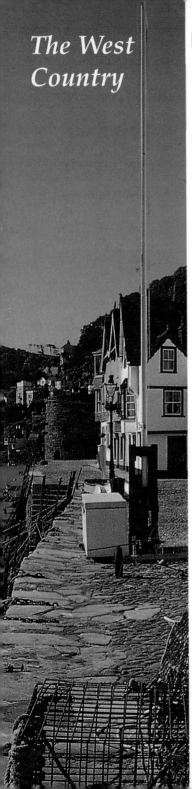

The West Country

March

1-Sept 30. **Cornwall '99.** World Watersports Festival, Various venues. Includes Cutty Sark Tall S hips Race & Int'l Sailing Championships.

April

3. **Bournemouth Easter Parade.** From Boscombe Pier to Bournemouth Pier, Dorset.
12*. Lyme Regis, Dorset. **Art Group Exhibition & Sale**

May

1. **Old Custom Hobby Horse Celebrations.** Town Centre, Padstow, Cornwall
1-4*. **The Great Cornwall Balloon Festival.** Venues in St Austell, Newquay, Cornwall. Hot air balloon festival.
1-3. **Bath** Annual Spring Flower Show.
6-9. **Badminton Horse Trials.** Badminton House, Badminton, Avon.
2-3. **South West Custom & Classic Bike Show.** Royal Bath & West Showground, Shepton Mallet, Somerset
2-3. **Weymouth International Beach Kite Festival.** Weymouth Beach, Dorset.
7-16. **Daphne du Maurier Festival of Arts & Literature.** Venues ar'd Fowey, Cornwall.
2-4. **Bath Annual Spring Flower Show.** Royal Victoria Park, Weston Lane, Bath
7*. **Helston Flora Day.** Helston, Cornwall
9-24*. **Bournemouth International Festival.** Various venues, Bouremouth, Dorset.
20-22. **Devon County Show.** 103rd Show. Westpoint Showground, Clyst St. Mary,Devon
21 May-June 6. **Bath International Music Festival.** Various venues in and around Bath, Somerset.
22 -June 5. **Salisbury Festival.**Various venues, Salisbury, Wiltshire
21-Sept 15*.**The Minack Drama Festival.**The Minack, Porthcurno, Penzance, Cornwall
22-25*. **International Festival of the Sea.** Bristol Historic Harbour, The City Centre, Bristol.

2-5. **Royal Bath & West Show.** Showground, Shepton Mallet.
4-8*. **Lamborne Folk Festival.** Lamborne Minster, Dorset.
4-8*. **Royal Cornwall Show.** Royal Cornwall Showground, Wadebridge, Cornwall
5-13*. **Ilfracombe Victorian Celebration**. Various venies.
12-18. **International Military & Veterans Festival.** Various venues, Weymouth.
12*. **Bristol to Bournemouth Vintage Vehicle Run.** Ashton Court Estate, Long Ashton, Bristol, Avon
19*. **Port of Brixham International Trawler Race & Quay Festival.** New Fish Quay, The Harbour, Brixham, Devon.
27*. **42nd Amateur Radio Rally.** Longleat, Warminster, Wilts.

July

2-18. **Exeter Festival.** Various venues, Exeter, Devon.
4-9. **Newquay 1900 Week.** Various venues, Newquay, Cornwall.
9-16. **'Ways with Words' Literature Festival.** Dartington Hall Gardens, Dartington, Devon.
17. **Yeovilton International Air Day.** RNAS Yeovilton, Ilchester, Somerset.

17. **Hearts of Fire '99 -** Christian Arts Festival. Glastonbury Abbey, Somerset.
18. **Tolpuddle Rally.** Trade Union March.
22-24. **West Wilts '99 Show.** Civic Hall & Town Park, Trowbridge, Wilts.
25-31. **Salcombe Town Regatta.** Var. Venues, Salcombe.
30-Aug 6. **Sidmouth Int'l Festival of Folk Arts.** Var. venues, Sidmouth, Devon.

August

August. **Cornish Cycle of Mystery Plays** - The Ordinalia. Piran Round, Perranporth, Cornwall.
5-7. **English National Sheepdog Championships.** Powderham Castle, Kenton, Nr. Exeter, Devon.
8-11. **RAF St Mawgan Int'l Air Day.** RAF St Mawgan, Newquay, Cornwall. International air show with flying displays, stalls, funfair, helicopters etc. Includes **Eclipse '99** on August 11th.
5*. **Bristol Balloon Fiestas Night Glow.** Ashton Court Estate, Long Ashton, Bristol.
6-8*. **Bristol International Balloon Festival.** As above.
7-8*. **Yeovil Festival of Transport.** Yeovil Showground, Yeovil, Somerset.
19-23. **Torbay Royal Regatta.** The Harbour, Torquay, Devon
26-28. **Port of Dartmouth Royal Regatta.** Various venues, Dartmouth, Devon.
28-30. **Plymouth Navy Days.** HM Naval Base, Plymouth.
28-4 Sept. **Bude Jazz Festival.** Various venues, Bude, Cornwall.

September

3-5. **National Amateur Gardening Show.** Royal Bath & West Showground, Shepton Mallet.
11. **Exeter Carnival.** Various venues, Exeter, Devon.
14. **Widecombe Fair.** Old Field, Widecombe-in-the-Moor, Devon
11-12. **Countryside Cavalcade** Royal Bath & West Showground, Shepton Mallet.

October

13*. **Tavistock Goose Fair.** Town Centre. Street stalls, fun fair, livestock market.
18. **Trafalgar Day Service.** Exeter Cathedral, Devon.
24-1 Nov. **Halloween Magic Lanterns Day.** Crealy Park, Sidmouth Rd, Clyst St Mary, Devon. Witches Halloween Party on 31 Oct. Pumpkins &c

November

4. **Bridgwater Guy Fawkes Carnival.**
6. **North Petherton Guy Fawkes Festival.**
8. **Highbridge & Burnham-on-Sea Guy Fawkes Festival.**
14. **Glastonbury Chilkwell Guy Fawkes Festival.**

December

31. Exeter Millenium Ball. University of Exeter, Devon

** denotes provisional dates.
For further information contact:*

TOURIST BOARD

The West Country Tourist Board. 60 St. Davids Hill, Exeter, Devon EX4 4SY
Tel: (01392) 276351

The West Country

England's West Country

The counties of Cornwall, Devon, Somerset, Dorset and Wiltshire comprise England's West Country, the great southwestern peninsula stretching out into the Atlantic Ocean.

The popularity of the region owes much to its geography and landscape. The coastline alone offers great variety and choice for the holiday maker. Around the coast you can also seek out the little ports and villages where visitors rub shoulders with the fishermen. If imposing scenery and bracing cliff walks are for you, then make for North **Cornwall**. The north coast is famous for its surfing beaches,

whereas the south coast has the picturesque tree-lined Helford River and its subsidiary Gillan Creek. There is the historic county town of Bodmin, the cathedral city of Truro and Launceston, once the ancient capital of Cornwall.

Plymouth, the largest city in **Devon**, is a happy blend of holiday resort, tourist centre, historic and modern city. The famous Hoe has its associations with Sir Francis Drake

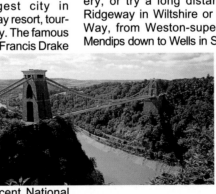

and the Barbican with the Pilgrim Fathers. Exeter is the cultural capital of the county with its university, theatre, medieval cathedral and Maritime Museum. 19th-century dramatist Richard Ford wrote: "This Exeter is quite a capital, abounding in all that London has, except its fog and smoke".

Inland are the two magnificent National Parks of Dartmoor and Exmoor. Dartmoor lies in the south of Devon, 365 square miles of great natural beauty and rugged grandeur where you can sense the history and legend and discover peace and quiet. From the sparkling streams of the outskirts to the starker

granite tors of the *high moor*, new pleasures unfold. The wild heather moorland and deep, wooded valleys are the home of red deer and of the legendary Doones of R D Blackmore's novel.

Exmoor, in the north of Devon is famous for its ponies. It is a place for relaxation, for walking perhaps, or resting in one of the sleepy villages.

The West Country also suits those who look for activity on their holiday. Fishing, for example - whether sea, game or coarse, is available in the five counties. The varied coastline is ideal for all watersports, with much opportunity for surfing, windsurfing, sailing and diving. Golf, with over 80 courses on breezy cliffs, amid the dunes, in parkland or on the moor, the West Country is a paradise for the golfer, The walker can choose to follow part of the Southwest Peninsula Coast Path, 515 miles of the finest coastal scenery, or try a long distance path like the Ridgeway in Wiltshire or the West Mendip Way, from Weston-super-Mare along the Mendips down to Wells in Somerset. Details of

shorter nature trails and walks around historic cities are available from Tourist Information Centres.

Bristol, the largest city in the West Country, is steeped in history. You can stroll down cobbled King Street, famous for its Theatre Royal, Almshouses and Llandoger Trow. The city docks are of great interest, providing a home for the SS Great Britain, Brunel's famous iron ship, the Industrial Museum and The Watershed shopping area.

A few miles up the river Avon is Britain's oldest and most famous spa, the City of Bath. Bath's 2000-year old fame started with its popularity as a resort for the Romans, who discovered its hot springs, still operative today. A second great era dawned in the 18th century Regency period, characterised by the Assembly Rooms, Royal Crescent, Circus, Lansdowne Crescent and other notable architecture. Tea in the Regency *Pump Room*, with a string quartet playing, should not be missed.

The county town of **Dorset** is Dorchester, founded by the Romans and later to become the fictional "Casterbridge" of Thomas Hardy's novels. Judge Jeffreys lodged in High West Street during his Bloody Assize. There are fine walks around Chesil Beach and on the Studland peninsula, part of the 7000-acre Corfe Castle estate. Bournemouth, with a population of 160,000 is the largest town in Dorset, representing a quarter of the county's population, is famous for its multitude of hotels and guesthouses, its theatre and concert hall with one of the few permanent non-Metropolitan orchestras of Britain in residence, its exhibition centre, its English Language Schools and for some reason often the highest priced fruit and vegetables in National comparative surveys!

In **Somerset**, visit the city of Wells, dominated by the great cathedral, with its magnificent west front. And do not miss Vicar's Close, one of the oldest medieval streets in Europe, and the moated Bishop's Palace. On the West coast of he county are the resorts of Weston-super-Mare and Minehead. Cheddar Gorge and the Wookey Hole caves in the Mendip Hills should not be missed. Glastonbury Tor, another Druidic site and now home to an annual popular music festival, is also striking.

Also dominated by its cathedral with its 404 ft spire, is Salisbury in **Wiltshire,** and around it, set back from the close, are many

fine historic buildings. 20 miles north of the city is Stonehenge, one of the most visited Druidic sites of Britain, dating back 3000 years. Amesbury, with its Roman burial mound and seemingly random stones, dates form the same period.

Every county in the West Country has its share of stately homes and gardens (see *Historic Houses, Gardens and Parks* on page xi). With a coastline of 650 miles, the West Country is to this day strongly influenced by the sea.

England is a nation of garden lovers and the mild climate, which makes the West Country so popular with tourists, offers a long growing season. Some gardens, like Abbotsbury and Tresco (in the Scillies) specialise in subtropical plants. Spring is the best time for visiting the gardens of the Southwest. Few sights can compare with the flowering of the rhododendrons and azaleas across the lake at Stourhead. At gardens like Killerton, with its hardwood trees, the warm tones of Autumn create another riot of colour to reward the late visitor.

Photographs reproduced by kind permission of the West Country Tourist Board. This page, top to bottom: Roman Baths at Bath, Wells, Westbury White Horse. Previous page Bowermans Nose, Hells Mouth, Clifton Suspension Bridge, Bristol.

St Benets Abbey Hotel

Truro Road, Lanivet. Nr Bodmin,
Cornwall PL30 5HF
Tel: (01208) 831352; Fax: (01208) 832052
E-mail: host@stbenetsabbey.demon.co.uk

Built in 1411, St Benets Abbey is a unique
building standing right in the heart of Cornwall. Offering all the comforts you would
expect to find in a 20th century hotel, the
building retains the charm and character of its
rich historical past. The Gatehouse of the old
abbey is now the hotel lounge and the chapel
tower still stands. The Abbey was the only
local building not to escape the Dissolution of
the Monasteries, being seized by the crown
and sold to a merchant in 1549. It was restored
in the 1980s to become a country house hotel.
Being the only hotel at the half way point of
the Saints Way, St Benet's is an ideal overnight
stop on this medieval pilgrims' route between
Ireland and France which crosses Cornwall
from Padstow to Fowey, a two-day walk. Also
for the energetic there is walking or cycling on
the Camel Trail, horse riding on Bodmin Moor,
golf at St Mellion or fishing and watersports
nearby. The area is rich in historic houses
(Lanhydrock being the closest 3 miles away)
and gardens like the Lost Gardens of Heligan.
St Benet's is an ideal location for the business
traveller, being near Cornwall's main commercial centres or for the holiday maker seeking a
break in a 'different' and unique small hotel
with so much to see and do in the area.

*Rates: Single room with breakfast from £42.50;
double room from £56.*   Ⓥ

● *6 en suite non-smoking bedrooms all with colour
TV, direct-dial telephone, hairdryer, tea/coffee
making facilities, music/radio/alarm clock, trouser
press. No facilities for children.*
● *A la carte (non-smoking) restaurant. Special
diets catered for. Last orders 9 pm.*
● *Fishing 1/2 mile; golf, fitness centre, indoor
swimming pool 3 miles; riding 5 miles.*
● *Two meeting rooms - cap. 15; car parking for 20.*
● *Open Feb to December. Major credit cards accepted.*

**Bodmin 3, Liskeard 10, Newquay 16, St
Austell 11, Truro 26, London 233.**

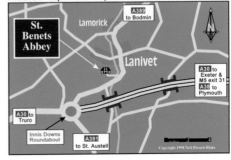

Tredethy Country Hotel

Helland Bridge, Nr. Bodmin, Cornwall
TR11 4NX
Tel: (01208) 841262; Fax: (01208) 841707

Tredethy is one of Cornwall's best kept secrets. Nestling just below the brow of the hill
on one side of the Camel estuary, the hotel
has some of the finest country views in Cornwall. There are nine acres of grounds with
many specimen trees and shrubs. It offers a
more sedate pace of life in tranquil surroundings. The house was originally Tudor but was
almost completely rebuilt in Victorian times.
It was formerly owned by the cricket loving
Anglophile Prince Chula of Thailand who,
with his cousin Bira, ran a successful motor
racing team in the 1930s. Their most famous
cars were the E.R.As *Romulus* and *Remus*,
which still compete in special events today.
With the rugged grandeur of the cliffs inter-
spersed with pretty sandy coves, plus the
beauty of its inland valleys , it is no wonder
that Sir John Betjeman spent much of his life
here. The area has become known as Betjeman
Country. For a relaxing break, walk through
the woods, swim in the secluded heated
swimming pool, rest in Prince Chula's summer house and then enjoy your meal in the
splendid restaurant with panoramic views
over the Camel estuary.

*Rates: Room and breakfast from £38.00 single,
£68.00 double/twin, per person inc. VAT.* **Ⅴ**
Bargain breaks*. Special discounted prices for longer
stays. Contact hotel for details.*

● *11 en suite bedrooms, all with direct dial telephone
and TV, hairdryer, tea/coffee making facilities, music/
radio/alarm clock. Ten cottages, of which two are all
ground flooor.*
● *Last dinner orders 8.30 p.m, vegetarian & special
diets available.*
● *Three conference rooms, capacity up to 20; A/V
equipment available. Car parking for 60.*
● *Outdoor swimming pool; fishing half mile; golf
four miles.*
● *Open all year. All major credit cards accepted.*

**Bodmin 4, Wadebridge 6, Launceston 22,
Truro 24, London 233**

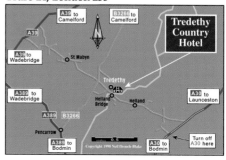

Royal Duchy Hotel

Falmouth, South Cornwall TR11 4NX
Tel: (01326) 313042; Fax: (01326) 319420

Set in the historic, maritime resort of Falmouth
on the riviera coastline is the Royal Duchy
Hotel. This seafront hotel is just a short, level
walk from the town centre and harbour, and
with its beautiful gardens and terraces, has
fantastic views across Falmouth Bay to
Pendennis Castle. The Royal Duchy Hotel is
part of the Brend Hotel Group, the West
Country's leading hoteliers (see also Carlyon
Bay Hotel, near St. Austell on pages 20/21).
The hotel is expertly managed by Darryl
Reburn and his staff whose friendly, attentive
service is second to none. The reception
rooms and most bedrooms enjoy spectacular
sea views and all are well furnished to create
a relaxing, comfortable atmosphere. The recently refurbished restaurant has a renowned
reputation and boasts two AA rosettes for
cuisine. The interesting selection of dishes is
beautifully cooked, well presented, and is
complemented by an extensive selection of
fine wines. I can thoroughly recommend a stay
at the Royal Duchy in any season. Whether you
opt for a quiet relaxing break or a more active,
fun-filled holiday, you will always enjoy the
best in accommodation and cuisine with impeccable service. Please write for their brochure or for details of special seasonal breaks.

*Rates: Room and breakfast from £55.00 single,
£51.50 double/twin, per person inc. VAT.* Ⅴ
Dinner, room and breakfast *from £68.25 single, £64.00 double/twin, per person inc. VAT.*
Bargain breaks. *Winter breaks from £90; Autumn
breaks from £109; special June and July breaks from
£128 and special July breaks from £124. All prices are
per person for a minimum stay of two nights and
include dinner, room and breakfast.*

● *50 en suite bedrooms, all with direct dial telephone
and satellite TV; room service; baby listening; night
service; lift.* ● *Last dinner orders 9.00 p.m, bar meals
available lunchtime, à la carte and table d'hôte menu.*
● *Children welcome; dogs accepted at manager's
discretion; conferences max. 40.* ● *Open all year.*
● *Small snooker/billiards table, table tennis; indoor
heated swimming pool; sauna; solarium; spa pool;
sea bathing; free golf to hotel residents at Carlyon
Bay; sailing, boating, riding, shooting and fishing.*
**Redruth 10, Truro 11, Lizard 20, Penzance
25, Bodmin 34, London 267.**

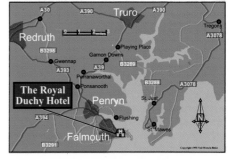

The Green Lawns Hotel

Western Terrace, Falmouth, Cornwall
TR11 4QJ
Tel: (01326) 312734; Fax: (01326) 211427
E-mail: green.lawns@dial.pipex.com

This hotel is the epitome of what a town
house should be. It is small enough to retain
the atmosphere of a country house and yet
large enough to provide all the facilities for
which a business traveller or holidaymaker
could wish. The staff are friendly, courteous
and efficient and the furnishings and decor
are superbly comfortable and in sympathy
with the building.

The immaculate gardens, *Britain in Bloom*
winners from 1994 to 1997, are a beautiful
backdrop to any function but it is for the
cuisine in the *Garras* restaurant for which
Green Lawns has built up a well deserved
reputation. The finest of ingredients are prepared with care, cooked to perfection and
pesented with flair and style. This is an hotel
which competes with any on an international
scale. There are a number of historic houses
and gardens nearby and riverboat trips and
coach outings can be arranged to sample the
natural beauty and views of this part of Cornwall. There are a wide variety of attractions
nearby for the whole family.

Single room inc. breakfast from £50. [V]
Double room inc. breakfast from £90.
*Bargain breaks: From £110 per room per day,
dinner b&b; minimum two days. Other breaks on
application. Dinner: Table d'hôte £20; à la carte,
lunch and special diets available.*

● *4 double, 26 twin, 6 single bedrooms, 4 deluxe
rooms, all en suite, with colour TV+ satellite,
direct-dial telephone, hairdryer, laundry/valet
service, 8 non-smoker bedrooms, tea/coffee making
facilities, music/radio/alarm clock, trouser press.*
● *Car parking for 60. Facilities for disabled.*
● *Fitness centre/gym, jacuzzi/whirlpool, sauna/
solarium, indoor swimming pool.*
● *Billiards/snooker, tennis, squash adjacent. Golf
1/2 mile. Watersports, riding, sailing/boating by
arrangement.*
● *Business services; 4 conference rooms to 200 cap.*
● *All credit cards accepted. Open all year.*

Penzance 26, Plymouth 65, Truro 11, London 308

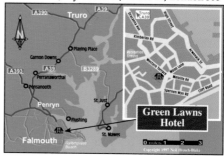

The Cormorant Hotel

Golant by Fowey, Cornwall PL23 1LL
Tel: 01726 833426; Fax: 01726 833026

Single room including breakfast from £42. **[V]**
Double room with breakfast from £84
Leisure Breaks: 3-night break offered throughout the year. Special winter bargains.
Enquire at hotel.

'What a delightful hotel' was my first reaction to The Cormorant, situated high above the waterfront in an unspoilt Cornish fishing village. This charming house makes a comfortable retreat for anyone wanting to "get away from it all", but is also close enough to Fowey and within easy driving distance of many of the beautiful treasures of Cornwall to do exactly the opposite! The setting of the Cormorant is an attraction in itself for all rooms enjoy magnificent views over the Estuary, or you can relax by the indoor pool to get the same experience. The hotel has recently been taken over by Mr and Mrs Elworthy who have modernised the public rooms to reinforce the atmosphere of friendliness and comfort. The bedrooms too, with that view, are very pleasing - warm in the winter and airy in the summer. The attractively decorated restaurant enjoys a well deserved name for good fare with its emphasis on fresh seafood, complemented by a full wine list. For those seeking more energetic pursuits the hotel has easy access to all water sports including water skiing and sailing. However, I shall return again before too long simply to relax in this exquisite place.

● *11 en suite bedrooms with radio, colour TV.*
● *Last orders for dinner 21.00 hrs. Special diets available.*
● *Indoor pool. Car parking for 15 cars.*
● *Open all year. All major credit cards accepted.*

St. Austell 7, Plymouth 28, Bodmin 9, Truro 23, London 277

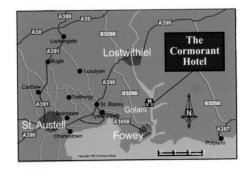

Polurrian Hotel

Mullion, Lizard Peninsula, Cornwall
TR12 7EN
Tel: 01326 240421; Fax: 01326 240083

Three hundred feet above Polurrian Cove, and surrounded by wonderful National Trust coastline, the Polurrian Hotel enjoys an enviable position overlooking some of Cornwall's loveliest scenery. Steps lead down from the hotel to the sandy beach where bathing is safe and clean, or there is an alternative of indoor or outdoor heated swimming pools. The hotel's leisure club includes a hairdressing and beauty salon, sauna and solarium, a gym for the more energetic, a tennis court and light snacks can be enjoyed in the Aqua Bar. An inviting 18 hole golf course is nearby. Small children can enjoy a safe-play area within the hotel's gardens, an indoor activity room, and during my visit, a conjuror! The attractive restaurant romantically overlooks the sea. The dishes are expertly cooked and presented and seafood is a speciality. Early rising guests can help catch the latter in a local fishing boat! The bedrooms are luxurious and are all en suite, some having four-posters. The Polurrian Hotel also has its own self-catering apartments and bungalows. Do write for the brochure and enjoy a really exceptional family holiday.

Dinner, room and breakfast from £42 + VAT
Bargain breaks: For a special occasion or a break from the stress of life, our Feature Breaks and Leisure Breaks in this unspoiled part of Cornwall will provide you with a memory to treasure. 3 day breaks - dinner, room and break fast from £100 per person. **V**

● *39 en suite bedrooms (5 ground floor), all with direct dial telephone and TV, room service; baby listening; night service.*
● *Last orders for dinner 9. 00 p.m.; special diets.*
● *Children welcome; dogs accepted; conferences to 100*
● *Games room; snooker/billiards; outdoor and indoor heated swimming pools; leisure centre; sauna; solarium; spa pool; gymnasium; squash; tennis; sea bathing 200 yards; golf $^1/_2$ mile; shooting/fishing $^1/_2$ mile; sailing/boating 5 miles.*
● *Hotel closed from 3rd January -17th February inc.; all major credit cards accepted.*
The Lizard 4$^1/_2$, Penzance 22, Truro 26, London 323

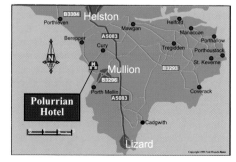

Coombe Farm

Widegates, Nr. Looe, Cornwall
PL13 1QN
Tel: (01503) 240223; Fax: (01503) 240895

Prices: room with breakfast from £30 per person; Room, breakfast & dinner from £46 per person. **Ⅴ**
Short Break: *Terms available.*
Dinner: *Four course table d'hôte from £16. Last orders 1800 hrs.* （Ⅹ）

This award-winning hotel is the epitome of what we, as inspectors, are always looking for. Using the time-honoured Signpost criterion of "Would we stay there again?", the answer is an emphatic 'Yes'. Coombe Farm is a delightful 10-bedroomed country house superbly situated in 10 $^{1}/2$ acres of lawns, meadows, woods and streams with magnificent views down an unspoiled wooded valley to the sea. It offers extremely comfortable lounges and bedrooms together with beautifully prepared and presented food served in a pretty dining room. There are acres of gardens with woods, swimming pool, croquet etc and a games room - a converted stone barn - with snooker and ping-pong tables, card and board games for inclement weather. Whilst not a working farm, a further attraction for children are the family dogs, cats, ducks, horses, peacocks and rabbits. For the holiday maker almost every historic house, garden, beach and tourist attraction in Devon and Cornwall is within an easy drive. Truly this is an excellent venue from which to get to know this idyllic area.

● *10 en suite bedrooms (3 double, 3 twin, 4 family), all non-smoking, with satellite colour TV, direct-dial telephone, hairdryer, music/radio/alarm clock, tea/coffee making facilities.*
● *Billiards/snooker, board games, swimming pool, golf two miles, watersports and tennis three miles, squash six miles.*
● *Open 1st March-31st October. All major credit cards accepted.*

Looe 3$^{1}/2$, Liskeard 9, Plymouth 15, Bodmin 16, Saltash 18, Fowey 22, St Austell 27, London 224.

Nansidwell Country House

Mawnan, Nr. Falmouth, Cornwall
TR11 5HU
Tel: (01326) 250340; Fax: (01326) 250440
E-mail: BOMBEROB @AOL.COM

Lying at the head of a wooded farmland valley, Nansidwell Country House is bounded by several acres of grounds between National Trust coastland and the Helford river. The house has wonderful views across Falmouth Bay towards the Roseland peninsula and is only an 8-minute walk to a small beach and the coastal path. Bearing witness to the mild climate, the five acres of sub-tropical gardens are splashed with colour from January, when the camelias appear, through to autumn when the banana trees bear fruit. The proprietors, Jamie and Felicity Robertson, feel that their guests should experience the ambience of staying in an amiable, well-run country house and the fact that so many guests return each year is testimony to the success of this policy. The bedrooms are prettily furnished and offer every comfort. Chef Anthony Allcott places an emphasis on fresh local produce, particularly seafood, accompanied by an interesting wine list. For the sports enthusiast, there are five 18-hole golf courses within a short drive and sea and trout fishing, windsurfing, sailing, riding and bowls can all be enjoyed in the vicinity.

Single room with breakfast from £95.
Double room with breakfast from £102.
Dinner: Table d'hôte £27.50 per head.
Bargain Breaks: Special prices from £65 per person inc. continental breakfast, dinner & VAT during November, December & February (exc. Xmas/New Year)

● *13 en suite bedrooms with colour TV, direct-dial telephone, hairdryer, laundry service, tea/coffee making facilities, trouser press.*
● *Last orders for dinner 21.30 hrs. Special diets.*
● *Fishing, riding, sailing & boating, golf nearby; tennis on premises. Airport pickup by arrangement*
● *Closed 2-31st January. Visa & Access accepted.*
● *Directions: From Truro follow signs to Falmouth. After about 8 miles, you will see brown road signs for Trebah and Glendurgan Gardens. Follow these and at Mawnan Smith bear left at Red Lion. Nansidwell is at the top of the hill.*

Falmouth 5, Helston 8, Redruth 12, Truro 13, London 259

Crantock Bay Hotel

Crantock, Newquay, Cornwall TR8 5SE
Tel: (01637) 830229; Fax: (01637) 831111;
E-mail: stay@crantockbayhotel.co.uk

The charming owners of this hotel, Mr & Mrs Eyles, have been here for over 40 years and in that time have continuously upgraded the hotel. It is now one of the foremost establishments in the area and, as a venue for either a family holiday or a conference, I cannot recommend it more highly. It is sutuated high above Crantock Bay, commanding the most stunning views over the sea and cliff. Beautifully tended gardens merge into and complement the natural landscape. There are numerous sporting and fitness facilities and for those who hanker after more sophisticated entertainment, Newquay is but five miles away. Beware, however, lest any benefit gained in the leisure complex is easily eroded in th dining room. Cooking at its best, using locally produced ingredients where possible and with a well chosen wine list from which to select an accompanying vintage, is a temptation too much to pass up. The North Cornwall coastal path runs through the hotel grounds and provides
access to miles of spectacular coastline. The Gannel estuary nearby is famous for walking, riding and windsurfing. Wild flowers abound in May and June.

Single room, dinner, bed & breakfast from £51.50
Double room, d, b & b from £103. **Ⅴ**
Dinner: Table d'hôte £18.95 per head; lunch & special diets available; last orders 8.30 pm
Bargain Breaks: Various breaks available, including special interest weekends - prices on application.

● *34 en suite bedrooms with colour TV, direct-dial telephone, laundry service, tea/coffee making facilities, radio/alarm clock.*
● *Heated indoor swimming pool, saunas, jacuzzi, children's pool, all-weather tennis court, gymnasium, indoor games, watersports.*
● *Fishing, riding, sailing & boating, golf, squash nearby; airport pickup by arrangement.*
● *Business centre. Conferences for up to 50 people*
● *Major credit cards accepted. Open all year.*

**Bodmin 20, Penzance 38, Truro 16,
Wadebridge 16, London 255**

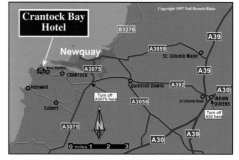

Cross House Hotel

Church Street, Padstow,
Cornwall PL28 8BG
Tel: (01841) 532391;
Fax: (01841) 533633

My visit to Cross House was the discovery of a new oasis in Cornwall. The Grade II Listed Georgian building was once owned by John Tredwen, the last of the local sailing ship builders. It is located slightly away from the bustling port in an area of quiet tranquility. The recent refurbishment and expansion shows a quality of taste and luxury normally only seen and enjoyed in much larger hotels and in more exotic locations. It is difficult to leave the comfort of the hotel for the short walk to the harbour, but leave one surely must in order to explore the colourful tableaux there or possibly to sample Padstow's many fine restaurants including the famous Seafood Restaurant. The more energetic can take a walk along the coastal footpath with its breathtaking views of the North Cornwall coast or hire bikes and follow the Camel Estuary to the town of Wadebridge. The estuary is also an ideal spot for many watersports and two excellent 18-hole golf courses are nearby - Trevose and St Enodoc at Rock. Riding and fishing are also available as are pleasure trips from the harbour.

Rates: Single room with breakfast £60; double room £80-120.   V
Bargain Breaks: For three-day stays or more we offer a reduction in tariff of £20 per room per night.

● *9 en suite bedrooms with airconditioning, colour TV + video, direct-dial telephone, hairdryer, tea/coffee making facilities; all rooms non-smoking; smoking lounge available.*
● *No restaurant. Car parking for five cars*
● *Fishing, golf, watersports, massage, sailing/boating, riding all available locally*

Wadebridge 7, Newquay 14, St Austell 18, Truro 23, London 246

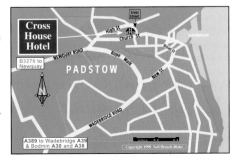

The Beachfield Hotel

The Promenade, Penzance, Cornwall
TR18 4NW
Tel: (01736) 362067; Fax: (01736) 331100

Whether on business or holiday the Beachfield must be the only place to stay in Penzance. Originally a Victorian hotel, built in about 1840, it occupies a prime seafront location, central for all local services, and has panoramic views over Mounts Bay, from the Lizard to Newlyn Harbour. It has recently been refurbished to a high standard and Ian James, the new owner, is justifiably proud of the transformation. The Minack Theatre, St Michael's Mount, Newlyn, Land's End and even the Scilly Isles are within easy reach. Those not wishing to drive can even use the hotel's own chauffeur-driven Rolls Royce, or better still, walk the coastal footpaths or the endless quaint back streets of Penzance. Amongst these you will find smugglers' pubs, maritime museums and sub-tropical gardens. At the end of the day, retire to this charming hotel with all its modern facilities and enjoy an excellent table d'hôte or à la carte menu, including fresh locally caught fish, in the raised restaurant which affords open fires in winter and views of the ever-changing seascape in summer.

Single room, inc breakfast from £37.50;
Double room, inc breakfast from £75.   **V**
Bargain Breaks: Reductions on three nights plus - prices on application. Special rates for children.

● *18 en suite bedrooms with colour TV+ satellite, direct-dial telephone, hairdryer, laundry service, music/radio/alarm clock, safety deposit box, tea/coffee making facilities, trouser press; non-smoker bedrooms available.*
● *Table d'hôte dinner £14.95; à la carte, bar lunch and special diets available; last orders 9.15 pm.*
● *Golf, sea/river bathing, watersports, clay pigeon shooting, riding all available nearby.*
● *Business services inc 2 meeting rooms, capacity 15 to 350. Car parking for 6 cars.*
● *Major credit cards accepted. Open all year.*

St Ives 8, Lands End 10, Helston 13, Redruth 17, Truro 25, London 281

Penventon Hotel

Redruth, West Cornwall TR15 1TE
Tel: (01209) 214141; Fax: (01209) 219164
E-MAIL: PENVENTON@BTINTERNET.COM
WEB SITE: See YAHOO   AA ★★★ ☺

To walk into the Penventon is to walk into a
gracious Georgian manor with the finest
antiques in every corner yet with all the ad-
vantages of the end of the 20th century. The
conference facilities would suit the most de-
manding of companies - the *Edith Suite* and
Forum Rooms being a self-contained area for
10 to 200 persons with own private bar and
dancefloor if required. The leisure centre is
unparallelled in this part of Cornwall, with a
health suite and *Statz* vertical sunroom.
Unlike most hotels in this part of England
which face the sea, Penventon stands fairly in
its own extensive grounds in the centre of the
county bringing it within 10-50 minutes'drive
of all Cornwall's major attractions. After a
day's exploring, it is a connoisseur's dream to
choose from more than 100 classic French,
Italian and English dishes in the restaurant
and be serenaded by the grand piano. The
hotel's staff of ten chefs prepare AA rosetted
menus specialising in local meat, fish and
shellfish. As well as the main bar and lounge,
there is the *Spice of Life* pub for younger
clientèle. For a small conference, leisure or
health break, the Penventon stands head and
shoulders above the competition in this area.

Rates: Single room inc b'fast £28-48; double £48-99
Bargain breaks: available all year. Weekends Ⓥ
from £25 pp daily inclusive; Gourmet occasions in
AA Rosetted Restaurant; Singles welcome at no
supplement; Party rates a speciality; Xmas, New
Year, Eclipse and Millenium Packages available.

● *55 en suite bedrooms & suites, all with direct dial*
telephone, colour TV, hairdryer, laundry/valet serv-
ice, music/radio/alarm clock, safety deposit box, tea/
coffee making, trouser press; 24-hr room service;
non-smoker bedrooms available.
● *Table d'hôte dinner £16; à la carte, lunch & spe-*
cial diets available; last orders 9.30 pm.
● *Business services inc 4 meeting rooms, cap. 6-300*
● *Indoor heated swimming pool; sauna, solarium,*
massage, jacuzzi; robes & towels provided; beauti-
cian. Fishing, bathing, sailing, shooting, squash,
tennis riding all within 1-3 miles.
● *Car parking for 200; airport pickup. Night Club*
● *Amex, Visa & Mastercard accepted. Open all year*
Truro 9, Falmouth 10, Helston 10, Newquay
15, Penzance 17, Bodmin 30, London 263

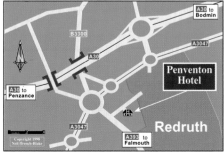

Rose-in-Vale Hotel

Mithian, St Agnes, Cornwall TR5 OQD
Tel: (01872) 552202; Fax: (01872) 552700

Rose-in-Vale is an hotel which truly lives up to its name. Romantically covered in climbing roses, this elegant 18th century country house, its past rooted in Cornish history, lies secluded in its own lovely 11-acre valley of woodland, pasture and gardens with gliding stream and waterfowl ponds. The pervading atmosphere is of peace and seclusion, where guests can relax by flower gardens and heated pool in summer or around log fires in winter. The hotel has been sympathetically extended, up-graded and refurbished. Dining in *Opie's Room*, with softly draped sweeping bay windows overlooking the gardens, offers a choice from à la carte and table d'hôte menus , complimented by fine wines, and special Cornish Lobster and Flambé menus. Bedrooms, four-poster suites and puiblic rooms are elegantly furnished with dark woods and floral themes prevailing. AA / RAC Three Stars and a Hospitality and Service RAC Merit Award means that you will be comfortable and cosseted during your stay. National Trust and privately owned great houses and gardens as well as six golf courses are within easy reach, with a host of other attractions close by. Rose-in-Vale's central location and proximity tp the coast makes it the natural choice for touring and sightseeing throughout the year.

Rates: Single room inc b'fast fm £48; double fm £86
Bargain breaks: *available 1st March-14 May & 18 Sept-31 Dec exc. Xmas/New Year/Bank Hols. Any 2 nights fm £102.90; longer breaks available; Special Xmas, New Year, Valentines, Romantic and various activity breaks also available.*

⬤ *18 en suite bedrooms, all with direct dial telephone, colour TV, hairdryer, laundry/valet service, minibar, music/radio/alarm clock, tea/coffee making. Facilities for the disabled. Car parking for 40.*
⬤ *Table d'hôte dinner £21.95; à la carte, lunch & special diets available; last orders 8.30 pm.*
⬤ *Business services inc 2 meeting rooms, cap. 12/50.*
⬤ *Billiards/snooker; outdoor swimming pool, croquet, badminton, indoor games, massage, solarium. Fishing, golf, bathing, watersports, tennis, riding, gliding/power flying all within five miles.*
⬤ *Amex, Visa, Mastercard, Switch, Delta, Diners accepted. Open February-December.*
Truro 8, Redruth 8, Helston 10, Newquay 11, Penzance 26, Bodmin 26, London 269

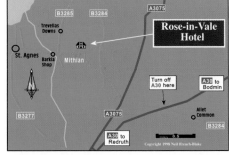

Trevaunance Point Hotel

Trevaunance Cove, St Agnes, Cornwall
TR5 ORZ
Tel: (01872) 553235; Fax: (01872) 553874

For a decade or more I have walked from
Chapel Forth over the coastal path past de-
funct tin mines and down the hill to St Agnes.
Each year, tired and dishevelled, I have
passed the Trevaunance Point Hotel fearing
that my appearance and muddy boots would
not be welcome within such august portals.
This year I decided to risk embarrassment and
what a wise decision this was! The welcome,
liquid refreshment and open fire showed the
warmth of a bygone age. On entering the
hostelry, you surrender to a tempo far re-
moved from the 20th century. There is no
reception desk or chattering typewriter to
greet you, but a smiling face behind the bar.
The hotel hangs to the cliff face, with some of
the quaint bedrooms, all of which overlook
the sea, below ground floor level. The loudest
noise is the lapping of waves 60 feet below.
Food is given a high priority with three chefs
preparing a variety of fresh fish, meat and
vegetarian dishes. Special Activity Weekends
can be organised, with sufficient notice, on
Natural History, Hard Rock Mining, Visits to
Country Houses & Gardens etc and for the
energetic, surf- and sailboarding tuition, riding,
golf, flying and gliding are all available nearby.

*Rates: Single room inc breakfast from £50; double
inc. breakfast from £75.* **V**
*Bargain breaks: 2 or 3 nights, dinner, b & b
from £60 per person per night (inc. full board &
3- course dinner). 4 or 5 night breaks (Sun-Thurs
only) from £40 pppn.*

● *8 en suite bedrooms, all with direct dial tel-
ephone, colour TV, hairdryer, laundry/valet service,
music/radio/alarm clock, tea/coffee making.*
● *Table d'hôte dinner £19.25; à la carte, lunch &
special diets available; last orders approx. 21.00.
Junior menu available.*
● *Gossips hair & beauty salon; fishing, sea bath-
ing, garden, watersports; riding 1 mile; golf 4 miles.*
● *The Porthole gift shop. Car parking for 20.
Airport pickup by arrangement. Dogs accepted.*
● *Amex, Visa, Mastercard, Diners accepted. Open all
year.*

**Truro 8, Redruth 8, Helston 10, Newquay 11,
Penzance 26, Bodmin 26, London 269**

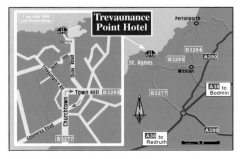

St. Austell Bay Hotel, Carlyon Bay Cornwall

3 Miles from St. Austell, 2 miles from Par, 7 miles from Lostwithiel, and 6 miles from Fowey.
(For position see map on page 16, square D.7).

A perfectly equipped, splendidly conducted and entirely modern hotel—Magnificent site overlooking fine sands—De luxe hotel atmosphere allied with first rate cuisine and wide choice of indoor and outdoor sports.

THE white form of St. Austell Bay Hotel, standing on the cliff above the famous Carlyon Bay sands and rising from gardens in which flourish many semi-tropical flowers and plants, completely dominates the surrounding country. But its somewhat stern exterior gives no indication of the warmth, hospitality and luxury that its interior provides. Being a modern hotel it suffers from none of the disadvantages that accrue from the conversion or modernisation of older houses. It was designed throughout as a luxury hotel and a luxury hotel it certainly is. There is an air of spaciousness, freshness and general ease about the place that is kindly and comforting in itself, quite apart from the actual amenities of the building. When I stayed there I had the room next to the suite usually occupied by the Prince of Wales on his visits to the Duchy of Cornwall and was at once intrigued by the system of signalling by silent bells which is standard throughout the hotel. Indeed the restfulness of the place was one of the things that most impressed me, for apart from the swish of a passing sea-gull

The Carlyon Bay Hotel

Nr. St Austell, Cornwall PL25 3RD

Tel: (01726) 812304; Fax: (01726) 814938

The Carlyon Bay Hotel, which 60 years ago was called the St Austell Bay Hotel, featured in the first edition of SIGNPOST in 1935 (see page at left) and was then described as an "entirely modern hotel". Today the hotel maintains its fine, art déco features, combined with every luxury that you would expect from a four star hotel. The hotel's setting is truly unique, positioned in 250 acres of beautiful secluded gardens on the cliff top overlooking St Austell Bay. As part of the Brend Group, the West Country's leading hoteliers, the hotel is operated under the personal supervision of the Brend family. It is a place of character and luxury with the public rooms and most bedrooms having unsurpassed sea views and all comfortable and stylish. In the Bay View Restaurant you can take in the wonderful view and be assured of fine cuisine, presented with skill and imagination. The wine list is well chosen and extensive, and perfect compliments the table d'hôte and special reserve menu. Carlyon Bay is a sportsman's paradise with its renowned 18-hole, 6500-yard golf course, 9-hole approach course set in the secluded palm-fringed gardens, indoor and outdoor heated swimming pools, two tennis courts and a lovely children's play area. Whether embarking on sport or leisure, the hotel offers a superb family holiday throughout the year. And with a full children's entertainment programme available during the school holidays, you are free to enjoy the extensive facilities which the hotel has to offer.

● *72 en suite bedrooms, all with direct-dial telephone and satellite TV with Guest Link facility, room service, baby listening, night service & lift*
● *Last orders for dinner 9 pm; bar lunches, special diets available; children welcome; conferences max. 125.*
● *2 snooker tables, indoor and outdoor heated swimming pools, sauna, solarium, spa bath, sea bathing, golf free to residents, 2 tennis courts, health & beauty room and playroom. Sailing, boating, riding, shooting and fishing all nearby.*
● *Open all year. All major credit cards accepted*

Bodmin 11, Truro 14, Falmouth 25, Exeter 75, Bristol 147, London 242

Rates: Single room with breakfast from £76; Ⅴ *double/twin from £73 per person. Dinner, bed & breakfast £88 single; £86 double/twin per pers.* **Bargain Breaks:** *Minimum 2-night stay Winter (Nov-Feb) from £48; Spring (Mar-May exc. Easter) from £59. All prices are per person and include room, dinner, breakfast, golf & VAT.*

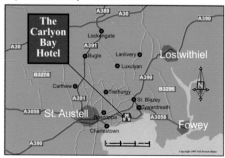

THE WEST COUNTRY

Boskerris Hotel

Carbis Bay, Nr. St. Ives, Cornwall TR26 2NQ
Tel: (01736) 795295; Freephone (0500) 121491; Fax: (01736) 798632

Room and breakfast from £36.50 per person, or with dinner £48.75, including VAT. Other terms on application. Open Easter till November.
***Bargain breaks:** Low season breaks from two to four days - prices on application. Golfing packages available.*   **V**

Boskerris stands in attractive gardens above the safe golden sands of Carbis Bay, with fine views across St. Ives Bay. This delightful hotel is owned and personally cared for by the Monk family, who have created a friendly, happy atmosphere. The public rooms are attractive and furnished to a high standard and together with the Cocktail Bar have extensive views over the Bay. In the dining room a carefully chosen menu is offered. The dishes are interesting, well presented and nicely served. Similar care is given in the selection of wines, which is excellent. The majority of the comfortable and well appointed bedrooms, all with private bathrooms, enjoy sea views and overlook the well kept gardens. Boskerris is an ideal centre for a wide range of activities, including a golfing package which enables you to play at 14 major golf courses in Cornwall, all within easy distances, plus the many beautiful moorland and coastal walks.

● *16 en suite bedrooms (some ground floor), with remote control colour TV, direct dial telephone and tea/coffee making facilities, hairdryer.*
● *Diets available; children welcome.*
● *Drying and games rooms; heated outdoor swimming pool; putting green; sea bathing, boating, surfing, rock climbing and tennis all nearby, ample car parking facilities.*

St. Ives 1, Penzance 8½, Helston 13 , Redruth 14, London 277

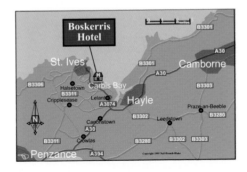

The Garrack Hotel & Restaurant

Burthallan Lane, St. Ives, Cornwall
TR26 3AA
Tel: 01736 796199; Fax 01736 798955
E-mail: garrack@compuserve.com

The discerning traveller seeking a classic small country house hotel could hardly do better than to stay in the family-run Garrack with its spectacular views over the old town of St. Ives and the sea. It has two acres of gardens , is near a coastal footpath and its excellent leisure centre caters for most eventualities. The personal touch and friendliness of the Garrack is reflected in the main lounge with its log fire in winter, books, magazines and board games. In addition there is a small TV lounge and a bar lounge. Whilst the bedrooms in this the main house are traditional as befits the building, an extension houses additional rooms of more modern design and equally comfortable. Some rooms have four posters, others whirlpool baths. There are family rooms and a room for the disabled. The hotel restaurant is justifiably renowned for its seafood with lobsters fresh from the hotel's storage tank, as fresh as is the other locally produced food with many of the vegetables coming from the garden. It would take several weeks to work through the wine list. The Garrack is a rarity - one of those places which it was a delight in itself to visit - and so hard to leave.

Single room including breakfast from £56.00. V
Double room with breakfast from £48.00 p.p.
Bargain breaks available November to end March

● *18 en suite bedrooms with TV, direct-dial telephone, hairdryer on request. Morning tea service. One room for disabled. Baby monitoring.*
● *AA 2 Rosetted Restaurant. Last dinner orders 20.30.*
● *Conferences for up to 25 guests.*
● *Indoor whirlpool and swimming pool, sauna, solarium and fitness area. Access to fishing, riding, shooting (clay),golf, water sports, squash and tennis.*
● *Airport pick-up and car rental by arrangement. Car parking for 30 cars.*
● *Open all year. All major credit cards accepted.*

Penzance 10, Redruth 14, Truro 25, London 319

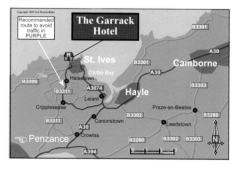

Talland Bay Hotel

Talland by Looe, Cornwall PL13 2JB
Tel: (01503) 272667; Fax: (01503) 272940

Imagine a beautifully furnished Cornish country house with superb gardens overlooking the sea, situated between picturesque Polperro and Looe, and you begin to understand what award-winning Talland Bay has to offer. Barry and Annie Rosier, your hosts, are experienced hoteliers and their attention to detail is legendary. Talland was first mentioned in the Domesday Book in 1089 but the present house dates back some four hundred years.

Each of the 19 bedrooms is individually furnished to a high standard. Public rooms are comfortable and service is unashamedly 'old-fashioned', presided over by a friendly and hard-working staff. Little touches such as free afternoon buffet teas and morning newspapers enhance the picture.

The food, for which the hotel has an AA rosette, is superb. The menu specialises in seafood from Looe - locally caught lobster, crab and scallop, West Country cheeses and tender Cornish lamb - all complemented by a fine 100+ bottle wine list. If you are looking for a venue in which to relax away from the crowds, where comfort and service are second to none, then the Talland Bay represents one of those far too rare hotels.

Prices from £62 per person dinner, bed and breakfast, inc. VAT and service. **V**
Bargain breaks available - details on request.

● *19 en suite bedrooms all with direct dial telephone, colour TV; haidryer, laundry service, tea/coffee making facilities, trouser press, music/radio/alarm clock*
● *Table d'hôte dinner £22; à la carte, bar snacks and special diets available; last orders 9 p.m*
● *Games room, croquet, sauna, outdoor heated swimming pool. Fishing, golf, watersports, riding, squash and tennis nearby.*
● *Meeting rooms to 20; car parking (20); car rental by arrangement.*
● *Major credit cards accepted. Open all year*

Fowey 14, Saltash 18, Bodmin 24, Plymouth 25, Truro 35, London 268

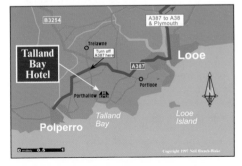

Bovey House

Beer, Nr. Seaton, Devon EX12 3AD
Tel: (01297) 680241; Fax: (01297) 680270

This historic 16th century manor house is situated in rolling farm and parkland between the seaside villages of Beer and Branscombe, only two miles from the sea and readily accessible to many places of interest in east Devon and west Dorset. Bovey House is now owned and personally cared for by Mr & Mrs LLorente. Much refurbishment has been carried out, but this lovely old country house, its historic surroundings and atmosphere have retained their charm. Bovey House once belonged to Catherine Parr, presented to her by Henry VIII as part of her dowry. Rumour has it that Charles II slept in the room named after him, which has one of the most flawless coffered ceilings I have seen. All bedrooms are comfortable and well appointed, some with splendid four-posters, all with fresh flowers. Log fires burn in the inglenook fireplaces in the bar and in the drawing room which was originally the medieval hall and reached up to the roof. The dining room, with its Tudor linen fold panelling and heavy beamed ceilings, provides interesting menus using local produce and serving fine wines. With its attractive walled garden and homely interior, Bovey House is truly a haven where you can relax as if staying with friends.

Rates: Single room inc. breakfast from £50; double room inc. breakfast from £70. Ⓥ
Bargain Breaks: 25% discount October-June, b & b. From £45 pppn dinner, b&b for two+ nights.

● *9 bedrooms (8 en suite) all with telephone, colour TV, hairdryer, tea/coffee making facilities; music/radio/alarm clock.*
● *Table d'hôte dinner £19.50. Special diets available. Last orders 8.30 p.m.*
● *Children welcome. Dogs welcome.*
● *Croquet. Watersports, riding, sailing/boating, tennis, indoor swimming pool nearby.*
● *Open all year exc 3 weeks January. Mastercard, Amex & Visa cred it cards accepted.*

Seaton 3, Lyme Regis 9, Exeter 19, London 153.

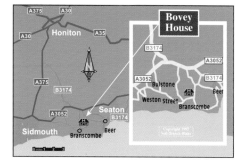

THE WEST COUNTRY

Yeoldon House Hotel

Durrant Lane, Northam, Bideford,
Devon EX39 2RL
Tel: (01237) 474400; Fax: (01237) 476618

This lovely Victorian Gentleman's Residence commands spectacular views over lawns to the river Torridge below. The house has been sympathetically converted into a most comfortable hotel and guests here are treated not only to being in the most beautiful part of Devon but also to delicious food, supplied, wherever possible, from the locality. Mr & Mrs Jelley, the owners, are justifiably proud of their Charters restaurant. A nice touch is the complimentary glass of sherry given to guests before dinner. The bedrooms are individually decorated; one having its own lounge and balcony, another having a four-poster, and it is a joy to return to dine and to relax here after what can be a tiring day touring the area. Within an hour's drive of the hotel there is an exceptional range of places to see and things to do. Almost on the doorstep is Lundy Island with its outstanding bird and marine life. Exmoor, Lorna Doone country, and the picturesque village of Clovelly are near to the hotel. Guests can enjoy miles of coastal footpath and for bathing and watersports, some of the finest sandy beaches in the country are near at hand.

Single room including breakfast from £42.00   [V]
Double room including breakfast from £70.00.
Dinner à la carte; vegetarian/special diets available; last orders 2100 hrs.

● *10 en suite bedrooms (7 double, 3 twin), all with direct dial telephone, colour TV and full central heating; hairdryer, tea/coffee making facilities, music/radio/alarm clock, ironing board.*
● *Meeting room - capacity 40.*
● *Open all year. All major credit cards accepted.*

Bideford 2, Barnstaple 11, Holsworthy 17, Bude 23, Okehampton 28, London 204

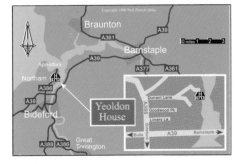

The Berry Head Hotel

Berry Head Road, Brixham, Devon
TQ5 9AJ
Tel: (01803) 853225; Fax: (01803) 882084

The Berry Head Hotel is set in a superb water's edge position in six acres of its own gardens and woodland, in the seclusion of the Berry Head Country Park, which is noted for its bird life and rare wild flowers. The hotel is steeped in history. It was built as a military hospital in the Napoleonic Wars, and was later the home of the Reverend Francis Lyte, who wrote the famous hymn *Abide with Me* at the hotel, no doubt inspired by the glorious sunsets. The historic fishing port of Brixham, where William of Orange first landed on English soil, is only a short walk away. The hotel offers relaxing accommodation and all the en suite bedrooms have colour television, radio and tea and coffee making facilities. The comfortable lounge and the restaurant, which overlook the terrace, enjoy spectacular views of Torbay and the Devon coast. The emphasis here is upon good food, wine and company in a very special setting.
Set in national parkland at the water's edge, with miles of coastal walks, fishing, birdwatching and sailing, yet close to the major resort of Torquay, this is an ideal hideaway for a short break.

Room and breakfast from £38.00, and dinner, room and breakfast from £45.00 including VAT.
Bargain breaks: *Two nights, dinner, bed and breakfast from £70.00*   [V]

● 32 en suite bedrooms all with direct dial telephone, TV; hairdryer; tea/coffee facilities; room service; baby listening; night service.
● Last orders for dinner 9.30p.m; bar meals until 9.30p.m; special diets; children welcome.
● Dogs accepted; conferences 100 max.
● Boules; sea bathing 30 yds; indoor heated swimming pool; outdoor seawater pool 200 yds; squash courts ¹/₂ mile; sailing and boating, shooting and fishing ¹/₄ mile; tennis one mile; golf and riding two miles.
● Open all year. Amex, Visa and Mastercard accepted.

Torquay 10, Exeter 30, Bristol 100, Birmingham 200, London 180

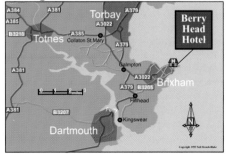

Wigham

Morchard Bishop,
Devon EX17 6RJ
Tel/Fax: (01363) 877350

IN CONVERSION

This extraordinary 16th-century thatched Devon longhouse accepts visitors for an unbelievable experience. Unique furnishings and log fires when appropriate contribute to the extreme comfort of guests as do the heated outdoor swimming pool, the delightful garden and, above all, the delicious and imaginative food which, whenever possible, is organically grown or reared on Wigham's own 30-acre organic farm. Dinner is the highlight of the day, with guests sitting around a communal table *'en famille'*. The views are stunning and the only sounds are those of sheep, cows and birds. This is indeed a bucolic retreat where one can simply relax and unwind or explore, as it is situated virtually in the centre of Devon, one hour from both coasts, and between Dartmoor and Exmoor, within easy reach of many National Trust properties. The owners regret that they do not cater for smokers or very small children. Booking is essential as Wigham is rapidly being discovered by those who like an 'away from it all' holiday in beautiful surroundings. For non-European postal enquiries, please enclose £2, refundable on booking.

Double room £55-79 per person including breakfast, three-course dinner and VAT.
Single occupancy - 75% of double rate.
Dinner separately £20. Lunch & special diets available
Bargain breaks available at various times; details on application.
Flexibreak: 3 nights £299 for two persons, dinner, bed and breakfast

● *Five en suite bedrooms, inc. one four-poster.*
● *Colour TV with video films, hairdryer, laundry/valet service, non-smoker bedrooms, tea/coffee making facilities.*
● *Swimming Pool, billiards/snooker. Golf and tennis two miles; riding & squash four miles.*
● *Open all year (tho' some restrictions Dec/Jan/Feb). Major credit cards accepted (subject to small charge).*

Exeter 15, Okehampton 16, Tiverton 16, Barnstaple 25, London 179

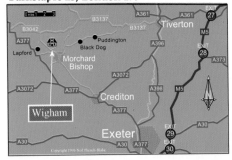

The Lord Haldon Hotel

Dunchideock, Nr. Exeter, Devon EX6 7YF
Tel: (01392) 832483; Fax: (01392) 833765

This large country house set high up on the edge of Dartmoor makes a superb journey break for travellers heading to or from the southwest. The present building is a reconstructed part of the original mansion built by Sir Richard Chudleigh in the 1700s, with views landscaped by Capability Brown over the surrounding rolling hills. It became an hotel some 50 years and was acquired by the Preece family in 1978, the personal touch being always evident. It is also an ideal base from which to explore the historic cathedral and university city of Exeter, only four miles away, and the south coast of Devon. It represents a haven of peace and quiet, being only three miles from the rush of both the A30 and A38 trunk roads. The *Chandelier* Restaurant has gained an enviable reputation locally for its high standard of service and cuisine and has recently been awarded an AA Rosette. Menus are changed daily to ensure that only the freshest products are used. This is indeed a delightful hotel for the country lover, the adventurous or for the weary traveller wishing to "wind down".

Rates: Single inc breakfast from £55; double inc breakfast from £75. **Ⅴ**
Bargain breaks *available; ask for details.*

● *22 en suite bedrooms (13 double, 6 twin, 3 four-posters) with colour TV+ satellite, direct dial telephone, tea/coffee making, hairdryer, music/radio alarm clock, laundry service, non-smoker bedrooms available.*
● *Table d'hôte dinner £ 19.50; lunch & special diets available; last orders 9 pm.*
● *Business services inc. 6 meeting rooms, cap. 300*
● *Croquet. Fishing, shooting & riding can be arranged.*
● *Airport pickup by arrangement. Car parking 200*
● *Open all year; Access,Visa, Switch, Diners, Delta accepted.*

Exeter 4, Airport 10, Okehampton 16, Torquay 20, Honiton 21, London 175

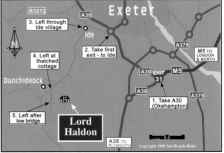

Combe House

Gittisham, Nr. Honiton,
Devon EX14 0AD
Tel: (01404) 540400; Fax: (01404) 46004
E-mail: stay@combe-house.co.uk
Internet: http://www.combe-house.co.uk

This lovely Elizabethan mansion is approached up a winding drive and lies in 3000 acres of private estate - woods and meadow lands with magnificent views over the Devon countryside. It has the atmosphere of a country house and one is received like a member of the family. Combe is just off the A30 and is thus accessible easily by road, rail and air. Ken and Ruth Hunt, having spent 16 years in Australia, now care for the hotel and restaurant and enhance the historic country mansion with treasured antiques and fresh garden flowers. The staff work as a cheerful, efficient and attentive team. The spontaneous restful bedrooms are dignified and well appointed. Among the magnificent rooms downstairs are the Entrance Hall - a fine example of Carolinian grandeur - and the large panelled drawing room - perfect for that board meeting, house party or special celebration.
A wonderful candlelit dinner is served in two lovely dining rooms. The wine list is exceptional in its quality and range. Lunch can be taken in the cosy Cocktail Bar.

Rates: Single room with breakfast from £75; Double/ twin from £98, both prices inc. VAT.   **V**
Short breaks July 1998-March 1999 Stay any two nights from £140 per person twin share, dinner, bed & breakfast. Children under 12 sharing parents's rooms stay free. Extra nights 15% less.
Conference Tariffs: 24-hour residential single fm £120; twin fm £97 per person. Day delegate £28 per hd. inc. standard equipment. **Weekend House Parties** *- groups of 8+ friends especially catered for; also* **Golf Breaks** *- calendar of events available.*

● *15 en suite bedrooms (inc two suites, one four-poster), all with colour TV, direct dial telephone, hairdryer and central heating.*
● *Non-residents, children and dogs most welcome.*
● *Croquet, riding, 1¹/₂ miles trout fishing; wonderful walking through private estate or country nearby.*
● *Member of* **Pride of Britain***. Open all Year.*
Major credit cards accepted.

Honiton 2, Airport 14, Exeter 16, Bristol 60, Birmingham 149, London 155

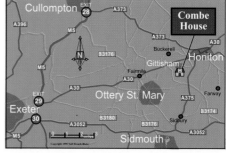

The Cottage Hotel

Hope Cove, Kingsbridge, South Devon
TQ7 3 HJ
Tel: (01548) 561555; Fax: (01548) 561455

The Cottage Hotel enjoys a superb position,
overlooking the picturesque harbour and
cove, with spectacular sea views and sunsets.
The gardens descend to the beach, where you
can bathe in safety. The hotel is delightful and
has 35 beautifully furnished bedrooms, with
23 of them having private bathrooms / showers. I always enjoy visiting The Cottage; it has
a happy and relaxing atmosphere thanks to
the owners, John and Janet, Sarah and
William Ireland, who, with Patricia Bazzano
Bazzano personally care for this pleasant and
comfort, which has lovely views of the cove
and coast, offers table d'hôte and à la carte
menus. I chose the former, which was excellent, cooked with great interest and attention,
served by cheerful, efficient and courteous
staff of many years' standing. The meal was
supported by a selective wine list. This hotel
still remains one of the best family hotels I
visit, well illustrated by the preponderance of
sun-tanned, well-fed families.

Rates: Dinner, room and breakfast from £47.50.
Bargain breaks *are available from 1st November*
to 9th April inclusive.2-night stay £27.25-£42.50;
7-night stay from £26.75-£41.50 according to
room. Prices are per person per night and include
accommodation, 6-course dinner plus coffee, full
English breakfast, service and VAT. **V**

- *25 en suite bedrooms (7 ground floor), all with*
direct-dial telephone and colour TV, room service,
baby listening. 12 other bedrooms.
- *Last orders for dinner 8.30 pm; bar meals 12-*
1. 30 pm. ● *Conferences, max. 50*
- *Children welcome; dogs accepted.*
- *Games room, sea bathing, sailing/boating,*
riding three miles, golf four miles, tennis & squash
six miles.
- *Hotel closed 2-30th January. No credit cards.*

**Totnes 18, Torquay 21, Plymouth 25,
Exeter 36, London 236**

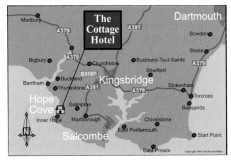

Ermewood House Hotel

Ermington, Ivybridge, Devon PL21 9NS
Tel/Fax: (01548) 830741

This delightful establishment, originally a rectory, is the epitome of the Country House Restaurant with Rooms for readers looking for a quiet backwater in which to relax. Whilst every comfort is provided, this is not one of those 'international' places where a bevy of staff can so often intrude on one's privacy. At Ermewood the owners personally supervise everything to make sure that your stay is memorable. Cuisine is predominantly English, using fresh local produce - the village of Ermington boasting two trout farms. The table d'hôte menu changes daily and the wine list is extensive. The food is bought locally whenever possible, to ensure freshness, and the straightforward cooking is lovingly prepared and presented. Here is a place to relax and reflect on the glories of the South Hams countryside, to go down to the uncrowded sea shore, to idly watch the river Erme flow along its bucolic valley or to reflect on the pace of life away from the city. Here life is perfect, whether for a break on the way to Plymouth, a gateway to Cornwall, en route to the ferry to France or Spain or as a holiday destination in its own right, from which to explore the south coast of Devon and Dartmoor.

Rates: Single room including breakfast from £38; double from £63. **V**
Bargain Breaks: Three nights dinner, bed & breakfast from £123; extra nights from £41; seven nights from £280.

● *10 en suite bedrooms with radio & TV, hairdryer, laundry/valet service, tea/coffee making facilities. Non-smoker bedrooms available.*
● *Table d'hôte £16.50; special diets available; last orders 20.30.*
● *Sea bathing, fly fishing. Sports complex 3 miles. Golf three miles. Riding & sailing can be arranged.*
● *No children under 12. Airport pickup by arr't.*
● *Small meetings (8) catered for. Wedding receptions. (Bridal suite available)*
● *Open all year. Visa & Mastercard accepted.*

Plymouth 11, Totnes 12, Ashburton 15, London 140

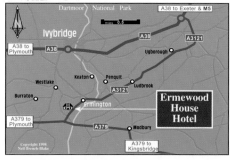

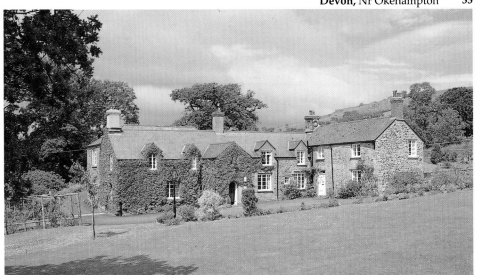

Collaven Manor Hotel

Sourton, Okehampton,
Devon EX20 4HH
Tel: (01837) 861522; Fax: (01837) 440961

Those readers looking to stay in a small
country manor house need look no further.
Collaven is a picturebook Devon Manor
both externally and internally. Dating from
the 15th century, it stands in four acres of
picturesque gardens and paddocks. It has
been sympathetically restored to cater for
discerning guests as it would have done in
the days of its earlier owners. Notable
amongst these are the Hamilton family (of
Nelson fame) and the house positively exudes Devon history. On entering the manor
via the Baronial Reception Hall, the visitor
is greeted by a feeling of warmth and comfort, enhanced by log fires in winter and
cooled by medieval thick walls in summer.
The Hamilton Restaurant offers a 4-course
dinner, changing daily, with the emphasis
on the Best of British cuisine, with Continental and Oriental influences. A vegetarian speciality is always on the menu.
Here the atmosphere is serene, the setting
tranquil but, for the adventurous, the
moors are on the doorstep, to delight the
walker, naturalist or outdoor sportsman.

*Single: inc. breakfast from £53; **double** from £82.*
***Bargain Breaks:** Oct 6-mid Dec, Jan to end
April, for a two nights+ stay, dinner b & b is at
the b & b price.* **Ⓥ**

● *9 en suite bedrooms (inc one family room), all
with direct dial telephone, colour TV, hairdryer,
laundry/valet service, tea/coffee making facilities,
trouser press, music/radio/alarm clock*
● *Table d'hôte £19.50; lunch and vegetarian diets
available; last orders 20.30.*
● *Croquet, bowls, badminton.*
● *Meeting room to 16. Car parking for 30.*
● *Master card, Visa, Delta, Switch accepted.
Open all year*

**Okehampton 3, Tavistock 16, Crediton 17,
Exeter 22, Plymouth 25, London 192**

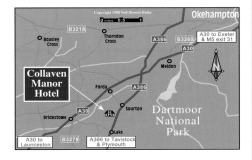

Heddon's Gate Hotel

Heddon's Mouth,
Parracombe, Barnstaple,
North Devon EX31 4PZ
Tel: (01598) 763313;
Fax: (01598) 763363;
E-mail: info@hgate.co.uk

When the English poets discovered this corner of Exmoor, they named it the 'Switzerland of England'. The wealthy soon followed, choosing all the best sites for their country estates and building in the 'Swiss-Victorian' style. Heddon's Gate was no exception to this fashion and in 1890 a single storey lodge was built high above the stunningly beautiful Heddon Valley. Bob De Ville bought it in 1967 with the intention of turning it into an hotel. In fact a Country House has been created which guests feel they can call 'home' during their stay. Accommodation at Heddon's Gate is divided into individually designed bedrooms or free-standing cottages below the hotel. The proprietor supervises the cuisine which is modern English with a Mediterranean bias. West Country Farmhouses Cheeses abound and fresh local fish and game are used. Even the hotel's water supply comes from a natural spring rising on the hill behind. Exmoor and North Devon contain a wide choice of places to visit: stately old homes and castles, fine churches and craft centres including the famous Dartington Glass Works where 'seconds' can be bought cheaply. Sheepskin goods and antiques can also be picked up reasonably in the area. There are spectacular walks from the hotel and a further 700 miles of marked Exmoor footpaths are on the doorstep.

Rates: Single room with breakfast from £33; **V** *double room inc. breakfast from £66.*
Bargain Breaks: *available from £170 for three nights b & b inc 3 afternoon teas & 3 5-course dinners.*

Lynmouth 5, Ilfracombe 11, Barnstaple 12, South Molton 15, Dunster 24, London 188

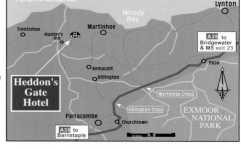

● *14 en suite bedrooms with colour TV, direct-dial telephone, hairdryer, tea/coffee making facilities*
● *Table d'hôte dinner £25; picnic lunch & special diets on request. Last orders 8 pm. Car parking for 20*
● *Walking the southwest footpath from hotel; fishing; golf ten miles; riding three miles.*
● *Open Easter-end November. Mastercard, Visa, Switch accepted.*

The Bolt Head Hotel

Salcombe, South Devon TQ8 8LL
Tel: (01548) 843751; Fax: (01548) 843060
E-mail: info@bolthead-salcombe.co.uk
Internet: www.bolthead-salcombe.co.uk

Blessed with a climate that is said to be the mildest in Devon, and set amid imposing scenery that ends with the fantastically shaped black rocks of mighty Bolt Head, this most southerly hotel in Devon commands a marvellous view of the Salcombe Estuary and coastline, and overlooks the sheltered golden cove of South Sands Beach. There are always yachts and fishing boats to be seen in this unspoilt estuary. The hotel has been completely refurbished to a very high standard under the ownership of Mr. Colin Smith. A sun terrace leads off the main lounge. The bedrooms are also very comfortable and equipped as one would expect of this well run hotel. The hotel is renowned for its warm welcome and friendly service and the staff are courteous, attentive and cheerful. The table d'hôte menu with specialities, is interesting and provides a splendid choice carefully served, in an attractive restaurant which has panoramic views of the estuary. In spite of all that is offered at this first class establishment, it also provides peace and quiet with lovely walks in the National Trust property adjoining the grounds.

Rates: Dinner, bed and breakfast from £66.00 per person per night inclusive of VAT. **V**
Getaway Breaks available; details on request.

● *29 en suite bedrooms (four ground floor), all with direct dial telephones, remote control colour TV with satellite, radio, tea/coffee making facilities; full central heating.*
● *Meals to 9p.m.; diets available.*
● *Children welcome, baby listening; dogs at manager's discretion.*
● *Games room; outdoor heated swimming pool; sailing, boating, private moorings; sea fishing; tennis 1/4 mile; riding two miles; golf eight miles.*
● *Closed mid November to mid March, but office open. A Best Western Hotel. Major credit cards accepted.*

Kingsbridge 7, Totnes 18, Exeter 43, Plymouth 25, London 214

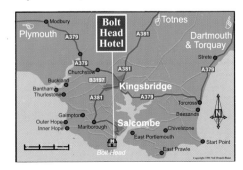

South Sands Hotel

South Sands, Salcombe, Devon TQ8 8LL
Tel: (01548) 843741; Fax: (01548) 842112

Single: dinner, bed and breakfast from £50; **Ⅴ**
Double: dinner, bed & breakfast from £88.
Bargain breaks: available: £108 two days, dinner, b&b; £196 4 days.

This hotel, owned and run by the same family as the Tides Reach Hotel (see following page) has been completely refurbished and it now represents superb value for anyone contemplating a holiday in Devon. Relaxation in this hotel can take several forms - having a 'naughty but nice' Devon Cream Tea in the comfortable main lounge, sweating it out in the Turkish Steam Room, perfecting your tan in the solarium, swimming in the indoor swimming pool, sunbathing on the beach in front of the hotel or partaking in the many watersports on offer. The South Sands Beach offers safe bathing with dinghy sailing, windsurfing and canoe hire and tuition available from The Boathouse. The hotel restaurant has a fine reputation and uses fresh local produce, from both the land and the sea. Nearby are magnificent walks along the cliffs and the attractions of Salcombe are only ten minutes away by ferry in summer months. Squash, sauna, multi-gym, hair & beauty salon and snooker are all available nearby at the sister Tides Reach Hotel Leisure Complex. South Sands' outstanding position in the sheltered Salcombe Estuary makes it an ideal spot for a short break or for a relaxing family holiday.

● *30 en suite bedrooms (9 double, 9 twin, 2 single, 10 family), all with direct dial telephone, colour TV, hairdryer, music/radio/alarm clock, tea/coffee making facilities; laundry service.*
● *Table d'hôte dinner £18.75; bar lunches; special diets available; last orders 9 pm.*
● *Jacuzzi, steam room, watersports, sailing/boating, indoor heated swimming pool. Squash & tennis 1/2 mile; riding two miles; golf five miles.*
● *Open all year. Visa and Mastercard accepted.*

Kingsbridge 7, Totnes 19, Plymouth 26, Exeter 43, London 214.

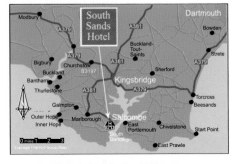

Tides Reach Hotel

South Sands, Salcombe, South Devon
TQ8 8LJ
Tel: (01548) 843466; Fax: (01548) 843954

The position of Tides Reach is perfect - a
beautiful secluded sandy cove. The quiet
luxury of the hotel strikes you as you enter
the conservatory-style hall with its indoor
water garden and the flower garden lounge-
hall so full of sunshine and scented blooms.
The décor throughout was chosen and supervised by Mrs. Edwards and the colours are
wonderfully vibrant and original. The indoor
heated swimming pool, around which has
been built a new bar and coffee shop, is as
glamorous as a Hollywood film set - there is
an outdoor sun patio and sun deck leading off
and below, a new hairdressing and beauty
salon, multi gym, sunbed, Whirlpool Spa
bath, sauna, steam baths and squash court. In
addition to the new facilities the dining room
has been extended and the bedrooms and
public rooms have been refurnished throughout in a most comfortable and luxurious manner. The food is superb, both à la carte and
table d'hôte dishes being really first class.

*Rates: Dinner, room and breakfast from £62.00
to £104.00 per person including VAT according*

to season and length of stay.   **Ⅴ**
Bargain Breaks *available from mid February -
22nd May 1999 (excluding Easter) and Oct,Nov
1999. 2-day breaks from £136 for dinner, bed and
breakfast. 4-day breaks from £260 for dinner,bed and
breakfast. Extra days pro rata.*

● *40 en suite bedrooms with colour TV, radio,
direct dial telephone; some family suites.*
● *Lift; children over eight welcome; dogs by arrangement; some diets available.*
● *Games room; snooker room; indoor heated pool;
solarium; sauna; spa bath; squash; indoor and
outdoor water gardens; drying room; golf, tennis,
riding nearby; sea bathing; boating; fishing,
windsurfing, water sports from own boathouse.*
● *Closed 2nd December-mid Febryary*
● *Resident proprietor - Roy Edwards FHCI*

**Kingsbridge 7, Totnes 19, Plymouth 26,
Exeter 43, London 214**

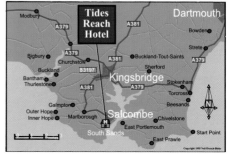

Saunton Sands Hotel, Braunton

ON THE
COAST ROAD FROM BARNSTAPLE TO ILFRACOMBE
8 Miles from Barnstaple and 9 miles from Ilfracombe.
(For position see map on page 16, square E.4).

*An hotel with a view adjoining a paradise for golfers and a playground
for children—Very modern appointments and atmosphere.*

COMMANDING an unrivalled stretch of sandy shore,
Atlantic ocean and a distant view across two estuaries
stands Saunton Sands Hotel. The formal white oblong
mass set alone on the cliff, with its storied rows of windows,
balconies and canopies conforms to a modern school of
architecture, in contrast to the homely little place which it
recently supplanted. But inside there is a gracious and
spacious air of comfort and freedom with a feeling that the
people there know how to appreciate the better things of life.
I don't want to be snobbish but the Saunton atmosphere is
very different from that of so many seaside holiday hotels
during the rush season. For one thing it's a place for golfers,
two of the best 18-hole courses in the West of England adjoining
the hotel. For another the sands are unrivalled for children
and so extensive that there is none of that dreadful herding
effect you encounter so much in the south. Yet for a de luxe
sort of place with every modern convenience, this great
solitary home with it spirit of health and happiness does not
set its charges too high for the average paterfamilias. Here
they are : Weekly from 4 to 5½ guineas. Breakfast from 3/-,
lunch from 3/6 and dinner from 5/- according to season.

The Saunton Sands Hotel

Saunton Sands, Nr. Braunton, Devon
EX31 lLQ
Tel: (01271) 890212; Fax: (01271) 890145

Lots of sun, miles of golden sands and tiered
silvery waves advancing eagerly up the beach
is what you look down on from the warm and
luxurious rooms of The Saunton Sands, a
member of the Brend Group of Exclusive
Hotels. The hotel is light and sunny as most of
the rooms face the south, the sea and the
sands, and there are panoramic views from
most. All the staff are efficient and attentive,
creating an air of warmth and friendliness.
The furnishings are elegant and comfortable,
and the bedrooms have all the modern facilities that you could want. Food is of a very
high standard and the wine list is well chosen.
Other seafront hotels in the Brend Group
include *Carlyon Bay* near St. Austell and The
Victoria Hotel in Sidmouth (see pages 20/21
and 41). This splendid hotel provides a truly
outstanding holiday for all the family, all year
round.

Rates: *Room and breakfast from £65.00 single,
£60.00 per person double, all inclusive of VAT.*
Bargain Breaks: *A Luxury Breaks tariff is available in addition to the hotel's main tariff, with
reduced rates for stays of two nights or more.* **V**

---

*Spring, June and Autumn Breaks represent excel-
lent value with prices from £56 per person per
night for dinner, room and breakfast. Child reductions are also available. Telephone the hotel and
ask for the Luxury Breaks Tariff.*

● *92 en suite bedrooms, all with telephone, satellite TV, tea/coffee making facilities; lift; 24-hour
room service; baby listening; no dogs*
● *Last orders 9.30 pm; bar meals (lunch); afternoon teas; vegetarian and vegan diets.*
● *Children welcome. Conferences max. 200.*
● *Games room; dancing frequently; full size
snooker table; children's paddling pool; supervised
nursery; heated indoor and outdoor swimming
pools; sauna/solarium; hairdressing salon; mini
cinema; miles of beach below; sailing; tennis;
squash; riding; shooting; fishing; helipad; golf
nearby.*
● *Open all year. Mastercard, Amex, Diners, Visa
credit cards accepted.*
**Barnstaple 8, llfracombe 9, Bideford 17,
Exeter 48, London 203**

Ten exclusive Westcountry Hotels.
Just a phone call away. Brend Hotels

The Victoria Hotel

Sidmouth, Devon EX10 8RY
Tel: (01395) 512651; Fax: (01395) 579154

Sidmouth was discovered as a resort by the affluent in Queen Victoria's day - hence the name of this imposing hotel which dominates the west end of the promenade, and has an uninterrupted view of the wide sweeping bay. The Victoria is owned by the Brend family who own other luxurious hotels, including the Royal Duchy at Falmouth (see page 8), Carlyon Bay at St. Austell (see pages 20/21) and The Saunton Sands Hotel at Saunton Sands (see pages 38/39) . Mr. John Brend, Managing Director, is very much in evidence looking after the needs of the guests, with the help of his efficient and friendly staff. The ground floor creates an impression of space and good taste; everything is planned for your comfort and well-being. The restaurant has a first class reputation for its cuisine, the table d'hôte and à la carte menus reaching high levels in quality, presentation and service. The wine list is comprehensive and well chosen. Upstairs, the well appointed bedrooms are comfortable and pleasantly furnished. The Victoria is set in 5 acres of landscaped gardens, with many outside attractions. I can recommend it to all ages.

Single room and breakfast from £66.00 single, Ⓥ *Double per person from £61 (including VAT). Bargain Breaks available at various times of year. Winter, Spring and Autumn breaks are particularly good value with single rooms from £62 and doubles from £52 per person, dinner, b & b, min. two nights.*

● *61 en suite bedrooms, all with telephone and TV; lift; night service.*
● *Meals to 9 p.m.; diets & vegeterian menus available.*
● *Children welcome; no dogs; conferences max. 100; hairdressing salon.*
● *Entertainment; snooker room, indoor and outdoor heated swimming pools and lido, sauna, solarium, spa bath, tennis courts, 18 hole putting course, sea bathing, sailing and fishing by arrangement; squash, badminton and riding all nearby.*
● *Major credit cards accepted.*
Honiton 9, Exeter 15, Torquay 35, Bristol 70, Birmingham 159, London 161

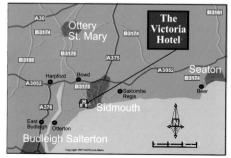

The Royal Glen Hotel

Sidmouth, Devon EX10 8RW
Tel: (01395) 513221 / 513456;
Fax: (01395) 514922

Originally built in 1700 as a farmhouse, the Royal Glen Hotel has been managed by a member of the Crane family for over 100 years. This historic and lovely hotel stands in its own grounds, 200 yards from the sea-front at Sidmouth. The cricket club is nearby as well as the golf course and shopping centre. Mr. Orson Crane proudly showed me around his lovely hotel, with its wonderful antique furniture and memorabilia from the time of Queen Victoria, whose family, the Kents, used it as a holiday cottage until the untimely death of the Duke. During the course of the young Victoria's stay, she came close to death when an apprentice boy who was shooting at birds in the garden, hit a window in the nursery, narrowly missing the future Queen. The hotel has a great deal of old world charm; the upstairs drawing room is oval with period furniture, and the dining room of the same shape houses an intriguing collection of period chairs. The food is excellent, including a superlative pudding trolley and an extensive wine list. It is possible for visitors to the hotel to stay in a Royal bedroom or Princess Victoria's nursery.

Rates start from £30.00 per night for bed and breakfast, and from £43.50 dinner, bed and breakfast in the winter. ▣
Bargain breaks available November until the end of April, excluding Christmas and Easter. Details on application.

● 32 bedrooms with bathroom/shower, three on ground floor; all with colour TV, radio, tea-making facilities, telephone and full central heating.
● Dinner - last orders 8.30 p.m.
● Special terms for children; dogs allowed.
● Indoor heated swimming pool; sea bathing; golf and tennis nearby.
● Open all year. Mastercard and Visa accepted.

Torquay 35, Birmingham 159, London 161

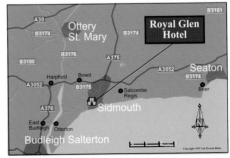

Thurlestone Hotel

Thurlestone, Nr. Kingsbridge,
South Devon TQ7 3NN
Tel: (01548) 560382; Fax: (01548) 561069
AA ★★★★ RAC ETB 👑👑👑👑 ⚜ Food

This luxurious hotel has been owned and run
by the Grose family for over 100 years and
during that time they have gained a 71% AA
4-star award - the highest graded hotel in the
district. The standard of rooms, especially the
beautifully appointed suites, testify to this.
The AA have also awarded a rosette for their
cooking and Hugh Miller, the chef, is striving
for a second one. The food is balanced, well
presented and simply delicious and the menu
is accompanied by a comprehensive wine list.
The staff, many of whom are long serving
members, are courteous, discreet and efficient. The hotel caters for everyone in that
conferences can be arranged for the business
traveller, there are all manner of facilities for
the sportsman and there is something for
every member of the family, whatever the
weather. Even the dog is welcome.
The hotel has its own golf course, which was
the venue for the British Professional
Shortcourse Championship in 1980 and which
brought Edward VIII, when Prince of Wales,
to Thurlestone on a number of occasions.

Single room including breakfast £37-100.   Ⅴ
Double room including breakfast £74-200.
Bargain breaks Dinner, b&b from £47 per per-
son per night Nov-March. Others on application.
Dinner table d'hôte £25; à la carte, lunch &
special diets available; last orders 2100 hrs.

● *65 en suite bedrooms (inc 3 suites & 19 deluxe),
all with colour TV (+Sky), direct-dial telephone,
music/radio/alarm clock, hairdryer, laundry/valet
service, tea/coffee making facilities, 24-hr room
service, trouser press.*
● *Outdoor & indoor swimming pools; billiards/
snooker, croquet, fitness centre, 9-hole golf course,
indoor games, jacuzzi, massage/sauna, squash,
tennis, children's playrooms. Fishing, watersports,
riding, sailing/boating nearby.*
● *Hairdressing/beauty salon. Conferences to 120.*
● *Open all year. Mastercard,Visa & Amex accepted*
**Kingsbridge 4, Plymouth 20, Torquay 21,
Exeter 36, London 236**

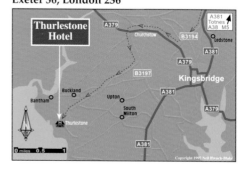

The Osborne Hotel

Hesketh Crescent, Meadfoot, Torquay,
Devon TQ1 2LL
Tel: (01803) 213311; Fax: (01803) 296788

The Osborne Hotel, known by the discerning
as "the country house hotel by the sea", is the
centrepiece of an elegant Regency crescent.
Rooms provide a panoramic view of five acres
of hotel gardens and the broad sweep of
Torbay, yet the neighbouring woodland is a re-
minder that the countryside is just a few minutes away. There are two hotel restaurants: the
gourmet *Langtry's* which combines innovative
dishes with tempting regional specialities and
the more informal *Brasserie*, open all day for
lighter meals, coffee and Devon cream teas.
The hotel has a fully equipped gymnasium and
many other sporting facilities in the grounds.
Conferences are catered for in the library and
social occasions such as weddings and birth-
days take place in the elegant Drawing Room.
Most of the luxurious bedrooms have sea
views and are individually designed with
every modern convenience. The Osborne is a
hotel big enough to be luxurious and small
enough to be able to care for every guest individually. Torquay is an ideal touring centre,
easily accessible via the motorway network
and within easy reach is Dartmoor, Exeter and
the romantic West Country coasts, with their
picturesque harbours and cliff walks.

*Rates: Single inc. breakfast from £43; double/
twin from £86. Dinner, room and breakfast from
£60 per head per night.*   Ⓥ
*Bargain Breaks: 2 nights or more from £58 per
head, dinner, b & b.*

● *29 en suite bedrooms, all with colour TV+ satellite, direct dial telephone, hairdryer, laundry/valet
service, music/radio/alarm, trouser press, tea/coffee
making facilities, 24-hr room/meal service.*
● *Table d'hôte dinner £17.95; à l carte & special
diets available; last orders 9.45 pm.*
● *Conference room - cap. 25. Car parking for 90.*
● *Billiards/snooker, gymnasium, sea/river bathing, sauna/solarium, indoor & outdoor swimming
pools, tennis, putting green. Fishing & watersports 1 mile; golf 5 miles.*
● *Open all year. All major credit cards accepted.*

**Newton Abbot 6, Totnes 8, Exeter 23, Ply-
mouth 32, Bristol 106, London 223**

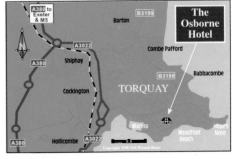

Watersmeet Hotel

Mortehoe, Woolacombe,
Devon EX34 7EB
Tel: (01271) 870333; Fax: (01271) 870890

Watersmeet, with its south facing terraced gardens and private steps leading to the beach below, commands a unique position with extensive sea views from Hartland Point to Lundy Island. This lovely hotel is owned and personally looked after by Brian and Pat Wheeldon, both very experienced, who have taken great care to preserve the comfort and style of a country house. All the public rooms and bedrooms are delightfully furnished with soft colour schemes complemented by lovely fabrics. There are two bars, one an exclusive cocktail bar with comfortable lounges leading off; the other a newly f urnished and superbly decorated terrace restaurant/bar for coffees, light lunches and teas. Candles light the octagonal Restaurant which is designed so that every table enjoys a spectacular view of the sea. The award winning cuisine, always imaginative, has gone from strength to strength, and is simply superb. The menus are changed daily, and guests may choose from English or an International cuisine. The selection of wines is well chosen. I can thoroughly recommend this well run family hotel, where the service is efficient and conveys a happy atmosphere. Do write for their most attractive and informative brochure.

Rates: Dinner, room and breakfast from £56-107; Other terms, including special breaks on application. Bridge and painting holidays arranged.
Spring and Autumn Breaks, three or more days. All prices on application. **V**

● *26 bedrooms (one ground floor suite) all with private bathroom, remote control colour TV; direct dial telephones; children welcome.*
● *Meals till 8.30 p.m; light lunches; diets.*
● *Indoor heated pool and spa; snooker room; outdoor heated swimming pool; grass tennis court; bathing, sandy beach - private steps to seashore; surfing and sailing, boating, sea and river fishing, riding and three golf courses all nearby; lovely walks - National Trust.*
● *Closed December to February but office open for enquiries. All major credit cards accepted.*

Barnstaple 14, Exeter 56, Taunton 62, Bristol 79, London 203

THE WEST COUNTRY

Woolacombe Bay Hotel

Woolacombe, Devon EX34 7BN
Tel: (01271) 870388; Fax: (01271) 870613

Rugged moors, rocky tors, endless National Trust walks on beach and headland; picturesque villages of "olde worlde" charm are the feel and freedom of Devon. Set amidst six acres of quiet gardens running to three miles of golden sand is the luxurious Woolacombe Bay Hotel, built in the halcyon days of the mid 1800's. It exudes a relaxed air of friendliness, good living, comfort and traditional service. The hotel has been extensively but sensitively modernised, combining discreet old fashioned ambience with modern charm. Dining is simply a delight, the best of English and Continental cooking, using the freshest local produce with special diets catered for. Complementing the menus is an interesting wine list, and you can also enjoy a drink in one of the relaxed bars. Guests have unlimited use of the extensive leisure and sporting amenities (see facilities below), and the hotel's *MV Frolica* boat is available for charter. A magnificent ballroom and spacious lounges, combined with the outstanding facilities at the Woolacombe Bay Hotel, enables everyone to have the holiday of their choice. Energetic or relaxed - the decision is yours.

Rates: room and breakfast from £55 per person, *Dinner*, room and breakfast from £75 per person including VAT.   **V**
Bargain breaks: Special seasonal offers available. Please enquire for details.

- 64 en suite bedrooms, all with telephone and TV, room/night service; baby listening, lift.
- Last orders for dinner 9 p.m; bar meals in bistro; special diets; children welcome; conferences max. 200.
- Games room; snooker/billiards; short mat bowls; tennis coaching; indoor and outdoor heated swimming pools; the 'Hot House' fitness centre with aerobics studio, fitness room, beautician, masseur, trimtrail; 2 squash courts; 9 hole approach golf course; 2 floodlit all-weather tennis courts; sea bathing (blue flag beach); sailing/boating; own motor yacht; riding, shooting and fishing nearby.
- Hotel closed Jan.-mid Feb.; all credit cards accepted.

Barnstaple 14, Exeter 56, Taunton 62, Bristol 79, London 203

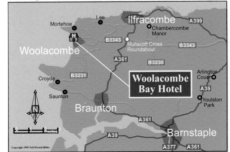

Dukes Hotel

Great Pulteney Street, Bath, Somerset
BA2 4DN
Tel: (01225) 463512; Fax: (01225) 483733

Rates: *Single room inc breakfast £55-70; double
room inc. breakfast £70-100.*   ¥
Bargain Breaks: *rates on application.*

Dukes Hotel is situated in one of Bath's most
elegant boulevards, and yet is just a few minutes' stroll from the city centre. The architect-
urally important Grade I listed Georgian
building has been fully restored externally
and modernised internally. Mouldings, cor-
nices and other original Georgian features
have been retained and the magnificent staircase, cosy fully licensed bar and relaxing
drawing room instill a sense of well-being as
soon as you set foot in the hotel. The varied
dinner menu is prepared from the finest local
produce and the reasonably priced wines
have been selected by a Master of Wine.
Breakfast is complemented by Duke's own
marmalade. Bedrooms are individually furnished to a high standard.
Bath is one of only three World Heritage
Centres in Europe and as well as the many
places to visit - the Roman Baths, Pump
Room, Assembly Rooms, Museum of Costume, Theatre Royal, Royal Photographic
Society etc, it is also a renowned shopping
and artistic centre and a good jumping-off
point for touring the Mendips and Cotswolds.

● *24 en suite bedrooms, all with colour TV + satellite, direct-dial telephone, hairdryer, tea/coffee making facilities.*
● *Table d'hôte dinner £15.95; special diets available;
last orders 9 pm.*
● *Open all year. Mastercard, Visa, Amex credit
cards accepted.*

**M4 (junc 18) 9, Bristol 12, Chippenham 13,
Frome 13, Wells 19, London 104**

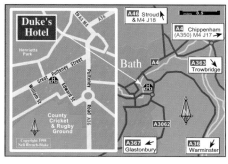

Bindon Country House Hotel & Restaurant

Langford Budville, Wellington, Somerset TA21 ORU
Tel: (01823) 400070;
Fax: (01823) 400071
E-mail: Bindonhouse@msr.com

Bindon House is not just an hotel but also a home. Owned by a succession of aristocrats and distinguished families documented since1237, it clearly has been and still is a centre of gracious living. The present buildings date from the 17th century. It became a hotel in 1997. The staircase is a delight to behold. One almost needs a map to find one's way through the labyrinth of old passages on the first floor. Furnished with beautiful antiques and nestling in seven acres of stunning woodland gardens, the house's motto is, unsurprisingly, *Je trouve bien*, (I find well). One need venture no further than the hotel grounds to find this 'well-being'. Guests can also hire a bicycle or stroll in the nearby 180-acre Langford Heath nature reserve. The 12 bedrooms are sumptuously decorated with many pampering extras in the bathrooms. The *Wellesley* Restaurant specialises in an eclectic mix of classical French style and imaginary British cuisine, with fine wines complimenting the meal. There are two private conference rooms with all modern facilities. Truly an atmospheric spot for a short leisure break or small business conference.

● *12 en suite bedrooms with colour TV, direct-dial telephone, hairdryer, laundry service, 24-hour room/ meal service, music/radio/alarm clock, trouser press. All bedrooms non-smoking. Facilities for disabled.*
● *Table d'hôte dinner £29.50; à la carte, lunch & special diets available; last orders 9.45 pm.*
● *Croquet, outdoor swimming pool, tennis at hotel; fishing 1 mile, golf, riding, shooting 4 miles.*
● *Business services inc 2 meeting rooms, cap'y 50.*
● *Open all year. Visa, Amex, Mastercard, Switch, Diners accepted. Car parking for 28/rental by arr't.*

Rates: Single room with breakfast from £75; **V**
double room inc. breakfast from £95.
***Bargain Breaks:** min two-day break, dinner, b & b £75 pppn standard or £95 pppn super.*

Taunton 6, Tiverton 15, Honiton 20, Dunster 22, Exeter 25, London 150

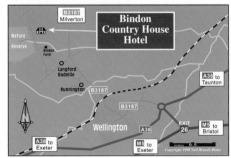

The Walnut Tree Hotel

North Petherton, Bridgwater,
Somerset TA6 6QA
Tel: (01278) 662255; Fax: (01278) 663946

Room and breakfast from £38 inc. VAT; **V**
Dinner, room *and breakfast from £50 inc. VAT.*
Bargain breaks: *Special weekend packages avail able.*

The Walnut Tree Inn is a former 18th Century coaching inn, set in the heart of the pretty Somerset village of North Petherton, on the A38. Traditional values have been maintained here over the years. All the rooms are quietly located at the rear of the Inn, and every possible comfort is provided for guests. Each of the thirty two bedrooms offer superb amenities. The décor is tasteful and warming, and the four-poster bed suite is a popular choice for those seeking a special or romantic weekend break. The Walnut Tree also specialises in receptions and parties, the public rooms having an abundance of charm and character. The popular bar with *Cottage Room* Restaurant, can tempt you with real ales, light bar snacks and succulent steaks. However, first class international cuisine can be savoured in the beautiful *Dukes* Restaurant, with presentation, service and excellent wines making for a memorable repast. The Walnut Tree Hotel is a hostelry of high standards with friendly staff attending to your every need. Well located for touring the South West. Do sample the charm of this hotel, and you are bound to return.

● *32 en suite bedrooms (inc. suites) (3 for the disabled), all with direct dial telephone and TV; room service; baby listening; night service.*
● *Last orders for dinner 10 p.m., bar meals, special diets.*
● *Children welcome; meetings/conferences to 110.*
● *Solarium; extensive parking facilities.*
● *Open all year; all major credit cards accepted.*

M5 (exit 24) 1, Bridgwater 1$\frac{1}{2}$, Taunton 8, Wells 12, Bristol 35, Exeter 40, London 150

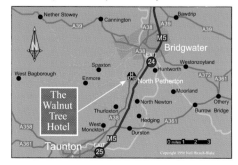

THE WEST COUNTRY

Crudwell Court Hotel and Restaurant

Crudwell, Nr. Malmesbury,
Wiltshire SN16 9EP

Tel: (01666) 577194; Fax: (01666) 577853
E-mail: Crudwellcrt@compuserve.com

What a lovely surprise to find this enchanting little hotel on my travels near to Cirencester and Malmesbury. It is a 1 7th century former vicarage, set alongside a Saxon church in three acres of beautiful walled gardens. It is really like staying in a private home - I had the most warm welcome and I certainly look forward to a return visit. The house has recently been completely refurbished and all fifteen bedrooms are individually decorated. The gracious panelled dining room and the beautiful conservatory overlook the church. The excellent cuisine is freshly prepared to order, all complemented by an extensive wine list. Crudwell Court is run by its resident owner, Nick Bristow, who gives that extra personal touch to the warm, country house atmosphere.

● *15 en suite bedrooms, all with telephone, remote control colour TV, radio, tea/coffee making facilities, full central heating, night service til midnight.*
● *Last dinner orders 9.30 pm; bar meals; diets.*
● *Childen welcome; baby listening; dogs accepted.*
● *Conferences max. 25.*
● *Heated outdoor swimming pool, croquet; leisure centre, sailing, golf tennis, squash, badminton, riding, shooting, fishing all nearby.*
● *Open all year. Mastercard, Visa, Amex & Diners credit cards accepted.*

Malmesbury 3, Cirencester 6, Swindon 12, London 97

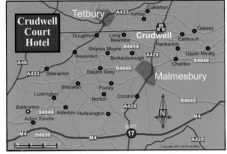

Beechfield House Hotel & Restaurant

Beanacre, Melksham,
Wiltshire SN12 7PU
Tel: (01225) 703700; Fax: (01225) 790118

Set in the pretty village of Beanacre between Chippenham and Melksham, Beechfield House is approached by a lovely, long leafy drive. This sets the scene for this delightful hotel built in Victorian times and set in a haven of eight acres of gardens and grounds. Antiques abound in this country house hotel but comfort is not lost and décor is exquisite. As you would expect, all 21 bedrooms are en suite, well appointed and include a charming four-poster room. The main dining room overlooks the heated outdoor swimming pool and a wisteria-clad walled garden. A private dining room caters for smaller functions or special occasions. Cuisine is largely modern English, offering a delicious and imaginative range of menus plus an excellent wine list. Hunting, shooting, fishing and golf can be arranged nearby. The hotel is one mile south of the National Trust village of Lacock. Beanacre is a good centre for visiting the Georgian city of Bath and the stately homes Bowood, Longleat and Corsham Court.

Single room inc. breakfast from £70;
Double room inc. breakfast from £90.
Bargain Breaks. £110 per night (minimum two night stay) to include 4-course dinner, bed & breakfast for two persons sharing twin or double.

● *21 en suite rooms (16 double, 5 twin), all with telephone, colour TV, laundry/valet service, hairdryer, tea/coffee making, music/radio/alarm clock, trouser press; non-smoker rooms available.*
● *Table d'hôte and à la carte dinner, lunch & special diets available; last orders 9 pm.*
● *Croquet, outdoor swimming pool. Fishing, golf, riding, shooting, squash, tennis nearby.*
● *Business services inc. three meeting rooms, cap-acity 25. Car parking for 45.*
● *Open all year. Major credit cards accepted.*

Melksham 1, Chippenham 7, Bath 12, Bristol 25, Swindon 28, Salisbury 35, London 94

Central Southern England

Berkshire
Beale Wildlife Gardens, Lower Basildon
Cliveden, Nr. Maidenhead
Dorney Court, Nr. Windsor
Forbury Gardens, Reading
Highclere Castle, Nr. Newbury
Mapledurham House and Watermill, Nr. Reading
Stonor House Henley-on-Thames
Stratfield Saye House, Nr. Reading

Buckinghamshire
Claydon House, Nr. Winslow
Hughenden Manor, High Wycombe
Stowe Landscape Gardens, Nr. Buckingham
Waddesdon Manor, Nr. Aylesbury
West Wycombe Park, Nr. High Wycombe

Dorset
Athelhampton House & Gardens, Puddletown, Dorchester
Forde Abbey & Gardens, Chard
Hardy's Cottage Garden, Higher Bockhampton, Dorchester
Kingston Lacey House, Nr. Wimborne

Hampshire
Breamore House & Museums, Nr. Fordingbridge Broadlands, Romsey
Exbury Gardens, Nr. Southampton
Furzey Gardens Minstead, Nr. Lyndhurst
Highclere Castle
Lymington Vineyard
Lymore Valley Herb Garden, Nr. Milford-on-Sea
Sir Harold Hillier Gardens & Arboretum, Ampfield, Nr. Romsey
Stratfield Saye House & Wellington Country Park

Oxfordshire
Basildon Park, Nr. Pangbourne
Blenheim Palace, Woodstock
Peoples Park, Banbury
Rousham House & Gardens, Steeple Aston
Waterperry Gardens, Wheatley

Berkshire
Riverside & Country Walk to Speen Moors
Heritage Walk, Reading
Look Out Countryside & Heritage Centre Nr. Bracknell
Reading Town Trails

Dorset
Brit Valley Walk
The Dorset Coastal Path
Hardy's Dorset Walk

Hampshire
Avon Valley Path, Salisbury to Christchurch
Itchin Way, Southampton to Hinton Ampner
Solent Way, Milford on-Sea to Emsworth
Three Castles Path, Windsor to Winchester

Oxfordshire
Guided Walking Tours of Oxford
Oxford Ecology Trail

Bedfordshire
Bunyan Museum, Bedford
Elstow Moot Hall, Church End
Stockwood Craft Museum & Gardens
Shuttleworth Collection, Biggleswade

Berkshire
Blake's Lock Museum, Reading
Foxhill Collection of Historic Carriages,   Nr. Reading
Newbury Museum
Reading Abbey
St. George's Chapel, Windsor Castle
Windsor Castle

Buckinghamshire
Buckinghamshire County Museum, Aylesbury
Chiltern Brewery, Terrick, Aylesbury

Hampshire
D Day Museum,   Portsmouth
Hurst Castle, Keyhaven
New Forest Museum & Visitor Centre,   Ashurst,
Portchester Castle
The Sammy Miller Museum, New Milton

Oxfordshire
Banbury Museum & Art Gallery
Broughton Castle, Banbury
Cogges Manor Farm Museum, Witney
Didcot Railway Museum
The Oxford Story, Oxford

Entertainment Venues

Berkshire
Bucklebury Farm Park Nr. Reading
Crown Jewels of the World Exhibition, Windsor
Holme Grange Craft Centre / Art Gallery, Wokingham Trilakes Country Park & Fishery, Sandhurst
Wyld Court Rainforest, Nr. Newbury

Buckinghamshire
Flamingo Gardens & Zoological Park, Olney
Glass Craft, Holtspur, Nr. Beaconsfield
West Wycombe Caves

Dorset
Brownsea Island, Poole
Lyme Regis Marine Aquarium
Lodmoor Country Park, Weymouth
Weymouth Sea Life Park

Hampshire
Lepe Country Park, Exbury
Marwell Zoological Park, Winchester
New Forest Buttefly Farm, Ashurst
Paultons Park, Nr. Lyndhurst
Portsmouth Sea Life Centre

Oxfordshire
Cotswold WildDife Park, Burford
CuriOXiTy (Science Gallery) Oxford
The Oxford Story, Oxford
Waterfowl Sanctuary, Nr. Hook Norton

DIARY OF EVENTS

January

2-4. **Challow Hurdle**. Racing at Newbury, Berks.

February

16. **Sway Pancake Race.** Village Centre, Sway, Hampshire

April

2. **Lambourn Racehorse Trainers Open Day.** Lambourn Stables, Berkshire.
2-3. **Thame Easter Antiques Fair.** The Spread Eagle Hotel, Cornmarket, Thame, Oxon.
5, **The Great Butser Easter Egg Roll.** Queen Elizabeth Country Park, Gravel Hill, Horndean, Hampshire.
5. **Old Berks Point-to-Point.** Lockinge, Abingdon, Berks.
11-12. **Beaulieu Boat Jumble**. Sale of Marine Equipment. National Motor Museum, Beaulieu, Hampshire.

May

1-3. **Newbury Steam Funtasia** Steam Rally. Newbury Showground, Chieveley, Berkshire.
2-3. **Weymouth International Beach Kite Festival.** The Beach, Weymouth, Dorset.
8, 11 & 24. **Cricket World Cup 1999** New Zealand v Hampshire / England v Hampshire / W Indies v New Zealand, County Cricket Ground, Southampton, Hants
8-22. **International Newbury Spring Festival.** Various venues, Newbury, Berkshire.
13-16. **Royal Windsor Horse Show.** Windsor Home Park, Berks.

June

11-13*. **Goodwood Festival of Speed.** Motor Sport Event, Goodwood House, W Sussex
15-18. **Royal Ascot Race Meeting.** Ascot Racecourse, Berks
26-July 10. **Bournemouth Musicmakers Festival**. Various venues, Bournemouth, Dorset.
30-July 4. **Henley Royal Regatta.** Henley-on-Thames, Oxfordshire.
19. **Ladbroke Handicap.** Ascot Racecourse, Berkshire

July

27-31. **Glorious Goodwood.** Goodwood Racecourse, W Sussex
31-7 Aug. Skandia Life Cowes Week

August

6-8*. **Portsmouth & Southsea Show,** Seafront, Portsmouth.
22-31*. **Arundel Festival,** Various venues, Arundel, West Sussex.

September

2. **Buckinghamshire County Show.** Seedon Park, Weedon, Aylesbury, Bucks.
10-19. **Southampton International Boat Show 99.** Western Esplanade, Southampton, Hants.
11*. **Romsey Show.** Broadlands Park, Romsey, Hampshire.
11-12*. **Farnborough International Air Show**, Farnborough, Hants.
18-19*. **Newbury & Royal Co Berkshire Show.** Chieveley, Berks
22-23. **ROA Foundation Stakes/ Charlton Hunt Stakes.** Goodwood, West Sussex.
25-26. **Queen Elizabeth II Stakes/Fillies Mile.** Ascot Racecourse, Berkshire.
25-27. **Holiday & Park Homes Exhibitions.** National Motor Museum, John Montagu Bldg, Beaulieu, Hampshire.

October

23. **Perpetual St Simon Stakes.** Newbury Racecourse, Berkshire.

November

20. **First National Bank Gold Cup Chase.** Ascot Racecourse, Berks

*Denotes provisional date
For further details contact:

The Southern Tourist Board
40 Chamberlayne Road, Eastleigh, Hampshire SO5 5JH.
Tel: (01703) 620006

CENTRAL SOUTHERN ENGLAND

Central Southern England

The Solent waterway between Southamp-ton and the Isle of Wight is the sailing playground of southern England.

Portsmouth Harbour is home to Nelson's *Victory*, the restored Elizabethan galleon recently brought to the surface The *Mary Rose* and *HMS Warrior*, Britain's first iron-clad warship.

Beaulieu on the west side of the Solent is the site of Lord Montagu's *National Motor Museum. Broadlands* at Romsey nearby was the seat of Lord Mountbatten and houses an exhibition from his life of public service.

On the way north from the south coast the visitor pasdses through Winchester with its 11-13th centruy cathedral and castle remains, where King Arthur's reputed Round Table can be viewed.

North of Winchester on the way to the Midlands, the visitor passes over the chalk Newbury Downs, site of some of the most famous racing stables in England, on his or her way to Oxford. The dreaming spires, echoing quads and cloistered lawns of the colleges have a timeless beauty. The *Ashmolean* Museum is Britain's oldest public museum, opened in 1683. It contains gold and jewellery beleived to have been the property of King Alfred, the lantern carried by Guy Fawkes and riches from ancient Egypt and Greece. The

Bodleian Library, founded in 1596, is one of six University Libraries in the British Isles which receives a copy of every book published in the UK.

Buckinghamshire, northeast of Oxford, contains Stowe, now a public school, with parks landsacped by Capability Brown, and Waddesdon, seat of the Rothschild Collection.

Neighbouring Berkshire's most visited monument is Windsor Castle, now fully restored after the fire of 1995.

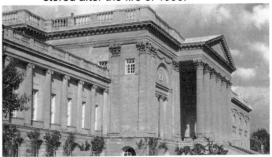

Isle of Wight, Totland Bay

Country Garden Hotel

Church Hill, Totland Bay, Isle of Wight
PO39 OET
Tel/Fax: (01983) 754521

Away from the main tourist areas lies the aptly named Country Garden Hotel in Totland Bay, near Yarmouth. The landscaping, the quiet garden pools and the rich colours are a joy. Bedrooms are light and airy and the public rooms are welcoming. The hotel organises gourmet evenings and lobster, wild boar, seafood and flambé dishes are a speciality. A good centre for walking or from which to explore the many attractions of the island by car.

Rates: Single room with breakfast from £38; **V** *double from £76. Visa & Mastercard accepted.*
Bargain Breaks: *October-June 2 nights or more at special rates.* ● *Open Feb-December. Car park 40.* ● *15 en suite bedrooms all with TV, telephone, hairdryer, laundry service, tea/coffee making.* ●
Last orders 21.30; facilities for disabled; no children.

The Swan Diplomat

Streatley-on-Thames,
Berkshire RG8 9HR
Tel: (01491) 873737; Fax: (01491) 872554
E-mail: sales@swan-diplomat.co.uk

Set on the banks of the River Thames in 23 acres of grounds, this well established hotel offers a welcoming and caring service to its guests. The spacious bedrooms, some with balconies, are individually designed and furnished and many look on to the river or have views to the Streatley hills. The comfortable lounge overlooks the river and the hotel's own island. Guests may choose to dine either in the elegant Dining Room or The Club Room, both of which offer traditional English, combined with European, cuisine. Other facilities include the Reflexions Leisure Club (free membership for hotel guests during stay) and the rebuilt 19th-century Magdalen College barge - a wonderful venue for meetings or cocktail parties. There are many short walks around the hotel, a number of National Trust properties and stately homes within easy reach and arrangements can be made for golf at local courses or the hire of a river cruiser. To sum up, this is a luxurious hotel in a marvellous setting which offers plenty to do and see - or you can even just relax by the river!

Rates: Bed and full English breakfast Monday to Thursday from £108.50 per single room per night; Friday-Sunday from £73.50 per single room per night **V**
Weekend breaks: From £85 per person per night(minimum two nights stay)

● *46 en suite bedrooms, all with telephone, colour TV+ satellite channels, minibar, hairdryer; 24 hour room service.*
● *Last orders 9.30p.m; light lunches; diets.*
● *Children welcome, baby listening; dogs by arrangement; conferences up to 90.*
● *Indoor, heated fit-pool; spa bath; multi-gym; sauna; solarium, row boat and bicycle hire, beauty treatments; golf, tennis and fishing 1/2 mile; shooting and riding five miles.*
● *Amex, Diners, Barclaycard and Mastercard accepted. Open all year.*

Reading 9, Newbury 13, Oxford 20, Henley 20, Windsor 30, London 50

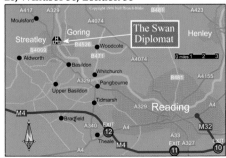

Grovefield Hotel

Taplow Common Road, Burnham,
Buckinghamshire SL1 8LP
Tel: (01628) 603131; Fax: (01628) 668078

The Grovefield Hotel was once the country re-treat of John Fuller of the well known brewing family. Now it is an elegant hotel, nestling in seven acres of lawns, surrounded by wood-land. Over the years the building has been ex-tended and renovated, but still retains its at-tractive character and architectural features. With a blend of tranquillity and quiet effi-ciency, the Grovefield is one of the finest and most versatile wedding and conference venues in the area. It is a popular choice for leisure breaks, private functions and company meet-ings. The bedrooms are a far cry from the run-of-the-mill hotel bedrooms. Some are very large, while others have unusual shapes and features. All have been completely refurbished to a high standard. *Hamiltons* restaurant is par-ticularly well regarded and has recently been awarded an AA rosette. Lunch is generally taken from a hot and cold buffet table. In the evening, an extensive à la carte menu is avail-able. Windsor, with its castle, river and antique shops is near-by and there are many National Trust properties in the area. Historic Runnymede Island is nearby and there are five local race-courses including Ascot, Kempton and Newbury.

Single room with breakfast £120 (weekends £70); V
Double room with breakfast £130 (weekends £90).
Bargain Breaks: 2-night weekend break £57.50 pppn sharing twin/double. Xmas package £280 pp 3-night stay.

● *40 en suite bedrooms, with radio and colour TV + satellite; direct-dial telephone; hairdryer; laun-dry service, 24-hr room/meal service, trouser press; non-smoker and disabled bedrooms available.*

● *Table d'hôte dinner £23.50; à la carte, lunch and special diets available; last orders 10 pm.*

● *Business services inc. 4 meeting rooms cap. 200; 200; car parking 150; wedding receptions a speciality.*

● *Croquet, fishing, golf. Watersports 8 m, riding, sail-ing, squash 5 m*

● *Amex, Visa, Mastercard, Switch ac-cepted.*

**Slough 3¹/₂,
Windsor 5¹/₂,
High
Wycombe 8¹/₂,
Henley 12,
Reading 16,
London 24**

Queens Hotel

Meyrick Rd, East Cliff, Bournemouth,
Dorset BHl 3DL

Tel: (01202) 554415; Fax: (01202) 294810

The Queen's Hotel, set in a prime position on
Bournemouth's East Cliff, enjoying southerly
views across Poole Bay. It is part of the Young
Hotel Group, (whose motto is *"Stay young,
stay happy"*) with The *Cumberland*, The
Trouville and The *Cliffeside*, all being 'sister'
hotels, within the central Bournemouth area.
A truly warm welcome awaits guests. All the
en suite bedrooms are stylishly decorated,
and many have their own balconies (some
with seaviews). A number of luxury four-
poster bedrooms and family suites are available. The restaurant has established an enviable reputation for its excellent cuisine, complemented by wines to suit every palate. The
Garden Room, leading out onto a sunny patio, is the ideal venue for either a coffee, or
perhaps cocktails with friends.
The *Queensbury Leisure Club* is the most superb addition. Facilities including the indoor
pool are of the highest standards, providing a
truly luxurious fitness centre. Conferences are
well catered for, with purpose built seminar
and syndicate rooms available, providing for
all your business needs. All in all, the Queen's
Hotel is an excellent venue, whether your stay
in Bournemouth is for business or pleasure.

Rates: Room and breakfast from £47.00.   **V**
*Bargain breaks: October-April '99 two night
stay £99.50 pppn, d, b&b. Mini breaks, Christmas,
New Year and Easter programmes.*

● *110 en suite bedrooms, all with telephone and
TV; room/night service; baby listening, lift.*
● *An AA Rosette has been awarded for the cuisine; last orders 9 p.m., bar meals, special diets on
request.*
● *Children welcome; no dogs; conferences max. 200*
● *Full size snooker table, games room, indoor
heated swimming pools, sauna, spa pool, solarium,
jacuzzi, gym, aroma-therapist/masseuse, sea bathing, sailing/boating, golf and riding 3 miles, shoot-
ing/fishing by arrangement.*
● *Open all year; major credit cards accepted.*

New Forest 10, Southampton 35, London 100

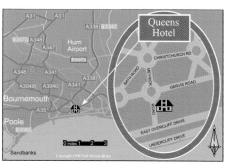

The Manor Hotel

West Bexington, Dorchester,
Dorset DT2 9DF
Tel: (01308) 897616; Fax: (01308) 897035

Rates: Room and breakfast from £44; diner, b & b weekly charge from £380. **Ⅴ**
Bargain breaks: Two-day stay - dinner, bed & breakfast £128 per person; five-day stay - dinner, bed & breakfast £305 per person.

The Manor Hotel, located amidst some of the most dramatic scenery on the South Dorset coast, is somewhere very special just waiting to be discovered. This ancient manor house is well mellowed with age, and offers a wonderful combination of flagstone floors, panelled walls, beamed ceilings, cellar rooms, yet has been provided with en suite bedrooms including every modern comfort and facility that guests could require. The décor of the en suite rooms certainly brings the vibrance of Dorset flowers and countryside through every window. Views are breathtaking. The natural gardens of the hotel are colourful and well established. Beyond is the sweeping geographical landmark of Chesil Bank with the clear seas of Lyme Bay lapping and ebbing over miles of pebbles. A more dramatic and scenic, yet quiet and relaxing situation for an hotel, one could not wish to better. The Cellar Bar provides a varied choice of bar meals through the day and in the evening, the elegant restaurant enjoys a fine reputation for well chosen culinary specialities, with fresh local produce, vegetables and especially seafood being used by the chef to present an excellent menu. A fine wine list satisfies all tastes. With the owners, Richard and Jane Childs stating that, for their guests *"nothing is too much trouble"*, please discover and pamper yourself with a visit to the Manor Hotel - a real treat!

● *13 en suite bedrooms, all with direct dial telephone and colour TV; room service; baby listening.*
● *Last orders for dinner 9.30p.m.; bar meals; special diets*
● *Children welcome; conferences max. 60.*
● *Sea bathing; golf five miles; riding two miles.*
● *Open all year. Credit cards accepted.*

Bridport 7, Dorchester 10, Weymouth 11, Lyme Regis 14, Bournemouth 50, Exeter 50, London 135

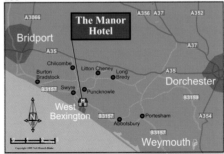

Manor House Hotel

Studland Bay, Nr. Swanage,
Dorset BH19 3AU
Tel: (01929) 450288

The site of the Manor House Hotel is mentioned in the Domesday Book and parts of the present rambling Gothic House date back to 1750. Set within 20 acres of elevated grounds, the hotel commands beautiful views overlooking the beaches and waters of Studland Bay. History and character are in abundance; the hotel's medieval carvings are said to have come from the residential quarters of Corfe Castle, home of the famous Mary Banks, who defended it so bravely against Cromwell's troops. Most of the en suite bedrooms (four with four-poster beds) have spectacular views over the bay and out to Old Harry Rocks. Wall carvings in the Westminster Bedroom are of particular interest, reputed to have been from the old Palace of Westminster, circa 1636. A delightful conservatory has extended the dining area, where décor is sophisticated, and the atmosphere and service is most warming. The menu has an excellent choice of fresh local produce and the delicious Studland Lobster is a must ! The Manor House is an ideal base from which to explore the beauty, beaches and nature trails of Studland and surrounding Dorset.

Rates: *Dinner, room and breakfast from £48.00*V
Bargain breaks: *3 or 5 night specials . 3 nights = 10% off daily rate; 5 nights = 20% off daily rate.*

● *18 en suite bedrooms, all with colour TV, radio, tea/coffee making facilities, telephone, hairdryer and full central heating.*
● *Last orders for dinner 8.30 p.m; bar lunches; vegetarian diets; AA award for good food.*
● *Children over five welcome; dogs allowed.*
● *Sea bathing three miles with sandy beach, sailing and boating; two tennis courts (hard); riding; golf within two miles;*
● *Hotel closed Christmas to mid-January.*
● *Mastercard and Visa cards accepted.*

Swanage 3, Corfe Castle 6, Bournemouth 8, Dorchester 26, London 113,

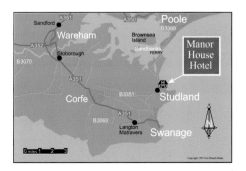

Knoll House Hotel

Studland Bay, Dorset BH19 3AH
Tel: (01929) 450450; Fax: (01929) 450423

This delightful hotel is situated on the finest stretch of Dorset heritage coastline surrounded by some of the prettiest countryside in the West and it is well worth a visit. It is within a National Trust Reserve and overlooks three miles of golden beach with first class swimming, fishing, boating and windsurfing. Knoll House is an independent country house hotel under the personal management of its family owners and is set in pine trees with the most attractive gardens where you can relax away from the cares of everyday life. The sporting facilities are numerous - tennis courts, a nine-hole par 3 golf course and outdoor heated swimming pool. For relaxation there is a sauna, steamroom, Jacuzzi, plunge-pool, solarium and gym set in a marvellous health hydro complex with fruit juice and coffee bar. Many of the bedrooms are arranged as suites, ideal for families. Log fires and an attractive cocktail bar add to the unique atmosphere of this

extremely efficiently run hotel. The quality, choice and presentation of the menus is excellent. At lunchtime a superb hors d'oeuvres selection and buffet table laden with cold meats, pies and salads is a speciality, followed by delicious puddings and a good English cheeseboard. Young children are catered for in their own dining room and there are many and varied facilities to keep them amused all day. Sandbanks and Bournemouth are easily reached via the car ferry. Dorchester, Corfe Castle and the picturesque villages of Dorset are only a short drive away.

Rates: *Half board from £64.00 daily or full board (weekly) £450 (April) - £720 (August) Generous full board terms for five nights out of season.*

Special breaks: *'Family Five' (two adults, one or two children under 13) - five nights full board in low season £939. Purbeck Five (single or twin rooms without private bathroom) five nights full board in low season £313.00 per person. September 19th-October 14th, two nights full board £138-£159 per person. Prices include VAT. There is no service charge.*

● *79 bedrooms (many ground floor), comprising 30 family suites, 29 single, 20 twin bedded rooms; 57 with private bathrooms.*
● *Five lounges; children's dining room; self-service laundry, giftshop, colour TV lounge.*
● *Three games rooms; solarium; children's disco* *in season; 9 acre golf course; two hard tennis courts, playground, outdoor swimming and paddling pools; full leisure centre; adjoins clean sandy beach, safe bathing; Isle of Purbeck Golf Club two miles, two courses.* ● *Open April to October.*
● *Mastercard, Visa, Access, Eurocard accepted.*

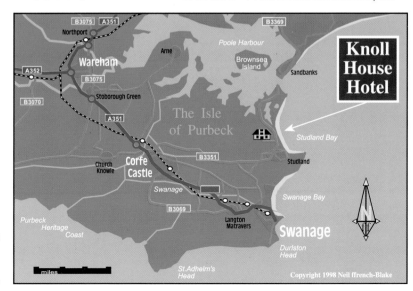

Studland 1,
Swanage 3,
Corfe Castle
6, Bourne-
mouth 8,
London 113,

Knoll · House Hotel, Studland Bay

ON THE FERRY ROAD FROM
BOURNEMOUTH TO STUDLAND AND SWANAGE
8 miles from Bournemouth, 2 miles from Studland and 3 miles from Swanage.
(For position see map on page 18, *square A.*8).

A paradise and playground for children of all ages among pines and rhododendrons near sea and sand—Directed by Mr. & Mrs. Chris. Smith—Generous inclusive terms—Really good all English food.

IN the space at my disposal I can only outline the wonderful charm of this most unusual place. The fact that most of its accommodation for this summer was booked last year is sufficient indication of its appeal while the tremendous extensions planned for next year afford other evidence of its remarkable rise to popularity. Knoll House is unlicensed and caters particularly for children, even to the extent of providing them with special food and accommodation. Its atmosphere is informal. It is an exceptionally lovely house, inside and out, and possesses an unusually attractive garden on which many hundreds of pounds have been spent. All-in terms include early morning tea, garage, beach huts, tennis, boats, coffee after meals and morning paper. Fresh fruit is always available free and the food is all English, much of it being grown and made on the premises. Terms form 4 to 7 gns. weekly. A number of family bungalows fitted with electric fires and running water adjoin the hotel. Three of them are complete suites with private bathrooms, and covered-in verandahs.

In front of the house is a lawn shaded by a few tall pines.

CENTRAL SOUTHERN ENGLAND

Plumber Manor

Sturminster Newton, Dorset DT10 2AF
Tel: (01258) 472507

This imposing Jacobean manor house hotel is set in idyllic countryside in the heart of beautiful Dorset "far from the madding crowd", where tranquillity prevails throughout. The Divelish stream weaves its way through delightful grounds, extensive lawns and fine old trees, making a rich and peaceful setting. Dating from the 17th century, the manor has been and still is the home of the Prideaux-Brune family. Since 1973 the careful management by Richard, Alison and Brian has indeed led to the creation of a first class hotel and restaurant. Situated halfway between London and Cornwall, the location is perfect for travelling or simply exploring the picturesque and unspoiled Dorset countryside. There are six elegant en suite bedrooms within the main house and a further ten in the courtyard and converted barn overlooking the stream and gardens. The highly acclaimed restaurant provides imaginative and traditional cuisine using the finest of fresh local ingredients where possible. The extensive wine list is excellent. Plumber Manor is welcoming, comfortable and has the most charming atmosphere in which to relax and savour first class hospitality, cuisine and service. A fine hotel.

Single room rate including breakfast from £75 Ⓥ
Double room rate with breakfast from £95.
Special breaks: *October-April, exc Xmas & Bank Hols, double room min. two nights from £85 per person b & b with 10% disc. on dinner menus*

● *16 en suite bedrooms, with radio & colour TV, tea/coffee making facilities, direct-dial telephone, hairdryer, trouser press.*
● *Table d'hôte dinner £17 (2 courses)/£19.50 (3 courses); last orders for dinner 9.30 p.m*
● *Meeting room for 25; photocopying, fax, o/head projector available. Car rental. Car parking.*
● *Croquet, tennis at hotel. Golf, fishing, riding, shooting, massage all nearby by arrangement.*
● *Open March-January. All major credit cards accepted.*

Blandford Forum 8, Sherborne 12, Salisbury 28, Bournemouth 30, Bristol 49, London 123

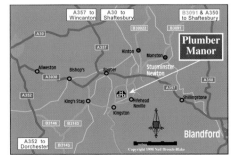

Tylney Hall

Rotherwick, Nr. Hook, Hampshire
RG27 9AZ
Tel: (01256) 764881; Fax: (01256) 768141
E-mail: sales@tylneyhall.co.uk

The approach to Tylney Hall, through avenues of chestnut and lime trees, gives a clue to the style of the hotel. The present hall dates from 1900. A fine Grade II building, it re-opened, after extensive renovation, as an hotel in 1985, owned by the *Elite* hotel group. (See also the *Grand* at Eastbourne (see page 91) and *Ashdown Park* (page 93). Honeymooners, weekenders, business executives or less hurried visitors cannot fail to appreciate the well appointed bedrooms and the views of lawns and lakes which surround the house. At different times of the year the various Gardens come into their own: The Italian, Rose and Azalea Gardens, the Water Gardens, Dutch Gardens and Water Tower. Tylney is convenient for Stratfield Saye, Broadlands, Highclere and Beaulieu. Activities from riding to hot air ballooning can be arranged. A focal point of the hotel is the glass-domed Oak Room Restaurant and there are 12 state-of-the-art conference and banqueting suites for meetings and special occasions. An exceptionally comfortable hotel for business and leisure traveller alike.

Rates: Single room inc. breakfast from £114 ; double/twin room from £140.   **V**
Bargain Breaks: Min 2-night stay inc table d'hôte dinner & breakfast from £181 per couple per night

● *110 bedrooms (inc. 25 suites), all with colour TV + satellite, direct-dial telephone, trouser press, hairdryer, laundry/valet service, radio/alarm clock, 24-hr room/meal service, safety deposit box.*
● *Oak Room Restaurant. A la carte; lunch & special diets avilable; last orders 9.30 pm.*
● *Business services inc 12 meeting rooms (largest 110 cap'y). Car parking for 120.*
● *Billiards/snooker, croquet, gymnasium, indoor & outdoor swimming pools, jacuzzi, sauna, massage, jogging track, clay shooting, tennis. Golf adjacent. Sailing, squash, riding, watersports within 8 miles.*
● *Open all year. Major credit cards accepted.*
M3 (junc.5) 1, Basingstoke 6, Camberley 11, Farnham 11, Reading 13, London 41.

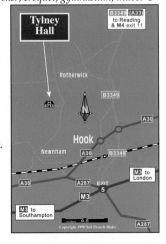

Passford House Hotel

Nr. Lymington, Hampshire SO41 8LS
Tel: (01590) 682398; Fax: (01590) 683494

The timeless magic of the New Forest has captivated visitors for centuries and the Passford House Hotel, set in nine acres of picturesque gardens and parkland, is the ideal base when visiting this part of the country. Passford House was formerly the home of Lord Arthur Cecil (of the Exeter-Salisbury family) and is steeped in the traditions of elegant country life. Comfort is paramount throughout. In winter months, log fires radiate throughout the oak lounge; the cocktail bar is refined and the courtyard lounge with its garden vista is a delightful fanfare of colour in summer months. The standard of cuisine is high. Menus are varied; fresh local produce well selected and the speciality wine list caters for all tastes. The hotel is well placed to explore the attractions of the New Forest and surrounding areas with Lymington, Beaulieu, Salisbury and Bournemouth all within easy reach. A lovely hotel to visit, relax at and enjoy with a charm of its own. A visit here for business or pleasure is an absolute must at any time of the year.

Single room inc. full English breakfast from £60 ; double/twin room from £85; deluxe double from £120. Special seasonal breaks available **V** *(min 2 nights).*

● *55 bedrooms (13 ground floor),1 suite, all with private baths, trouser press, hairdryer, telephone, radio, colour TV, tea/coffee making facilities.*
● *Children welcome; dogs by arrangement.*
● *Table d'hôte £22.50; vegetarian & healthy diets available.*
● *Indoor leisure complex with sauna, compact gymnasium, swimming pool; tennis court; croquet lawn; pétanque, outdoor swimming pool - heated in season; sailing, golf, riding, fishing all nearby.*
● *Open all year. Major credit cards accepted.*
Lymington 2, Brockenhurst 3¹/₂, Bournemouth 17, London 93

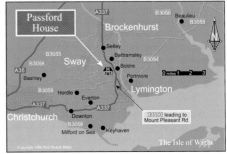

Stanwell House Hotel

High Street, Lymington,
Hampshire SO41 9AA
Tel: (01590) 677123; Fax: (01590) 677756

"Brilliant" is the first word that comes to mind in describing the Stanwell House Hotel. The whole establishment is colourful, dramatic, stylish, tasteful and standards throughout are superb. This exciting hotel under new ownership has dramatic colours and the mix of antique and modern, iron work sculptures and the freshest of flowers illustrate the complimentary contrasts of Stanwell House. In the sophisticated restaurant, award-winning chef Mark Hewitt and his team prepare exquisite menus, offering seasonal local produce with excellent presentation and a fine wine list. For informal dining the bar and bistro serve delicious meals in chic, comfortable surroundings. Coffee and afternoon teas can be taken in the artistic conservatory area. The elegant patio extends to a tranquil landscaped traditional walled garden area. *Stanwells* is an in-house clothing store where guests can acquire classic elegant designer leisurewear for the area's varied country pursuits and social activities. A hotel whose style will entice you back time after time!

Single room inc. breakfast from £50.00 ; Ⅴ
Double from £95; deluxe from £110; suites from £140; cottage from £150.
Seasonal breaks available.

● *31 en suite bedrooms (inc 3 suites & self-contained cottage), all with colour TV, direct-dial telephone, hairdryer, laundry service, minibar (in deluxe & suites), tea/coffee making facilities, 24-hour room/meal service, trouser press.*
● *Bar, bistro, restaurant, conservatory; table d'hôte £17; last orders 10 pm; lunch & diets available.*
● *Billiards, fitness centre/gym, indoor games, jacuzzi, sauna, riding, sailing/boating, squash, outdoor & indoor swiming pools, tennis all nearby.*
● *Open all year. Major credit cards accepted.*
Brockenhurst 4, Bournemouth 17, London 93

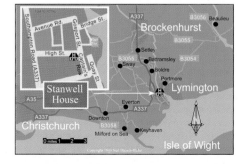

Fallowfields Country House Hotel

Faringdon Road, Kingston Bagpuize with Southmoor, Oxfordshire OX13 5BH
Tel: (01865) 820416; Fax: (01865) 821275

Fallowfields, once the home of the Begum Aga Khan, dates back more than 300 years. It has been updated and extended over the years and today boasts a lovely early Victorian Gothic southern aspect. The house is set in two acres of garden, surrounded by ten acres of grassland. The guest bedrooms, which offer a choice of four-poster or coroneted beds, are large, well appointed and have every modern amenity. There are welcoming log fires in the elegant reception areas. Home cooked cuisine is imaginative in style and presentation and there is a good choice of menu available. The walled kitchen garden provides most of the vegetables and salads and locally grown produce is otherwise used whenever possible. Weekend house parties are ever popular and additional accommodation can be arranged. Fallowfields is an ideal base from which to tour the surrounding countryside, being handy for the Cotswolds, Stratford, Oxford, Henley-on-Thames, and the Chilterns. Heathrow is less than an hour away.

Rates: Single inc. breakfast from £85; double from £105.   **Ⅴ**

● *10 en suite bedrooms, all with colour TV+ satellite, direct-dial telephone, hairdryer, laundry service, tea/coffee making facilities, music/radio/alarm clock, trouser press. Non-smoker bedrooms available*
● *Table d'hôte dinner £28.50; last orders 8.30 pm; à la carte, lunch & special diets available.*
● *Croquet, jacuzzi/whirlpool, outdoor swimming pool. Fishing 2 miles, golf 1 mile, fitness centre/gym 5 miles, riding 1/2 mile. Car poarking for 20.*
● *Three meeting/conference rooms, capacity 100*
● *Open all year. Visa, Amex, Mastercard accepted*

Abingdon 7, Oxford 9, Witney 9, Swindon 20, London 70

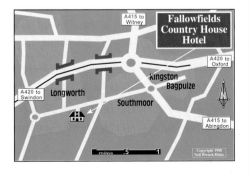

London & the Southeast

Historic Houses, Gardens & Parks

London
Carlyle's House, Chelsea
Fenton House, Hampstead
Kensington Palace, Kensington
 Gardens, W8
Osterley Park, Isleworth
Tower of London, Tower Hill, EC3
Westminster Abbey Chapter House,
 SWI

Kent
Bedgebury National Pinetum, Nr.
 Goudhurst
Chilham Castle Gardens, Nr
 Canterbury
Doddington Place Gardens, Nr
 Sittingboume

Godington House & Gardens,
 Godington Park, Ashford
Goodnestone Park, Wingham, Nr.
 Canterbury
Iden Croft Herbs, Staplehurst
Kent Garden Vineyard, Headcorn
Penshurst Place & Gardens, Nr.
 Tonbndge
Sissinghurst Garden

Surrey
Clandon Park, West Clandon
Claremont Landscape Garden,
 Esher
Ham House, Richmond

Hampton Court Palace, East Molesey
Hatchlands Park, East Clandon
Kew Gardens (Royal Botanic Gar
 dens), Richmond
Polesden Lacey, Great Bookham, Nr.
 Dorking
The RHS Garden, Wisley, Nr.
 Woking
The Savill Garden, Nr. Egham
Winkworth Arboretum, Hascombe,
 Nr. Godalming

East Sussex
Alfriston Clergy House, Alfriston
Battle Abbey, Battle
Brickwall House & Gardens,
 Northiam, Nr. Rye
Carr Taylor Vineyards, Hastings
Great Dixter House & Gardens,
 Northiam, Nr. Rye Michelham
Priory, Upper Dicker, Nr.
 Hailsham
Merriments Gardens, Hurst
Green
Pashley Manor Gardens Ticehurst
Preston Manor, Preston Park,
 Brighton
Royal Pavilion, Brighton
Sheffield Park Garden, Danehill, Nr.
 Uckfield

West Sussex
Denmans Garden, Fontwell, Nr.
 Arundel
GoodwoodHouse,Goodwood
Leonardslee Gardens, Lower
 Beeding, Horsham
Parham House & Gardens, Parham
 Park, Pulborough
Petworth House & Park
St. Mary's House,Bramber, Nr.
 Steyning
Standen, East Grinstead
Wakehurst Place Gardens, Ardingly,
 Nr.Haywards Heath

Walks & Nature Trails

Kent
Bewl Water Walks and Rides, Nr.
 Lamberhurst
Cobtree Manor Park Nature Trail
The Ecological Park, Elms Vale
Hastings Country Park, Hastings
Haysden Country Park Nature Trail
The Western Heights, Dover
White Cliffs Country Trail   (various
 walks), around
 Kent

West Sussex
Burton Pond
Nature Trail
Worth Way Walk,
from Worth Way to
 East Grinstead

Historic Sites & Museums

London
Bntish Museum Great Russell Street, WC1
Guinness World of Records, The Trocadero Centre
The London Dungeon, 28 -34 Tooley Street, SE1
Mall Galleries The Mall, SWl
National Portrait Gallery, St. Martin's Place, WC2
Natural History Museum, Cromwell Road, SW7
The Queen's Gallery, Buckingham Palace, SWl
Royal Mews Buckingham Palace Road, SWI
Science Museums, Exhibihon Road, SW7
The Tate Gallery, Millbank, SWl
Tower Bridge SEl
Victoria & Albert Museum, Cromwell Road, SW7

East Sussex
Anne of Cleves House Museum, Lewes
Bodiam Castle, Bodiam
Brighton Museum & Art Gallery
Filching Manor Motor Museum, Polegate
Hastings Castle and 1066 Story, West Hill, Hastings Hove Museum & Art Gallery
Quarry Farm Rural Experience, Robertsbridge

West Sussex
Arundel Castle, Arundel

Kent
Canterbury Cathedral
The Canterbury Tales, Canterbury
The Dickens Centre, Rochester
Dover Castle & Hellfire Comer
Eurotunnel Exhibition Centre, Folkestone
Guildhall Museum, Rochester
Leeds Castle, Nr. Maidstone
Lympne Castle, Nr. Hythe
Rochester Castle

Surrey
Brooklands Museum, Weybndge

Entertainment Venues

London
Madame Tussaud's & The London Planetarium, NWl
London Zoo, Regent's Park, NWl

East Sussex
The Bluebell Railway - Living Museum, Shenfield Park
Hastings Sea Life Centre

West Sussex
Butlins Southcoast World, Bognor Regis
Coombes Farm Tours, Lancing
Pulborough Brooks RSPB Nature Reserve

Kent
The Buttefly Centre, Swingfield Dover
Kent & East Sussex Steam Railway, Tenterden
Port Lympne Wild Annmal Park, Mansion & Gardens
Toy & Model Museum, Lamberhurst

Surrey
Birdworld, Nr. Farnham
Gatwick Zoo, Charlwood
Thorpe Park, Chertsey

Bank & Public Holidays in Great Britain 1999

1 January. *New Year's Day*

4 January. *Bank Holiday (Scot)*

17 March. *St Patrick's Day (NI)*

2 April. *Good Friday*

5 April. *Easter Monday*

3 May. *May Day*

31 May. *Spring Bank Holiday*

11 June. *TT Bank Holiday (IoM)*

5 July. *Tynwald Day (IoM)*

12 July. *Orangeman's Day. (NI)*

2 August. *Summer Bank Holdiay (Scot)*

30 August. *Summer Bank Holiday (all exc Scot.)*

NI = Northern Ireland only; IoM = Isle of Man only; Scot= Scotland only. Others national.

London & The Southeast

London & the Southeast

DIARY OF EVENTS

January

1-12*. **Hastings International Chess Congress.** Cinque Ports Hotel, Hastings.
1. **London Parade.** Parliament Square to Berkeley Square.
8-17. **45th London Internat'l Boat Show**, Earls Court, London SW5

February

20*. **Rugby International.** England v Wales, Twickenham
23-28. **Olympia Fine Arts & Antiques Fair,** London W14.

March

6*. **Rugby International.** Wales v Scotland, Wembley.
17-11Apr. **Daily Mail Ideal Home Exhibition**, Earls Court, London W5.
17-23. **British Antiques Dealers Fair,** Chelsea Town Hall, London SW3
27. **Head of the River Race** - Mortlake to Putney, London.
28-30. **London International Book Fair.** Olympia, SW5

April

3. **Oxford v Cambridge University Boat Race,** Putney to Mortlake, London
3. **Rugby International.** England v Ireland, Twickenham.
3. **Rugby International.** Wales v France, Wembley.
5. **London Harness Horse Parade.** Battersea Park, SW11
22-25*. **Chelsea Art Fair,** Chelsea Old Town Hall, London SW3

18. **London Marathon**
24. **Whitbread Gold Cup** Classic Race, Sandown Park Racecourse, Esher, Surrey.

May

1-23. **Brighton International Festival.** Various venues, Brighton, East Sussex
May 1-4*. **Eastbourne International Folk Festival.** Various venues, Eastbourne, E. Sussex.
15. **FA Challenge Cup Final** Wembley Stadium, Wembley, London.
16-30*. **Ramsgate Spring Festival.** Various venues, Ramsgate, Kent.
25-28. **Chelsea FlowerShow** Royal Hospital, London SW3.
27-278. **Glyndebourne Festival Opera Season.** Glyndebourne, Lewes, E Sussex.
31. **Surrey County Show.** Stoke Park, Guildford, Surrey.

June

3-13. **Olympia Fine Arts & Antiques Fair,** Olympia, London SW5.
4/5. **Vodafone Oaks/Vodafone Derby Days.** Epsom Racecourse, Surrey.
12. **Trooping the Colour.** Queen's birthday parade, Horse Guards, London SW1
8-14*. **Stella Artois Tennis Championships.** Queen's Club, London W14.
10-19. **Grosvenor House Antiques Fair.** Grosvenor Hse, London W1.
12-19*. **Eastbourne International Ladies Tennis Championship.** Int'l Lawn Tennis Centre, Eastbourne, E Sussex.
19-26. **Broadstairs Dickens Festival.** Various venues, Broadstairs, Kent.
19-13 July*. **City of London Festival.** Various venues, City

of London.

21-July 4. **Wimbledon Lawn Tennis Championships.** All England Lawn Tennis Club, London SW19.

27-July 12. **Chichester Festival,** Chichester, West Sussex.

23-Sept 1. **Arundel Festival.** Various venues, Arundel, West Sussex.

29-30. **Notting Hill Carnival.** Ladbroke Grove, London W14

26-30. **Glorious Goodwood.** Horseracing at Goodwood, Nr Chichester, West Sussex.

July

15-17. **Kent County Show.** Showground, Detling, Kent.

16 -Sept 11. **BBC Henry Wood Promenade Concerts** Royal Albert Hall, London SW7

20-1 Aug. **Royal Tournament** Earls Court, London SW5.

31-7 Aug. **Cowes Week 97.** High Seas, Cowes, Isle of Wight

August

6-14*. **Broadstairs Folk Week** Var. venues, Broadstairs, Kent

19-23*. **Kensington Art Fair,** London W8.

September

12. **Thames Festival**. Nighttime illuminated procession.

16-26. **Chelsea Antiques Fair** Town Hall, London SW3.

29-3 Oct. **Horse of the Year Show.** Wembley Arena, Wembley, Middx.

October

23-1 Nov.**London Motor Show** Earls Court, London SW5.

30*. **Grand Firework Spectacular.** Leeds Castle, Kent.

November

7. **London to Brighton RAC Veteran Car Run.** London

7. **Remembrance Sunday Ceremony.** Cenotaph, London SW1.

13. **Lord Mayor's Show**. City of London.

December

16-20. **Olympia Int'l Showjumping Championship.** Olympia London W14.

31. **Millenium Firework Display.** Battersea Park, SW11
● ● ● ● ● ● ● ● ● ● ● ● ● ● ●
*Denotes provisional date
For further details, contact

The South East England Tourist Board
The Old Brew House
Warwick Park, Tunbridge Wells, Kent
TN2 5TU. Tel: (01892) 540766

London Tourist Board & Convention Bureau. 26, Grosvenor Gardens Victoria. London SWIW ODU.
Tel: 0171 730 3450

The South-East

Kent is the garden of England - and its oldest city Canterbury, with its cathedral, is the centre of the Anglican faith. The impressive Knole Park, near Sevenoaks, was built in the 15th century by an Archbishop of Canterbury. Near Maidstone is the impeccable Leeds Castle, founded in 857 and later improved by Henry VIII. In East Sussex lies the peaceful Bodlam Castle (below), surrounded by its moat and never breached by an enemy.

Over the South Downs lies Brighton, Regency summer capital of Britain with the eccentric Pavilion and to the west of Brighton is the impressive Arundel Castle, Norman stronghold, now inhabited by the Duke of Norfolk (above). Chichester, west of Arundel, has an 11th century cathedral, narrow streets of timber-clad houses and an annual drama festival.

Ashdown Forest, now more heath than forest in East Sussex covers some 6000 acres and is home to badgers and fallow deer.

On the outskirts of London, near Bromley, Kent, Chislehurst Caves have long been a favourite with children. Further East Chatham's 400-year old dockyard provides a history of Britain's fighting ships. Ashford in southeast Kent is the mouth of the Channel Tunnel, Gateway to Europe. Dover Castle houses the White Cliffs Experience and Churchill's War Rooms - nerve centre for the Dunkirk evacuation and the Battle of Britain of 1940.

London

London's treasures are well chronicled. Most visitors prefer to stay in the west /central Knightsbridge/Kensington areas which are handy for shopping and allow quick access into the West End for theatres and other functions. London's main museums - the Natural History, Science and Victoria and Albert are also in this area.

In the Central/West End area most visited sights are the (now) public rooms of Buckingham Palace, the National Gallery in Trafalgar Square, Westminster Abbey and the Houses of Parliament, the Cabinet War Rooms by Admiralty Arch, whence Churchill directed the second world war when bombing made the rest of the capital unsafe (the 70 rooms, of which 19 are open to the public, cover a subterranean warren of three acres), the Tate Gallery on the Embankment, containing mainly 20th century masterpieces.

Westminster Abbey, nearly a thousand years old, has tombs of many English kings queens, statesmen and writers. The British Museum in Bloomsbury houses one of the world's largest collections of antiquities, including the *Magna Carta,* the Elgin Marbles and the first edition of Alice in Wonderland.

Further east in the city of London is St Paul's Cathedral, designed by Sir Christoher Wren after the original was destroyed in the Great Fire of London (1666), whose epitaph is below the dome *"if you seek his monument, look around you".* Other notable buildings of the city are the Guildhall, the Mansion House, official residence of the Lord Mayor of London and further East, the Tower of London, a medieval fortress dominated by the White Tower and dating from 1097. The Crown Jewels are housed in the tower, which is policed by the famous Beefeaters.

In North Central London (Baker St - home of the fictitious Sherlock Holmes) are the Planetarium and Madame Tussauds, although the London Dungeon, near London Bridge Station, has recently overtaken Tussauds' *Chamber of Horrors* as childrens' favourite collection of gruesome displays.

London's parks are its 'lungs' and a pleasant place to relax on a summer's afternoon. St James, the oldest one, was founded by Henry VIII in 1532, is the most central and covers 90 acres. Hyde Park, bordering Kensington, Mayfair and Marylebone is the largest at 630 acres and includes the famous Serpentine artificial lake where the hardy still swim on Christmas Day. Regents Park, lies north of Oxford Circus, and was given to the nation by the Prince Regent. Further out are Richmond Park in the southwest, where deer still abound, and Kew Gardens, with its famous tropical greenhouses and plants.

In the south-east of the capital, land to the East of the Tower of London has been reclaimed and Canary Wharf and the Docklands area provide an interesting study of urban renewal. On the south bank opposite Docklands is Greenwich Observatory and the National Maritime Museum. Visitors can see the Millennium dome taking shape here.

The Cavendish St James's

81 Jermyn Street, St James's, London
SW1Y 6JF
Tel: (0171) 930 2111; Fax: (0171) 839 2125
E-mail: 76213.171; Internet: 76213.171 @ compuserve.com

Rates: Single room incl. breakfast & service from £165; double from £195. All prices VAT exclusive.
Bargain Breaks: Midweek and weekend leisure breaks available from £78 per person sharing twin or double, b & b; from £99 pp dinner, b & b.

The most surprising characteristic of this stylish, modern hotel is its aura of tranquillity. It is an ideal base for shoppers - a short distance to Bond Street, theatre- and clubland - and just two minutes' walk from the bustle of Piccadilly. The calming ambience starts with the welcoming reception area and is continued in the Bar where wood panelling and leather seating make a popular meeting place for business or pleasure. An elegant staircase is dominated by a portrait of Rosa Lewis, the "Duchess of Duke Street", whose influence on an earlier Cavendish made it so much a part of the social scene that Edward VII preferred entertaining there to nearby Buckingham Palace. "The Lounge" on the first floor serves light menus; the more sophisticated *Tapas Bar* and *81 Restaurant* providing superb European cuisine and pre-theatre dinners. Travellers on vacation will enjoy the traditions of the Cavendish; business travellers will appreciate the modern facilities ranging from on-site parking to air-conditioned meeting rooms. Unsurprisingly, the hotel has won many top awards for quality, comfort and service.

● *251 en suite rooms with colour TV + satellite, direct-dial telephone; hairdryer, trouser press, laundry service, minibar, 24-hour room/meal service. 75% of bedrooms non-smoking.*
● *2-cse table d'hôte dinner from £13.50. A la carte, lunch & special diets available. Last orders 10.30 pm. Ring anytime for current special offers.*
● *Business services inc. 4 meeting rooms, capacity 100. Car parking. Massage/sauna nearby.*
● *Open all year. Mastercard, Visa, JCB, Diners Club, Amex credit cards accepted.*

LONDON & THE SOUTHEAST

The Cranley Hotel

10-12 Bina Gardens, South Kensington,
London SW5 OLA
Tel: (0171) 373 0123; Fax (0171) 373 9497
E-mail: thecranley@compuserve.com
Internet: http://www.thecranley.co.uk

Recapturing the age of grandeur, The Cranley
is set in the heart of the Royal Borough of
Kensington and Chelsea, one of London's
smartest residential districts. The antiques,
stylish décor and delicate period details of
The Cranley will captivate the most discerning guest. It's exclusive. Loving restoration
has been carried out to provide 36 air-conditioned rooms, including executive- type
suites and one-bedroom apartments, giving
the impression of a private residence rather
than a hotel. Antique furnishings and exquisite decoration make each room individual
yet luxurious. A fully equipped and con-
cealed kitchenette offers all the comforts of
home and each room is fully equipped with
every conceivable modern comfort and
luxury. Whether relaxing in the deep tub bath
or freshening up under a powerful shower, it
is the extra touches such as the soft white
towels and bathrobes that go to make a stay at
The Cranley an experience of luxury. The
Cranley is ideally situated for direct links to
Gatwick and Heathrow Airports and London's underground rail system. The famous
museums and shopping areas of
Knightsbridge and the King's Road are within
easy walking distance, as are the exhibition
areas of Earls Court and Olympia.

Single room incl. VAT & service from £140.00.
Double room incl. VAT & service from £160.00.
Continental breakfast £8.95. English breakfast
£12.95.   V

● *36 en suite rooms with air-conditioning, satel-*
lite TV, radio, direct-dial telephone; hairdryer,
trouser press, laundry service, tea/coffee making
facilities.
● *12-hour room service*
● *Open all year. Credit cards accepted.*

The Gainsborough Hotel

7-11 Queensberry Place,
London SW1 2DL
Tel: (0171) 957 0000; Fax: (0171) 957 0001;
E-mail: eeh@eeh.co.uk;
Internet: http://www.eeh.co.uk/eeh! Freephone UK: 0-500 826187; USA 1-800 270 9206; GDS Access Code HW;
Central Reservations: (+44) 181-906 9650 world.

The Gainsborough is located in the same quiet street as its "Elegant English Hotels" sister property, the Gallery (see following page), with which it has much in common. Having been totally refurbished, it now offers some of the best value for money accommodation in this part of London. Passing the discreet brass plate at the entrance you will find a similar town house ambience whose character is enhanced by reproduction works of art by, among others, the eponymous painter. His works surround the welcoming lounge/reception area whose wood panelling, sofas and draped floral curtains make you feel instantly at home. The cheerful Picasso Bar and breakfast room adjoin and here an eccentric display of cartoons, etchings and line drawings happily defy classification but serve to keep you entertained over the hotel's full English buffet meal. The recent facelift has added nine lovely new rooms. The mix of grand suites, quadruples, triples, doubles and singles are individually decorated with fine fabrics and quality furnishings. The 'new' Gainsborough guarantees a comfortable stay in a very English atmosphere.

Single *room, inc. breakfast £82;*　Ⓥ
Double *room, inc. breakfast £148.*

- *40 en suite bedrooms (15 double, 11 twin, 12 single, 2 suites), some with airconditioning, colour TV, direct-dial telephone, hairdryer, laundry/valet service, trouser press, 24-hr (butler) room service.*
- *Picasso Bar Restaurant open 24 hours.*
- *Business centre inc. meeting room for 40.*
- *Open all year. All major credit cards accepted.*

The Gallery Hotel

8-10 Queensberry Place,
London SW7 2EA
Tel: (0171) 915 0000; Fax: (0171) 915 4400;
E-mail: eeh@eeh.co.uk;
Internet: http://www.eeh.co.uk/eeh! Freephone UK: 0-
500 826187; USA 1-800 270 9206; GDS Access Code WW
Central Reservations: (+44) 181-906 9650

Situated down a quiet side street close to the
busy cultural and commercial area of South
Kensington and minutes away from Knightsbridge, these two fine Georgian residences
(*see previous page*) have undergone total restoration to create traditional town house hotels
themed around art as the names imply. Once
through the fine, pillared entrance, the guest
is faced by a reception area which was host to
an original exhibition of sculpture when we
visited. This is also a feature of the adjacent
Gallery Room which is also ideal for small
conferences or functions. Nearby the "4 Gats"
lounge bar, named after a famous Picasso
painting, reflects a typical private club ambience heightened by comfortable furnishing,
mahogany panelling and rich décor. A bright
breakfast room is reached down stairs and
through a pleasant working library area. Here

the Impressionists are on display and this
venue is popular for private dinners. The hotel's 36 bedrooms and studio suites are beautifully decorated and have such facilities as
voice-messaging and private fax. Bathrooms
have marble tiling, brass fittings and bathrobes.
It is hard to dispute the Gallery's claim that
"it is a discovery you would like to keep secret
and yet feel compelled to tell your friends".

Single/double *room, incl. breakfast from £148.* **V**

● *36 en suite bedrooms (34 double, 2 suites), some
with airconditioning, colour TV+ satellite, direct-
dial telephone, hairdryer, laundry/valet service,
minibar, trouser press, 24-hr (butler) room service,
music/radio/alarm clock, trouser press.*
● *4 Gats Bar open 24 hours.*
● *Business centre inc. meeting room for 15.*
● *Open all year. All major credit cards accepted.*

Harrington Hall Hotel

5-25 Harrington Gardens,
London SW7 4JW
Tel: (0171) 396 9696; Fax (0171) 396 9090
E-mail: harringtonsales@compuserve.com
Internet: http://www.harringtonhall.co.uk

Harrington Hall, a hotel of elegance located in the heart of London is one of the few remaining privately owned hotels. This luxury 200 bedroom, fully air conditioned property is situated in the exclusive Royal Borough of Kensington and Chelsea, within easy reach of Knightsbridge. Behind the splendour of the original period facade, Harrington Hall is a new hotel providing every modern convenience in a beautifully designed, classical setting. In the open plan lounge, which combines warmth and elegance with comfortable traditional furnishings and a beautiful marble fireplace, snacks and refreshments are offered. Wetherby's, the spacious and refreshingly airy restaurant, has a tempting selection of dishes available from the choice of buffet or à la carte menu. Harrington Hall's bedrooms are large and all contain an extensive array of facilities which include satellite TV, mini-bar, a state of the art message system and of course air conditioning. A number of rooms have been allocated for non-smoking guests. Harrington Hall's 9 conference and banqueting suites provide a sophisticated venue for conferences, or corporate hospitality and are ideal for luncheons, or receptions. Harrington Hall also has a Business Centre for the exclusive use of guests, which provides a range of secretarial services including word processing and facsimile. Guests can tone up in the private Fitness Centre which boasts a multi-gym as well as saunas and showers.

Room rates from £160.00 incl. VAT and service. Continental breakfast £9.75; Full English breakfast £13.75.   **V**

● *200 en suite air conditioned bedrooms with radio, satellite TV, direct dial telephones with personal numbers; hairdryer, trouser press, laundry service; tea/coffee making facilities, mini-bar, safety deposit box; 24-hour room service; non-smoker bedrooms available.*
● *Last orders for dinner 22.30 hrs. Special diets available.*
● *Fitness Centre/gym, sauna.*
● *Full business services inc. nine meeting rooms , capacity up to 250. Car parking off site. Car rental.*
● *Open all year. Credit cards accepted.*

The Howard Hotel

Temple Place, Strand,
London WC2R 2PR
Tel: (0171) 836 3555; Fax: (0171) 379 4547
E-mail: reservations@thehowardhotel. co.uk.
Internet: http://www.thehowardhotel.co.uk

Ideally located for business or leisure, this unique, luxury hotel is imposingly situated on the Thames where the City meets the West End. Many of the elegantly designed bedrooms which feature French marquetry furniture and tasteful marble bathrooms, enjoy the stunning panoramic view of the river as it winds between St . Paul' s and Westminster. All rooms are fully air conditioned and have every possible modern convenience, including 24 hour room service. The Surrey and Westminster suites cater for small parties, while larger meetings, to a maximum of 200, may be held in the Arundel and Fitzalan suites. One can relax over an aperitif in the Temple Bar overlooking an attractively 'landscaped terrace, planted with flowers and shrubs. I enjoyed an excellent luncheon, beautifully presented and served, in the justifiably

famous Quai d'Or Restaurant, where the Renaissance décor, domed ceiling and thoughtfully chosen paintings, complemented the International cuisine and wines. Attentive staff anticipate your every need, some having been at the hotel for many years. This rather special hotel is under the direction of Mr. Michael P. Day, Non Executive Chairman and Mr Harvey Pascoe, General Manager.

Single £260.00; twin/double £285.00 and suites from £318.00. Rates inclusive of 17½% VAT.
Luxury Weekend: Double or twin-bedded room with full English Breakfast and a Bottle of Champagne in your room on arrival @ £200 per night inc. VAT. Valid minimum of two nights, Friday, Saturday, Sunday.

● *135 en suite bedrooms, all with direct dial telephone, TV; 24 hour room service; three lifts;*
● *Last orders 10.30 p.m.; special diets.*
● *Children welcome; conferences 200 max.*
● *Open all year. Major credit cards accepted*
● *Fully equipped Business Centre.*

Heathrow 16, Gatwick 28, London City Airport 6

Kingsway Hall

Great Queen Street, London WC2B 5BZ
Tel: (0171) 396 1616; Fax: (0171) 396 1615
E-mail:kingswayhall@compuserve.com
Internet: http://www.kingswayhall.co.uk

Kingsway Hall, opening in the Spring of 1999, will be a superior four-star hotel situated in London's Covent Garden and adjacent to the New Connaught Rooms. Close to the British Museum, Royal Courts of Justice, Oxford Street and Theatreland it will have convenient access to the City. The hotels's 170 luxury air-conditioned bedrooms and suites will be furnished to the highest international standards. Kingsway Hall's nine air-conditioned conference and banqueting suites, featuring the most up-to-date facilities, will provide a sophisticatd venue for business or social events. A fully equipped fitness centre will be available for the exclusive use of our guests. The relaxing Lounge Bar and Restaurant, with superb cuisine, will combine to make your stay in this new hotel a memorable one.

Single room inc breakfast from £178.50; V
Double room inc breakfast from £191.50.
Bargain breaks: Weekend theatre rates: Executive Double Room £177 per night inc full b'fast. (Min 2-night stay inc Saturday)

● 170 en suite bedrooms (109 double, 59 twin, 2 suites) with airconditioning, colour TV + satellite, radio, direct-dial telephone, hairdryer, laundry service, minibar, tea/coffee making facilities, 24 hour room/meal service, safety deposit box, trouser press. Non-smoker & disabled bedrooms available.
● Table d'hôte dinner 3-courses £25; last orders 10.15 pm; lunch & special diets available.
● Fitness Centre/gym. Car rental.
● Nine meeting rooms, capacity up to 150.
● Open all year. All major credit cards accepted.

The Montcalm

Great Cumberland Place,
London W1A 2LF
Tel: (0171) 402 4288; Fax: (0171) 724 9180

Located on a delightful, tree-lined street behind Marble Arch, this sometime Georgian
town house lives up to the dignity and style
of the 18th century general, the Marquis de
Montcalm. A recent winner of the *AA Courtesy and Care Award*, the emphasis is on discreet service to each guest. This begins with
the welcome at the imposing entrance, continues in the club-like atmosphere of the foyer
and extends to the cosy bar and adjoining
area where a relaxing pianola plays classical
music. The ⚘⚘ AA *Crescent* restaurant is
dominated by an idyllic country garden mu-
ral and offers a variety of good value menus
as well as private dining and conference facilities and a special supper service for theatre-
goers. The 120 air-conditioned bedrooms (including 12 duplex suites) exude comfort, rein-
forced by luxury furnishings and marble tiled
bathrooms. If you would like to turn the clock
back to Georgian style and forward to flawless
comfort, The Montcalm is your connection.

*Single room from £205.00 + VAT; **Double** room
from £225.00 + VAT; breakfast extra.*
Bargain breaks: *Montcalm Interlude - Fri to
Mon and Bank Holidays from £176.25 for two
people   per night (min. two nights) inc. traditional English breakfast and VAT.*   [V]

● *120 en suite bedrooms (15 double, 46 twin, 45
single, 14 suites) with airconditioning, satellite
TV, radio, direct-dial telephone, hairdryer, laundry service, voice mail & fax machines, 24 hour
room/meal service, safety deposit box, trouser press*
● *Table d'hôte dinner or lunch 3-courses £22.50 inc
glass of wine, coffee & VAT; last orders 10.30 pm;
lunch & special diets available.*
● *Three meeting rooms - capacity to 80.*
● *Open all year. Access, Visa, Amex, Diners &
JCB credit cards accepted.*

Pembridge Court

34 Pembridge Gardens, London W2 4DX
Tel: (0171) 229 9977; Fax: (0171) 727 4982
E-mail: Reservations@pemct.co.uk

This privately owned Victorian town house hotel is situated in quiet tree-lined gardens close to the Portobello Road Antiques Market. The location is very appropriate, for the Pembridge Court has been beautifully restored and reflects the character of its distinctive environs. As you step up through a colourful array of shrubs and flowers you may be greeted by the two handsome, TV personality ginger cats Spencer and Churchill; and also by a fine display of Victoriana where artefacts and prints jostle for space on the walls. An unusual collection of framed fans decorates the bedrooms. The cosy cellar bar and *Caps* Restaurant - with its own unique display of headgear - are popular with guests notably for the imaginative room service menu. Several of the twenty comfortable rooms are spacious, most are de luxe and all are tastefully decorated with nicely coordinated fabrics and furnishings. The tone of this stylish hotel is set by the book-lined drawing room - with its deep sofas, open fire and fresh flowers it is as ideal for relaxation as it is for working in peace and quiet.

The Pembridge Court has won many prestigious awards for its sheer quality, but its greatest accolade is represented by the number of guests who return again and again to savour the welcome and charm of this hotel with a difference.

Single room inc. Eng. breakfast & VAT £115-150;
Double room inc. breakfast & VAT £145-185. **Ⅴ**

● *20 en suite rooms all with radio, satellite TV, direct-dial telephone, hairdryer, trouser press, laundry service, tea/coffee making facilities, 24-hour room/meal service, safety deposit box.*
● *Last dinner orders 11 pm; soup/snack lunch available.*
● *Business services; airport pick-up; car rental; car parking (2 cars).*
● *Temporary membership to nearby health club*
● *Open all year. Amex, Visa, Diners, Access credit cards accepted.*

The Clarendon Hotel

Montpelier Row, Blackheath,
London SE3 ORW
Tel: (0181) 318 4321;
Fax: (0181) 318 4378

The location of the Clarendon, on the edge of the beautiful Blackheath common and close to the many attractions of historic Greenwich makes it an alternative to staying in the centre when visiting London. It is a short walk to the railway station and a 20-minute journey to Central London. Stone from the old London Bridge is reputed to have been used in the construction of the hotel, which was later home to rich Georgian merchants and shipbuilders. The nautical background is reflected in the bar which has many maritime artefacts including sea charts. Home comfort is a feature of the bedrooms and the Meridian Restaurant, overlooking the gardens, serves a good choice of cuisine. Otherwise modest in appearance and price, the Clarendon also caters for wedding receptions and has conference facilities for 150 in 5 well-equipped suites.

Rates: Single inc. breakfast from £56.50; double/twin inc. breakfast from £79. **V**

● *200 bedrooms, 6 suites, most en suite, all with colour TV, radio, direct-dial telephone, hairdryer, tea/coffee making facilities.*
● *Table d'hôte £14.50; à la carte, lunch & special diets available; last orders 9.45 pm.*
● *Conference room, capacity 150. Car parking 80*
● *Open all year. All major credit cards accepted.*

Greenwich 1, Central London 6, Rochester 30, Canterbury 55, Dover 72.

The Langorf Hotel

20 Frognal, Hampstead, London
NW3 6AG. Tel: (0171) 794 4483;
Fax: (0171) 435 9055.
Toll-free from USA: 1-800-925 4731.

This delightful town house hotel is discreetly situated in a quiet residential street just ten minutes by public transport from the West End, and south of fashionable Hampstead Village with its quality shops, fine restaurants and historic Kenwood House, renowned for open air concerts. The first impression is of friendly, attentive staff for whom nothing is too much trouble, and the second of a welcoming ambience throughout the hotel. The bright reception area adjoins the restaurant-bar, which overlooks a leafy walled garden and is open for breakfast and snacks throughout the day. Accommodation includes a number of serviced apartments.
A deserved holder of "Commended" and "Highly Acclaimed" awards, the Langorf guarantees a comfortable stay, offering its guests amongst the best value in town.

Single room inc breakfast from £73; Double **V**
inc breakfast from £90. Apartments (4 pers) from £115 nightly. Leisure breaks: Rates on application

● *31 en suite bedrooms (+ 5 apartments) with colour TV + satellite, radio, direct-dial telephone, hairdryer, laundry service, tea/coffee making facilities, 24 hr light snack service, safety deposit box.*
● *Horse riding nearby. Leisure Centre 15 minutes.*
● *Open all year. All major credit cards accepted.*

Little Hemingfold Hotel

Telham, Battle, East Sussex TN33 0TT
Tel: (01424) 774338; Fax: (01424) 775351

This enchanting place answers perfectly to the description of a farmhouse hotel. The home of Allison and Paul Slater, this part 17th century and part Victorian building is situated well away from a busy road down a half mile track in a world of its own, comprising 40 acres of farm and woodland with a two-acre spring-fed trout lake. The warmth of the welcome is matched by the comfortable furnishings of the lounges and a cosy bar area. The beamed candlelit dining-room serves an ample farmhouse breakfast as well as a freshly prepared 4-course dinner using home grown fruits and vegetables in a daily changing menu. The personal touch and the charm extend to the individually designed bedrooms. In these magical surroundings, you could remain happily undisturbed and quietly spoiled for many weeks.

Rates: Single room inc breakfast from £38;double from £76.Weekly terms from £50 pppn, dinner b&b
Bargain Breaks: 2 nights dinner,b&b £54-58 pppn.

● *13 bedrooms (10 en suite) with radio, colour TV,* **V** *direct dial telephone, hairdryer, laundry/valet service, tea/coffee making facilities, radio/alarm clock.*
● *Table d'hôte 4 courses £22.50; last orders 7.30 pm.*
● *Croquet, fishing, boating, swimming in the lake, grass tennis court, boules. Squash, riding & golf nearby.* ● *Closed Jan 5th-Feb 12th* ● *Dogs welcome.*
● *Access, Visa, Amex & Mastercard accepted.*
Hastings 6½, Maidstone 30, Brighton 34, Folkestone 43, London 56.

Thanington Hotel

140 Wincheap, Canterbury, Kent CT1 3RY. Tel: (01227) 453227; Fax: (01227) 453225; E-mail: Thanington_hotel@compuserve.com

Originally a Georgian farmhouse listed Grade II for its architectural interest, Thanington became an hotel in 1987. Guests can enjoy a quiet drink in the bar or drawing room or sample the delightful walled garden - a real suntrap in the summer months. The indoor heated swimming pool is open all year round and, for the less energetic, there is the snooker room, darts board and various board games. The hotel is just a ten-minute stroll to Canterbury city centre and its host of cosmopolitan restaurants, shops and magnificent cathedral. It is close to the seaside towns and famous castles and houses of Kent and gives convenient access to the Channel terminals. Accommodation is modern and attractive with superior double rooms having queen size four posters or antique Victorian bedsteads.

Rates: Standard double or twin room with breakfast £68-72; superior double room £80-88.
Bargain Breaks: 2 persons for 2 nights Jan-Mar £130-£150, Apr-Dec £135-160.

● *15 en suite bedrooms with radio, colour TV, direct dial telephone, hairdryer, tea/coffee making facilities, trouser press, personal safe. Non-smoker rooms avail.*
● *Snooker room, indoor swimming pool.*
● *Open all year. Access, Diners, Visa & Amex credit cards accepted.*
Ashford 14, Dover 15, Margate 15, Folkestone 16, Maidstone 27, London 58.

Walletts' Court

Westcliffe, St Margaret's Bay, Dover, Kent CT15 6EW
Tel: (01304) 852424; Fax: (01304) 853430

This lovely old country manor house set in beautiful grounds is located just outside St. Margaret's and dates back to the Domesday Book but is essentially a celebration of a former Elizabethan era. The earlier part is explained on a frieze and the rest is evident in the atmosphere of the house. Built in 1627, it has many unusual features: carved wooden porch, ancient staircase, original wall-painting, even a priesthole, and historical associations with such eminent figures as Queen Eleanor of Castille, Gibbon and Pitt. Today Walletts'Court testifies to the Oakley Family philosophy of making a home of the place they discovered 22 years ago. The conservatory is an additional lounge designed for planning your dinner in the beamed, candlelit restaurant. This award-winning gourmets' paradise offers excitingly creative cuisine with menus changed regularly to incorporate fresh seasonal ingredients, and chosen with a Jacobean flavour reflecting the historical background of the house. The bedrooms are divided between the main house and converted barns whose comfortably furnished rooms are named according to original usage such as

Dairy or *Stable*. This year four new luxury bedrooms have been added: the *William Pitt*, the *Sir Edward de Burgh*, the *Lord Aylmer* rooms and *Crèvecoeur's* Tower. The Elizabethans built to last; happily enjoyment of all good things from that era lives on in Walletts' Court.

Single *room, inc. breakfast from £60;* **[V]**
double *room inc. breakfast from £70;*
Bargain breaks: *2 nights inc. dinner for two mid week £200; weekend £210.*

● *12 en suite bedrooms with colour TV, direct-dial telephone, hairdryer, laundry/valet service, tea/coffee making facilities, radio alarm clock.*
● *Table d'hôte & à la carte dinner in AA ⊕⊕⊕ restaurant; last orders 2030 hrs; special diets avail.*
● *Croquet, fishing, tennis, indoor swimming pool, jacuzzi, sauna & steam rooms. Golf 6 m, sea 1 mile*
● *Open all year. Visa, Amex, Mastercard, Switch accepted.*

Folkestone 7, Canterbury 15, Margate 20, London 74

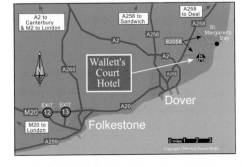

Stade Court Hotel

West Parade, Hythe, Kent CT21 6DT
Tel: (01303) 268263; Fax: (01303) 261803

Standing proudly on the seafront of the picturesque Cinque Port of Hythe stands Stade Court, which has been welcoming both business and leisure guests to this historic corner of Kent since 1938 and is thus nearly as old as *Signpost* itself! It provides a quieter and pleasing alternative to its big sister, the Hythe Imperial, just 600 yards away, for those who prefer smaller hotels and the personal service they provide. Many of the 42 beautifully furnished en suite bedrooms, including five family rooms, have lounges with views directly overlooking the Channel. Stade Court's charming location features a promenade along the beach and is a popular fisherman's haunt. Fresh local seafood is regularly featured on the menu in the award-winning Lukin Restaurant where a wide selection of quality wines at favourable prices are also available. Complimentary access is allowed to the excellent leisure facilities at the nearby Hythe Imperial, including a 9-hole golf course and a beauty parlour. The hotel is well situated for visits to Dover Castle and the White Cliffs Experience, the Romney, Hythe and Dymchurch Light Railway; also Howletts and Port Lympne wild animal parks.

Rates: Single room and breakfast from £72.00; Ⅴ *double room inc. breakfast from £101.00.*
Bargain breaks: *Marston breaks - 2 nights dinner, b&b per person sharing from £59 per night; Romantic Breaks from £67.75; Golfing Breaks from £66.50.*

● *42 bedrooms (38 en suite) with colour TV + satellite, direct-dial telephone, hairdryer, laundry service, minibar, tea/coffee making facilities, 24 hr room/meal service, safety deposit box, music/radio/ alarm clock, trouser press., safety deposit box.*
● *Table d'hôte dinner £19.50; à la carte, lunch & special diets available; last orders 9.30 pm.*
● *Business services inc 4 meeting rooms, capacity 60*
● *Billiards, croquet, gymnasium, golf, indoor games, jacuzzi, massage, sauna, squash, indoor swimming pool & tennis all available 600 yds at Hythe Imperial Hotel. Car rental and parking for 12.*
● *Open all year; Visa, Mastercard, Diners and Amex accepted.*
Folkestone 5, Ashford 11, Canterbury 17, Rye 21, London 66.

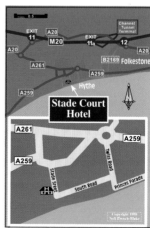

LONDON & THE SOUTHEAST

Hotel du Vin & Bistro

Crescent Road, Royal Tun-
bridge Wells, Kent TN1 2LY
Tel: (01892) 526455;
Fax: (01892) 512044

Once the country home of the Earl
of Egremont, the totally refurbished Hotel du Vin (formerly the
Calverley) has quickly become a
stylish base from which to explore
the historic town of Tunbridge
Wells and the surrounding Kent
and Sussex countryside. Charming
and unpretentious, the hotel combines simplicity with comfort and
offers excellent value for money.
The flair of the partners of the
Alternative Hotel Company has
already been well recognised
through the success of the sister
Hotel du Vin in Winchester, created in 1994. As a princess, Queen
Victoria stayed regularly at the
lovely sandstone house - extended
in the 1830s by Decimus Burton -
during the summer season. Reception rooms include the *Burgundy
Bar*, a celebration of the great wine
growing district, and the *Dom
Pérignon Gallery*, a comfortable and
elegant drawing room hung with
famous paintings. The *Havana
Room* offers a quiet game of billiards and a fine selection of Cuban cigars;
and the *Evian* function room provides state-
of-the-art meeting facilities. Enjoy lunch on
the *Bistro*'s terrace overlooking Calverley
Park. The menu changes twice daily depend-
ing on local supplies for its Mediterranean
cuisine. The bedrooms, each of which are
sponsored by an eminent wine company,
mirror the rest of the hotel, offering all modern luxuries with particular emphasis on good
quality beds, made up with Egyptian linen,
and bathrooms. The charm of this place, with
its many original features and understated
elegance, makes for a most relaxing stay.

● *25 individually decorated en suite bedrooms with
CD players, trouser press, satellite TV, minibar.*
●*A la carte lunch & dinner; last orders 9.30 pm;
special diets available.*
● *Two conference rooms to 70. Car parking.*
● *Billiards/snooker. Golf 1 mile.*

● *Open all year. Visa, Amex, Diners, Switch
accepted.*

Rates: *Double/twins £75-95; Principal rooms
£109. Prices include VAT but not breakfast.* Ⓥ

**Tonbridge 4, East Grinstead 13, Maidstone
16, Eastbourne 29, Hastings 27, London 36**

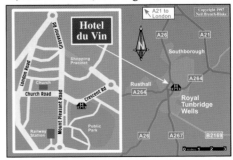

Coulsdon Manor

Coulsdon Court Road, Old Coulsdon.
Nr. Croydon, Surrey CR5 2LL
Tel: (0181) 668 0414; Fax: (0181) 668
3118

Set in 140 acres of beautiful Surrey parkland, a large part of it laid down as a chal-
lenging 18-hole golf course, yet just 15
miles from both central London and Gatwick and easily accessible to the motorway
network. Built for Thomas Byron in the
1850s and sympathetically restored, inside
you will discover a country house flavour
reflected in beautiful woodwork and chandeliers. Relax in the lounge or bars and
soak up the atmosphere as it is now and
imagine how life was at Coulsdon Manor
over 100 years ago. Dine in the award winning Manor House restaurant or choose
lighter fare in the popular Terrace Bar.
Many of the 35 bedrooms have views over
the golf course. Coulsdon Manor is an ideal
base from which to explore many places of
interest. Children of all ages will enjoy
Thorpe Park and Chessington World of
Adventures. Croydon Palace, Wisley RHS
Gardens, Wakehurst Place and Hever Castle are also near at hand. As well as golf,
many other activities are available at Coulsdon and there are five conference rooms
which can cater for up to 180 delegates.

Single room with breakfast from £104;   **V**
Double room including breakfast from £130.
Leisure Breaks: 2-night Marston Breaks, dinner, b&b £75 per head; Romantic Break £83.75
per head; Golfing Break inc 2 rounds per person
£84.50. Special Xmas/New Year/Bank Holiday
breaks avail. 5 nights d,b&b £350; 7 nights £450.

● 35 en suite bedrooms with colour TV+ satellite, direct-dial telephone, hairdryer, laundry
service, tea/coffee making facilities, minibar, 24-
hr room/meal service, radio, safety deposit box,
trouser press. Non-smoker bedrooms available.
● Table d'hote dinner £25. A la carte, lunch &
special diets available. Last orders 21.30.
● Fitness centre, golf, sauna/solarium, squash,
tennis. Riding,
dry ski slope, wa-
ter park nearby.
● Business serv-
ices inc 9 meeting
rooms - cap. 175.
● Open all year.
All major credit
cards accepted.

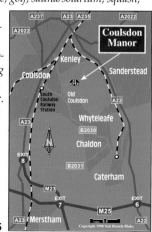

**Croydon 6,
M25 Motor-
way 6,
Gatwick Air-
port 15, Cen-
tral London 15**

The Bishop's Table Hotel & Restaurant

27 West Street, Farnham, Surrey GU9 7DR
Tel: (01252) 710222; Fax: (01252) 733494

This lovely small hotel is situated in the heart of the historic market town of Farnham, notable for its Georgian architecture of which the Bishop's Table is a classic example. Formerly owned by the Marquis of Lothian and once used as a training school for clergy - whence its name - it is now managed by the family owners. Their friendly style has won them national excellence awards for hospitality, comfort and cuisine, including the AA Courtesy and Care Award 1996. The character of the place is distinguished by quality furnishings and fresh flowers in the reception, bar and restaurant and by the 'home from home' atmosphere of the well furnished bedrooms. The gourmet fare is generally acclaimed as being amongst the finest in the area. A lounge leads to one of the hotel's most attractive features - a beautifully landscaped, secluded wall garden. The location makes the hotel an ideal venue for business and leisure traveller alike who return time and time again attracted by the relaxing ambience of this charming hotel.

Rates: Single room with breakfast from £88; **V**
Double room including breakfast from £105.
Leisure Breaks: Weekend - Fri, Sat, Sun £114 per double room to include 3-cse tdh dinner, b & b per night for two pertsons sharing.

● *17 en suite bedrooms with colour TV, direct-dial telephone, hairdryer, laundry service, tea/coffee making facilities, music/radio/alarm clock, safety deposit box, trouser press.*
● *Table d'hote dinner £22. Lunch & special diets available. Last orders 21.45. Car rental available.*
● *Tennis next door; golf 3 miles; riding 4 miles.*
● *Business services inc 2 meeting rooms - cap. 10.*
● *Open all year. All major credit cards accepted.*

Alton 9¹/₂, Guildford 10, Basingstoke 15, Reading 25, Winchester 28, London 45.

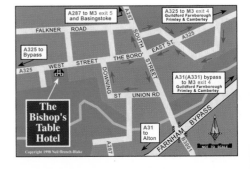

Chase Lodge Hotel

10 Park Road, Hampton Wick, Kingston-upon-Thames, Surrey KT1 4AS
Tel: (0181) 943 1862; Fax:(0181) 943 9363

Nigel and Denise Stafford Haworth own and
personally run this extremely popular little
gem of an hotel, situated just 20 minutes from
the heart of London. Chase Lodge has been
cleverly amalgamated from two old cottages
dating back to 1870, and Nigel himself has
done most of the work. Denise has designed
the style and décor of lounge, bar and bedrooms with such flair and charm that you will
immediately feel relaxed and at ease. Nigel
also runs the kitchen with equal aplomb. The
menu is imaginative, and the food is cooked
and presented to perfection. Avocado with
crab, langoustine and pernod, followed by
roast barbary duck with a kumquat or black
cherry sauce are just an example of the delicious dishes available, which can be complemented by a bottle from the very fine wine
list. Meals are served in the conservatory,
which is surrounded by the prettiest little
floodlit courtyard garden, and light bar
snacks can also be enjoyed in the adjoining
sitting room. I can thoroughly recommend
this hotel to anyone who is looking for comfort, relaxation and good food. They will
understand Chase Lodge's popularity.

Single *room and breakfast from £48 inc.VAT*
Double *room with breakfast from £71 (inc VAT).*
Dinner, *room and breakfast from £49.50, inc. VAT*
Bargain breaks: *Discounts available for stays of
3 nights or more. Also Xmas/New Year
programmes.*

● *12 en suite bedrooms, all with direct dial telephone and TV + satellite; tea/coffee making facilities; room service; baby listening; night service.*
● *Last orders for dinner 10.00 p.m; bar meals;
special diets.*
● *Children welcome; dogs accepted.*
● *Gymnasium 500 yds; tennis ¹/₂ mile; indoor
heated swimming pool, leisure centre, squash, golf
and riding 1 ¹/₂ miles; open all year; ample parking;*
● *All major credit cards accepted. AA Appointed.*

**Hampton Court 1¹/₂, Kew Gardens 4,
London 7, Wimbledon 7, Heathrow 8**

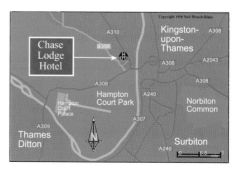

Oatlands Park Hotel

Oatlands Drive, Weybridge, Surrey
KT13 9HB
Tel: (01932) 847242; Fax: (01932) 842252

This majestic hotel is set in acres of parkland
overlooking Broadwater Lake in the heart of
the Surrey countryside, yet is only a 25-minute
train journey to central London. Records show
that Henry VIII had his hunting lodge on the
estate; it was used by many subsequent mon-
archs and rebuilt as a country residence for
the Duke and Duchess of York until 1820. It
became an hotel in 1856, patronised by many
famous writers such as Zola, Lear and Trol-
lope, and today the historic character remains
very apparent. You pass through the
porticoed entrance into the splendid galleried
lounge, with marble columns and and tapestries under a large glass dome, where refreshments and light meals are served throughout
the day. The lounge bar and Broadwater Restaurant are equally stylish offering table
d'hôte and à la carte menus, and a particularly popular traditional Sunday lunch. The
bedrooms are designed to high standards of
comfort. The hotel has everything for the leisure guest but also excels as a conference
venue with an expert staff and a variety of
rooms equipped for every need. The awards
won for customer care, whether corporate or
leisure, are much in evidence and Oatlands
Park's standards remain second to none.

Single room with breakfast from £111; **V**
Double room with breakfast from £152;
Bargain Breaks: *Weekend rates available from
£40 per person per night, bed & full Eng. b'fast*

● *128 en suite bedrooms (55 double, 43 twin, 25
single, 5 suites, all with colour TV + satellite,
direct-dial telephone, hairdryer, laundry/valet
service, tea/coffee-making facilities, 24 hour room/
meal service, music/radio/alarm clock, safety deposit box, trouser press; non-smoker bedrooms
available.*
● *Broadwater Restaurant table d'hôte £25; last
orders 9.30 pm; à la carte, lunch & special diets
available.*
● *Business centre inc. meeting rooms for 300.*
● *Croquet, gym, 9-hole golf course, massage. Car
parking for 100.*
● *Open all year. All major credit cards accepted.*
**Woking 7, Kingston-upon Thames 8,
Bagshot 11, Epsom 12, London 18.**

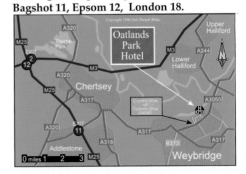

Grand Hotel, Eastbourne

King Edward's Parade, Eastbourne,
East Sussex BN21 4EQ
Tel: (01323) 412345; Fax: (01323) 412233

The commanding presence of the Grand Hotel overlooks the Western promenade at Eastbourne. Affectionately known as the 'White Palace', it was built in 1875 and epitomises the grandeur of Victorian and Edwardian eras. The *Elite* hotel group acquired the property in 1998 - see also the *Ashdown Park Hotel* (page 93) and *Tylney Hall* (page 64). The hotel's exterior is magnificently elaborate, whilst the lavishly appointed interior provides spacious reception rooms. During the summer months, the terrace beside the outdoor swimming pool is an alluring spot. A short stroll from the Grand are the famous grass tennis courts of Devonshire Park where the long-established pre-Wimbledon Ladies' Tournament takes place. In addition to tennis stars, the Grand continues to play host to political and business leaders. Communications are good, with Gatwick less than an hour away. Brighton, Beachy Head and the battlefield site at Hastings are also close by, as is Newhaven sea ferry terminal. Glyndebourne and the glorious South Downs countryside are on the hotel's doorstep. The hotel has recently extended its leisure facilities and impressive banqueting and conference rooms are available.

Rates: Single room with breakfast from £115; ☑
Double room with breakfast from £150.
***Bargain Breaks:** Min 2-night stay inc tdh dinner & breakfast from £181 per couple per night.*

● *152 en suite bedrooms (inc 48 suites), all with colour TV + satellite, direct-dial telephone, hairdryer, laundry/valet service, tea/coffee-making facilities (on request), 24 hour room/meal service, music/radio/alarm clock, safety deposit box, trouser press; non-smoker & disabled bedrooms available.*
● *Garden Restaurant 4-course table d'hôte £27; last orders 9.30 pm; à la carte, lunch &diets avail.*
● *Business centre inc. 8 meeting rooms up to 350.*
● *Billiards/snooker, fitness centre/gym, jacuzzi/whirlpool, massage, sauna/solarium, outdoor & indoor swimming pools. Tennis nearby; fishing, watersports, squash one mile; sailing, riding, shooting 3-5 m.*
● *Open all year. All major credit cards accepted.*

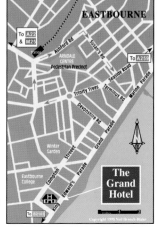

Newhaven 12,
Hastings 20,
Brighton 25,
Tunbridge Wells
29, Dover 61,
London 63.

Lansdowne Hotel

King Edward's Parade, Eastbourne,
East Sussex BN21 4EE
Tel: (01323) 725174; Fax: (01323) 739721
AA 'Courtesy & Care' Award 1992.
RAC Merit Awards for Hospitality, Service &
Comfort 1995/6/7/8.   RAC ★★★ AA

The Lansdowne Hotel commands a fine view
over Eastbourne's beach to the sea beyond.
Owned by the same family since 1912, this hotel has the true hallmark of hospitality and
comfort. Bedrooms are gracefully furnished
with many rooms overlooking the sea-front.
There is a choice of elegant lounges all of
which benefit from a view across the Western
Lawns as well as several refreshment places
from the attractive Regency Bar to the stylish
Devonshire Restaurant serving fixed price
menus of traditional English cuisine. A comprehensive bar and lounge menu is available
daily at lunchtime. Traditional Sunday lunch
and 4-course dinner is served every evening in
the restaurant. Conferences and seminars are
well provided for in a selection of rooms. Two
snooker rooms, table tennis, darts and a pool
table provide every opportunity for relaxation. Eastbourne is an active resort offering a
world famous tennis centre, a first class yachting marina, 200 acres of parks and gardens and
the Lansdowne hotel is the ideal base from
which to explore all that is offered in the area.

Single room rate including breakfast from £52.00.
Double room with breakfast from £84.00.   Ⅴ
Bargain Breaks *weekend/weekday from 15th Jan-
uary -16th May (exc. Easter) & 17 October- 22nd
December. Prices from £39 pppn d,b&b. Rubber
bridge weekends once a month exc. June, July, Sept.
& Oct; prices pp from £88 (2 nights) or £122 (3
nights). Duplicate bridge weekends (3 nights only)
from £130 Nov, Feb, March, May & August.
Golf Breaks all year from £130 per golfer for 2 days.*

● *121 en suite bedrooms with colour/satellite TV,
radio, direct-dial telephone, hairdryer, laundry
service, tea/coffee making facilities, 24-hour room
service, trouser press.* ● *Last dinner orders 20.30.*
● *Snooker, indoor games room. Special
arrangements for golf with seven local clubs.
Sky Sports TV in Jevington Room.*
● *Complete business service. Five fully
equipped conference rooms with capacity of 330.*
● *Car parking: 22 lock-ups.* ● *Hotel closed 1-
14 January.* ● *All major credit cards accepted.*
**Newhaven 12, Hastings 20, Brighton 25, Tunbridge Wells 29,
Dover 61, London 63.**

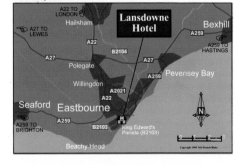

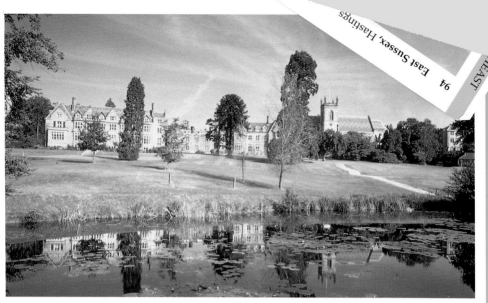

Ashdown Park Hotel

Wych Cross, Forest Row, East Sussex
RH18 5JR
Tel: (01342) 824988; Fax: (01342) 826206

Not much more than an hour's drive from
Central London, yet in the heart of Ashdown
Forest, lies Ashdown Park Hotel & Country
Club, sympathetically restored in the 1990s
and now part of the *Elite* Group (see also
Tylney Hall on page 64 and *The Grand Hotel,
Eastbourne* on page 91). Convenient for the
summer delights of Glyndebourne, Hickstead
and the stunning gardens and country houses
of Sussex, the hotel gives a marvellous sensa-
tion of comfort and space. There are some 186
acres of parkland in which to roam, with gardens, lakes and woodland trails - and no shortage of activities on site. The charms of
Tunbridge Wells and Brighton and the international connections at Gatwick and the Channel
Tunnel terminal at Ashford are nearby. The
recently expanded Country Club now has
some of the latest cardiovascular equipment
and a wide range of facial, body and hair treatments available. A magnificent Victorian building, Ashdown Park offers a range of short
breaks and musical evenings, sometimes in
connection with a wedding or private party.
It also has superb conference facilities.

*Rates: single room rate inc. breakfast from £114;
double room with breakfast from £140.* **V**
*Bargain Breaks: min 2-night stay inc tdh dinner &
breakfast from £181 per couple per night.*

● *95 en suite bedrooms with colour/satellite TV,
radio, direct-dial telephone, hairdryer, laundry
service, trouser press, safety deposit box*
● *Last dinner orders 21.30. Lunch & special diets
available. Car parking for 120.*
● *Billiards/snooker, croquet, fitness centre/
gym, jacuzzi/whirlpool, jogging track, massage,
sauna/solarium, indoor swimming pool, tennis,
barber shop/haidresser, beauty salon, 9-hole par
3 golf course. Fishing 7m. Riding three miles.*
● *Business services inc. 15 meeting rooms, cap 150.*
● *Open all year. All major credit cards accepted.*

**East Grinstead 3, Haywards Heath 10,
Tunbridge Wells 12, Lewes 17, London 33.**

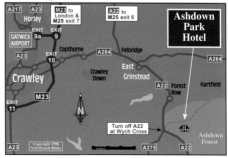

Beauport Park Hotel

Battle Road
Hastings, East Sussex TN38 8EA
Tel: (01424) 851222; Fax: (01424) 852465

This fine house was built in 1719 and remodelled by a former Governor of Quebec who named it Beauport after his summer home in Canada. It is unspoiled by its transition from residence to first class hotel and guests will particularly enjoy the three most attractive features - seclusion, the stylish elegance of the interior and the extensive range of leisure facilities. Set at the end of a winding drive in 33 acres of tranquil parkland, you are welcomed by a perfect example of a Georgian country house. The tastefully modernised lounge and bar areas are warmed by open log fires, and the candlelit restaurant, renowned for its cuisine, overlooks the formal Italian and sunken gardens. The bedrooms too are furnished to a high standard and leave nothing to chance in terms of additional luxuries. Beauport is close to the Channel ports and the many attractions of this beautiful part of Britain. Yet in these historic surroundings anyone seeking either peace and quiet or a more active holiday need look no further than this lovely hotel, whose rating of Highly Commended and awards for comfort we found to be fully justified.

Rates: Single room inc. breakfast from £80. Double room inc. breakfast from £105.
Bargain Breaks: *Minimum two night short breaks available all year. A four poster room, dinner & breakfast starts at £74 per night.*

● *23 bedrooms (10 double, 7 twin, 4 single, 1 suite), all with colour TV + satellite, direct-dial telephone, hairdryer, laundry/valet service, tea/ coffee making facilities, trouser press. Non-smoker bedrooms available.*
● *Table d'hôte dinner £22. A la carte, lunch & special diets available. Last orders 9.30 pm*

● *Golf, riding, outdoor swimming pool, tennis.*
● *Full business services inc, 3 meeting rooms - capacity 70. Car parking for 60.*
● *Open all year. Major credit cards accepted.*
Rye 11, Lewes 29, Brighton 37, Folkestone 37, London 65

Flackley Ash Hotel

Peasmarsh, Near Rye
East Sussex, TN31 6YH
Tel: (01797) 230651; Fax: (01797) 230510

This is one of Sussex' most charming small country house hotels. Rye is only a few miles away with its many historic buildings including the 15th century church, the Ypres Tower, the famous Landgate and Henry James' Georgian residence, Lamb House. Local activities are many and varied, with antique shops, potteries, local crafts and boutiques and a market on Thursdays. Camber Sands, with its beautiful beaches and safe bathing, is only a few miles further on; and of course there are castles, abbeys, a cathedral and many gardens in the locality to be visited.

The hotel has an indoor swimming pool and leisure complex, with whirlpool spa, mini gymnasium, steam room, sun bed, aromatherapy and beautician, sun terrace and croquet lawn. This Georgian house offers its visitors a warm and friendly atmosphere and comfortable en suite bedrooms. The dining room has an AA Rosette for its food. Dishes are interesting and well presented by friendly and willing staff. Most vegetables are locally grown and emphasis is on fresh local fish and seafood.

Rates: Room and breakfast from £57.50 sharing twin/double per person per night. **V**
***Getaway Breaks** from £72-£82 pppn - min. 2 nights. Winter price buster £135 pp for 3 nights. Summer price buster £199 pp for 3 nights or £309 pp 5 nights; weekly £325-£435.*

● *42 en suite bedrooms, all with direct dial telephone and TV.*
● *Last orders 9.30 p.m.; bar meals available.*
● *Children welcome; dogs accepted; conferences/receptions to 100 max.*
● *Indoor heated swimming pool; leisure centre; sauna; solarium; spa pool; steam room; gymnasium;*
● *Open all year; all major credit cards accepted.*

Rye 3, Hastings 11, Folkestone 29, Dover 36, London 60.

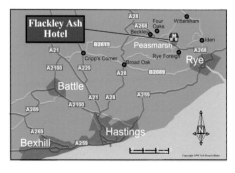

LONDON & THE SOUTHEAST

Rye Lodge Hotel

Hilder's Cliff, Rye, East Sussex TN31 7LD
Tel: (01797) 223838; Fax: (01797) 223585
E-mail: info@ryelodge.demon.co.uk

Rye - Ancient Town of the Cinque Ports. No town in England evokes the atmosphere of medieval times better than Rye with the charm and character of its cobbled streets, picturesque period houses, historic buildings and ancient fortifications. Situated on the East Cliff overlooking the estuary and Romney Marshes, yet within yards of the High Street of this beautifully preserved ancient town, stands Rye Lodge, acclaimed and acknowledged as one of the finest small luxury hotels of Southeast England. Much thought has gone into the décor, furnishing and equipping of the bedrooms and public rooms, creating an oasis of tranquillity and comfort for guests. The Terrace Restaurant is elegant, candlelit and its fine cellar houses some rare vintages. The hotel is centrally located, so that all antique shops, art galleries etc are within walking distance. This delightful privately owned hotel is run by the de Courcy family. It offers a degree of comfort and personal service rarely found in hotels these days and only achieved by experienced hoteliers through hard work and dedication to their art.

Rates: Single room with breakfast from £49.50-75; double room with breakfast £65-110. **V**
Bargain Breaks*: Midweek Short Breaks - any 2 nights dinner room & breakfast from £99-139. Mini Holidays - 3 nights+ from £95-135 pppn dinner b&b*

● *15 en suite bedrooms with radio, colour TV, direct-dial telephone; hairdryer, laundry service, tea/coffee making facilities; de luxe rooms with video films, trouser press & room safe.*
● *A la carte dinner - last orders 21.00. Special diets available. Car parking for 20.*
● *Open all year. Amex, Diners, Mastercard, Visa, Switch & Delta cards accepted.*

Hastings 11, Folkestone 25, Dover 32, Maidstone 33, Brighton 49, London 63.

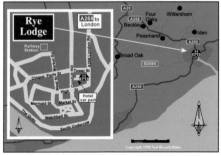

East of England

Historic Houses, Gardens & Parks

Bedfordshire
Luton Hoo, Luton
The Swiss Garden, Old Warden
Woburn Abbey, Woburn
Wrest Park House & Garden, Silsoe

Cambridgeshire
Anglesey Abbey Nr. Cambndge
Chilford Hundred Vineyard, Linton
Docwra's Manor Garden, Shepreth
Elton Hall, Elton, Peterborough
Hinchingbrooke House, Huntingdon
Kimbolton Castle
Peckover House, Wisbech
University of Cambridge Botanic Garden

Essex
Audley End House & Park, Saffron Walden
BBC Essex Garden, Abridge
Bridge End Gardens, Saffron Walden
Felsted Vineyard
New Hall Vineyards, Purleigh
Ingatestone Hall
Layer Marney Tower
Priory Vineyards, Little Dunmow
RHS Garden, Rettendon, Chelmsford

Hertfordshire
Ashridge Estate, Nr. Berkhampstead
Cedars Park Waltham Cross
The Gardens of the Rose, Chiswell Green, St Albans
Hatfield House

Knebworth House
The National Trust Wimpole Hall, Arrington, Nr. Royston
Priory Gardens, Royston
Verulamium Park, St Albans

Norfolk
Beeston Hall, Beeston St Lawrence
Bickling Hall
Fairhaven Garden Trust, South Walsham
Felbrigg HallFritton Lake Countryworld
Holkham Hall, Wells-next-the-Sea
Sandringham
Hoveton Hall Gardens, Wroxham
Mannington Gardens, Norwich
Norfolk Lavender Ltd, Heacham
Rainham Hall and Gardens, Tasburgh

Suffolk
Blakenham Woodland Garden, Nr Ipswich
Bruisyard Vineyard and Herb Centre
Euston Hall, Thetford
Haughley Park
Helmingham Hall Gardens
Kentwell Hall, Long Melford
Melford Hall, Long Melford
Somerleyton Hall & Gardens

Walks & Nature Trails

Bedfordshire
Greensand Ridge Walk from Leighton Buzzard to Gamlingay
Upper Lea Valley Walk, from Leagrave Common to E Hyde

Cambridgsehire
Bishops Way, north of Ely
Devil's Dyke, from north of Feach to south of Stechworth
Grafham Water Circular
Hertfordshire
The Lea Valley Walk, from Ware to Stanborough Lakes
Tring Reservoirs
Lincolnshire
Chambers Farm Wood Forest Nature Reserve, Aply, Lincoln

Hartwholme Country Park, Lincoln
Tattershall Park Country Club, Tattershall, Lincoln
Norfolk
Peddars Way & Norfolk Coast Path with Weavers Way
Marriott's Way, between Norwich & Aylsham

Suffolk
Constable Trail
Painters Way from Sudbury to Manningtree
Suffolk Coastal Path, from Bawdsey to Kessingland

East of England

Suffolk Way, from Flatford to Lavenham

Historical Sites & Museums

Bedfordshire
Bunyan Museum, Bedford
Elstow Moot Hall, Church End
Stockwood Craft Museum & Gardens
Shuttleworth Collection, Biggleswade

Cambridgeshire
Ely Cathedral
Imperial War Museum, Duxford
Fitzwilliam Museum, Cambridge
Oliver Cromwell's House, Ely
Cromwell Museum, Huntingdon

Essex
Central Museum and Planetarium, Southend-on-Sea
Colchester Castle
Hedingham Castle, Castle Hedingham
Maritime Museum, Harwich
National Motorboat Museum, Pitsea
Working Silk Museum, Braintree

Hertfordshire
Berkhamsted Castle
Hertford Castle
Roman Baths, Welwyn Garden City
Roman Theatre, St Albans
Verulamium Museum, St Albans

Lincolnshire
Bishop's Palace, Lincoln
Bolingbroke Castle, Spilsby
Lincoln Castle
Lincoln Guildhall
Woolsthorpe Manor, Nr. Grantham
The Incredibly Fantastic Old Toy Show, Lincoln

Norfolk
100th Bomb Group Memorial Museum, Dickleburgh
Alby Lace Museum and Study Centre
Ancient House Museum, Thetford
Bygones Collection, Holkham Hall, Wells-next-the-Sea Bygone Heritage Villa, Burgh St Margaret
Charles Burrell Museum, Thetford
City of Norwich Aviation Museum, Horsham St Faith
Maritime Museum, Great Yarmouth
Muckleburgh Collection, Weybourne
Shrine of our Lady of Walsingham, Walsingham
Wolverton Station Museum
Tales of the Old Gaol House, King's Lynn

Suffolk
Bridge Cottage, Flatford
Dunwich Underwater Exploration Exhibition, Orford
Framlingham Castle

Gainsborough's House, Sudbury
Guildhall of Corpus Christi, Lavenham
Moot Hall & Museum, Aldeburgh
National Horse Racing Museum, Newmarket
Sizewell Visitors Centre, Sizewell B Power Station
Sue Ryder Foundation Museum, Cavendish
Tolly Cobbold Brewery, Ipswich
Woodbndge Museum

Entertainment Venues

Bedfordshire
Stagsden Bird Gardens
Whipsnade Wild Animal Park, Dunstable
Woburn Safari Park, Woburn

Cambridgeshire
Grays Honey Farm, Warboys
Hamerton Wildlife Centre
Linton Zoo
Peakirk Waterfowl Gardens Trust, Peterborough
Sacrewell Farm & Country Centre, Thornhaugh

Essex
Colchester Zoo
Dedham Rare Breed Farm
Layer Marney Tower
Mole Hall Wildlife Park, Widdington
Southend Sea Life Centre

Hertfordshire
Maltings Centre, St Albans
Paradise Wildlife Farm, Broxbourne
Water Hall Farm & Craft Centre, Nr. Hitchin

Lincolnshire
Brandy Wharf Cider Centre, Gainsborough
Battle of Britain Memorial Flight, RAF Coningsby, Lincoln
The Butterfly & Falconry Park, Long Sutton
Skegness Natureland Sea Sanctuary, Skegness
Cobb Hall Craft Centre, Lincoln

Norfolk
Banham Zoo
Kingdom of the Sea, Great Yarmouth
Norfolk Wildlife Centre & Country Park, Great Witchingham
Otter Trust, Earsham
Park Farm & Norfolk Farmyard Crafts Centre, Snettisham
Pensthorpe Waterfowl Park
Thrigby Hall Wildlife Gardens, Filby

Suffolk
East of England Birds of Prey and Conservation Centre, Laxfield
Suffolk Wildlife Park, Kessingland

DIARY OF EVENTS

February

4-7. **Springfields Horticultural Exhibition,** Spalding, Lincs. Indoor spring flowers.
20-21*. **Motorbike '99.** Springfields, Spalding, Lincs. 2-wheeled show for the road.
27-6 Mar. **Bedfordshire Festival of Music, Speech & Drama.** Corn Exchange, St Paul's Sq, Bedford

March

8-13* **Celebration of Schools Music.** Snape Maltings Concert Hall, Snape, Suffolk.
20-21. **National Shire Horse Show.** East of England Showground, Alwalton, Nr. Peterborough, Cambs.
27-28. **Thriplow Daffodil Weekend.** Thriplow, Cambs.

April

2-5. **Aldeburgh Easter Festival.** Snape Maltings Concert Hall, Snape.
2-5. **Blickling Craft Show,** Norfolk Knebworth House Knebworth, Hertfordshire.
30-3 May. **Lincoln Folk Festival.** The Lawn, Lincoln.

May

1-2* **2000 Guineas/1000 Guineas Classic Race Meeting**. The Racecourse, Newmarket, Suffolk.
1-3. **Spalding Flower Show.** Streets of Spalding, Springfields Gardens and Festival Site, Spalding, Lincs

3.**Stilton Cheese Rolling/May Day.** North St, Stilton,Cambs
3-4*. **Knebworth County Show.** Knebworth House, Hertfordshire.
3-5*. **Horse Racing: The Guineas Meeting.** Racecourse, Newmarket, Suffolk.
6-9. **Living Crafts Exhibition.** Hatfield House, Herts
14-30. **Bury St Edmunds Festival.** Various venues in Bury St. Edmunds, Suffolk.
10. **South Suffolk Show.** Ampton Park, Ingham, Suffolk. Agricultural Show with show jumping, crafts &c
29-30. **Air Fête '99.** RAF Mildenhall, Mildenhall, Suffolk.
29-31. **Fellbrigg Coast & Country Craft Fair.** Fellbrigg Hall, Norfolk.
30-31.**Southend Air Show.** Southend-on-Sea, Essex
31. **Luton Carnival.** Luton, Bedfordshire
29-30. **Hertfordshire County Show.** Herts County Showground, Redbourn, Herts.

June

1-Aug 30*.**Stamford Shakespeare Co 99 Summer Open Air Season.** Rutland Open Air Theatre, Tolethorpe, Casterton, Leics
2-3. **Suffolk Show.** Suffolk Showground, Ipswich.
11-26. **52nd Aldeburgh Festival of Music & Arts.** Snape Maltings (and various venues), Aldeburgh, Suffolk. World renowned festival including operas, concerts, recitals etc.
18-20. **Essex County Show.** Essex Showground, Great Leigh, Essex.
30-July 1. **Royal Norfolk Show 1999.** (agricultural) Norfolk Showground, Norwich.
30-July 4. **Wisbech Rose Fair.** St Peters Church, Wisbech, Cambs.

East of England

1-4. Cambridge Music Festival. Kings & St Johns College, Cambridge.
9-17. International Organ Festival. St Albans Cathedral, St Albans, Herts.
17-18*. Holkham Country Fair. Holkham Hall, Norfolk
20-22. East of England Show 1999. Showground, Alwalton, Peterborough, Cambs
22-31. Kings Lynn Festival 1999. Various venues, Kings Lynn, Norfolk.
28. Sandringham Flower Show, Sandringham, Norfolk

1-31. Snape Proms. Maltings, Aldeburgh, Suffolk
19-20. Thorpeness Regatta & Fireworks. Thorpeness, Suffolk.
27-30. Clacton Jazz Festival. Clacton-on-Sea, Essex.

2-5. Burghley Horse Trials. Burghley Park, Stamford, Lincolnshire
24-26. Woodhall Spa Festival of Flowers. Var. venues, Woodhall Spa, Lincs.

1-17. Norfolk & Norwich Festival '99. Various venues, Norwich, Norfolk
16. Dubai Champion Stakes. Newmarket, Suffolk

* = Provisional Date. For further information contact:

TOURIST
BOARD

East of England Tourist Board. Toppesfield Road, Hadleigh, Suffolk, Suffolk IP7 5DN. Tel: 01473 822922

East of England

East of England Tourist Board area encompasses the predominantly agricultural counties of Bedfordshire, Hertfordshire, Norfolk, Suffolk, Cambridgeshire and Essex. Norfolk is thickly afforested in the west around Thetford, whereas the east is crisscrossed by waterways and Lakes known as *The Broads* - the remains of medieval man's peat diggings.

The county town of Norfolk and informal capital of East Anglia is the university city of Norwich, whose fine cathedral with walls decorated with biblical scenes dates from 1046. There are 30 medieval churches in central Norwich dominated by Norwich Castle Museum. Brideswell Museum and Church Museum should also not be missed.

Near King's Lynn in the northwest of the county is Sandringham, royal palace bought for King Edward VII while prince of Wales by Queen Victoria in 1862. Rising above the fens south of Kings Lynn is the magnificent 11th century Ely Cathedral, built on the site of a 7th century Benedictine Abbey.

East Suffolk's coast with its inlets and estuaries is popular with yachtsmen. Framlingham Castle, near Aldeburgh, stands intact since the 13th century. The hills and river valleys surrounding the Suffolk-Essex border open up to magnificent skies, captured in paintings by Constable and Gainsborough. Heart of Constable country is Nayland and Dedham Vale. Fine woollen towns are exemplified by Lavenham, Long Melford and Sudbury, among others.

Cultural capital of East Anglia is the tranquil city of Cambridge whose colleges, dating from the 13th century, were mostly founded as acts of piety. Most are open during daylight hours. Evensong at Kings College Chapel on Sundays is memorable. Rubens' *Adoration of the Magi* hangs there. The Fitzwilliam Museum is one of Europe's treasure houses, housing antiquities from Egypt, Greece and Rome as well as English and Chinese porcelain. Also worth a visit is the University Museum of Archaeology and Anthropology, with emphasis on prehistoric artefacts from the Cambridge area. Cambridge is also a centre for shopping and theatre.

Bedfordshire has the palace and theme park of Woburn to visit and Luton Hoo. Whipsnade open air zoo will appeal particulary to children.

St Albans in Hertfordshire has Verulamium Roman remains and Hatfield House was the home of Elisabeth I. Tewin Hoo is an example of a small Elizabethan Manor.

Old Palace Lodge Hotel

Church Street, Dunstable, Bedfordshire
LU5 4RT
Tel: (01582) 662201; Fax: (01582) 696422

This ivy clad hotel on the edge of Dunstable is an excellent alternative for those not wishing to stay in Central London. There are plenty of local attractions and Luton Airport is only 15 minutes away. The hotel, formerly a Victorian home, stands on the site of a Tudor palace. Interestingly the divorce between Henry VIII and Catherine of Aragon was decreed in the priory church of St Peter, opposite. Traditional, yet stylish furnishings and decoration create a relaxed atmosphere. The restaurant achieves high standards with the emphasis on modern British cooking, complemented by an unusually fine wine list. Wedding receptions and conferences are well catered for either in the *Catherine Room* for larger functions or in the *Henry VIII Room* which accommodates up to 20. The London Gliding Club is located nearby and the hotel can supply discounted ticket entry to Whipsnade Wild Animal Park and Woburn Abbey & Safari Park. Excellent shopping is available in Milton Keynes, Brent Cross or St Albans, with the West End only half an hour away down the M1.

Rates: Single room from £95; double from £105 (room only). **V**
Special Weekend Breaks: from £29.95 per person inc. breakfast.

● *68 en suite bedrooms, all with colour TV+ satellite, direct-dial telephone, hairdryer, tea/coffee making facilities, safety deposit box, 24-hour room/meal service. Non-smoker bedrooms available.*
● *Table d'hôte dinner £19.95; last orders 9.45 pm. A la carte, lunch and special diets available.*
● *Business centre inc. 2 meeting rooms, capacity 40. Car parking for 60. Car Hire can be arranged.*
● *Open all year. All major credit cards accepted.*

M1 Junc 11 2¹/₂, Luton 5, St Albans 13, Aylesbury 15, Bedford 19, London 34.

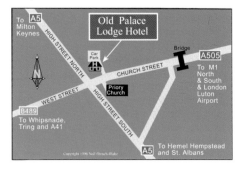

Arundel House Hotel

Chesterton Road, Cambridge CB4 3AN
Tel: (01223) 367701; Fax: (01223 367721)

The Arundel House Hotel occupies one of the finest sites in the City of Cambridge, overlooking the River Cam and open parkland. It is only a short walk across the park known as Jesus Green to the city centre with its wealth of historic buildings. The hotel is well known for its bar and restaurant. The bright, cheerful colours in the bar, coupled with beautiful chintz curtains, comfortable sofas and armchairs, sumptuous carpeting and leather bound books create a warm and refreshing atmosphere. With its magnificent Victorian-style bar, carved out of solid American red oak, and two beautiful fireplaces, it is a comfortable setting for a pre-dinner drink.
The restaurant has a reputation for providing some of the best food in the area. All tastes are catered for, thanks to the several different menus on offer, all featuring a wide range of imaginative dishes, freshly prepared in the hotel's award winning kitchen. As an alternative to the dining-room, there is a Victorian style conservatory, providing a luscious green environment. The Conservatory is open all day and offers a wide range of different op-

tions from cooked meals to cream teas, all of which can also be served in the hotel's secluded garden (weather permitting).

Single room with breakfast from £39.50 . Ⅴ
Bargain Breaks: £105 per person for two nights dinner, bed & breakfast.
● *105 bedrooms, 102 en suite with colour TV, direct-dial telephone, hairdryer, tea-coffee making facilities, radio/alarm clock. Non-smoker bedrooms available.*
● *Table d'hôte £15.95. Table d'hôte lunch, à la carte, special vegetarian and children's menu also available. Last orders 9.30 pm restaurant, 10 pm conservatory.*
● *Three meeting rooms, maximum capacity 50.*
● *Car parking for 70.* ● *Open all year.*
● *Visa, Mastercard, Amex, Diners accepted.*
Newmarket 13, Ely 16, Ipswich 54, Norwich 61, London 55.

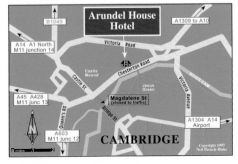

Redcoats Farmhouse Hotel

Redcoats Green, Nr. Hitchin,
Hertfordshire SG4 7JR
Tel: (01438) 729500; Fax: (01438) 723322
E-mail:priory@redcoats.co.uk
Internet: http://www.redcoats.co.uk

Near Little Wymondley village, set amidst
rolling Hertfordshire countryside, yet only a
few minutes from the A1, lies the 15th century
Redcoats Farmhouse. It has been in the
Butterfield family for generations and in 1971
Peter and his sister Jackie Gainsford converted
the building into an hotel. Today it retains its
relaxed and easy going country atmosphere.
The bedrooms, where pictures abound, are in
the main house or in the adjacent converted
stables, some having exposed beams. One
room is particularly suitable for a long stay,
opening onto the very pretty country garden,
where marquees can be erected for weddings.
Three intimate dining rooms and the new
conservatory serve outstanding cuisine. Menus
are changed every two weeks and include a
good choice of delicious dishes such as Danish
herring with dill sauce and new potatoes, half
a Gressingham duckling with peach and ginger sauce or a Fillet Steak Carpetbagger.
Redcoats is ideal for visiting Knebworth or
Woburn, Hatfield House or the Shuttleworth
Aircraft Collection.

Rates: Single room with breakfast from £70. **V**
Double room inc breakfast from £90.
*Bargain Weekend Breaks from £105 per person
for two nights, b & b.*

● *12 en suite bedrooms, 2 with shared bathroom/9
ground floor; all with colour TV, direct-dial tel-
ephone, baby listening facilities.*
● *Last orders 9.30 pm for Club Suppers; children
welcome; conferences max. 40; garden suitable for
wedding & other marquee receptions.*
● *Tennis one mile; golf 1½ miles.*
● *Visa, Mastercard, Amex, Switch accepted.*
● *Closed Dec 24-Jan 3 except Christmas lunch &
New Year's Eve dinner.*

**A1(M) 1 mile, Hitchin 3, Hatfield 10,
Woburn 15, Cambridge 25, London 35.**

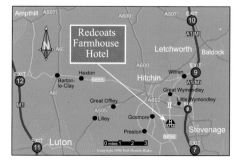

The Swan

Market Place, Southwold, Suffolk
IP18 6EG
Tel: (01502) 722186; Fax: (01502) 724800

The Swan has occupied its present site since the 14th century. Following the Great Fire of 1659, it was rebuilt in time to provide refreshments for bell-ringers pealing out the restoration of Charles II in 1660. In 1880 the owner at the time substantially remodelled the hotel and built himself a fine house next door, now the Town Hall. Subsequent alterations of great character were made in 1938 and in more recent times the Swan has been fully restored and refurbished in a most comfortable and attractive style. There are 27 bedrooms in the main building and a further 17 clustered round the old bowling green in the garden - a quiet place to enjoy a game of croquet. The public rooms have the traditional character of an English country house, enhanced by fine furniture, carved 18thC doorframes and mantelpieces, prints, paintings and photographs connected with the history of Southwold. The menu in the dining room, specialising in seafood, changes daily and is complemented by a fine wine list. The relaxed and homely atmosphere at The Swan, backed up by friendly and attentive staff, will ensure that your stay will be a memorable one.

*Single room with breakfast from £56; **double** from £98. **Midweek breaks** (Sun-Fri inc.) available annually Nov-March £60 pppn inc. breakfast, 3-course dinner, newspaper, early morning tea, VAT.*

● *44 en suite bedrooms with colour TV, direct-dial telephone, hairdryer, music/radio/alarm clock.*
● *Table d'hôte dinner £22. Last orders 2130. Lunch available April*

-November. Special diets.
● *Business services inc meeting room for 20.*
● *Croquet. Fishing, golf, riding, sailing/boating, tennis nearby. Car parking for 30.*
● *Open all year. Amex, Diners, Switch, Visa, Mastercard accepted.*

Darsham Station 9, Lowestoft 12, Norwich 34, Ipswich 34, Gt Yarmouth 24, London 108.

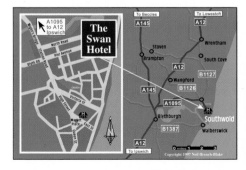

The Heart of England

Historic Houses, Gardens & Parks

Derbyshire
Calke Abbey Park & Gardens, Ticknall
Chatsworth House & Gardens, Bakewell
Eyam Hall, Eyam
Haddon Hall, Bakewell
Kedleston Hall, Derby
Lea Gardens, Matlock
Melbourne Hall, Gardens & Craft Centre
Sudbury Hall & Museum of Child Care, Sudbury

Gloucestershire
Berkeley Castle
Barnsley House Garden
Buscot House, Nr. Lechlade
Hidcote Manor Garden, Hidcote Bartrim
Painswick Rococo Garden
Snowshill Manor, Nr. Broadway
Stanway House, Nr. Winchcombe
Sudeley Castle & Gardens

Herefordshire
Abbey Dore Court Gardens
Berrington Hall, Nr. Leominster
Burford House Gardens, Burford
Eastnor Castle, Nr. Ledbury
Eastgrove Cottage Garden Nursery, Nr. Shrawley
Hergest Cloft Gardens, Kington
Hill Court Gardens, Nr. Ross-on-Wye
How Caple Court Gardens
Moccas Court, Moccas
Queenswood Country Park, Nr. Leominster

Leicestershire
Belgrave Hall, Belgrave
Stanford Hall, Lutterworth
Whatton Gardens, Loughborough

Northamptonshire
Althorp, Nr Northampton
Castle Ashby House & Gardens
Canons Ashby House, Nr Daventry
Coton Manor, Nr Guilsborough
Cottesbroke Hall, Cottesbroke
Elton Park, Peterborough
Deene Park, Nr Corby
Holdenby House Gardens, Nr Northampton
Lamport Hall, Lamport
Rockingham Castle, Market Harborough

Nottinghamshire
Naturescape Wildflower Farm, Langar
Newstead Abbey, Linby
Wollaton Hall Natural History Museum

Shropshire
Attingham Park, Nr. Shrewsbury
Benthall Hall, Broseley
Boscobel House, Nr. Albrighton
Goldstone Hall Garden, Market

Drayton
Hawkstone Hall, Weston
Weston Park

Staffordshire
Biddulph Grange Garden & Coun try Park,Biddulph
Chillington Hall, Codsall Wood
Greanway Bank Country Park, Nr. Biddulph
Hanch Hall, Lichfield
Shugborough, Milton
Trentham Gardens

Warwickshire
Arbusy Hall, Nr. Nuneaton
Baddesley Clinton House
Charlecote Park, Nr. Wellesboume
Coughton Court
Harthill Hayes Country Park, Nr. Nuneaton
Jephson Gardens, Leamington Spa
Kingsbury Water Park
Middleston Hall
Packwood House, Nr. Hockley Heath
Ragley Hall, Nr. Alcester
Ryton Organic Gardens, Coventry

West Midlands
Aston Hall, Birmingham
Birmingharn Botanical Gardans
Clent Hills Country Park, Nr. Stourbridge
Coombe Abbey Country Park, Nr. Coventry
Moseley Old Hall, Fordhouses
Selly Manor & Minworth Greaves, Bourneville
Sutton Park, Sutton Coldfield
Wightwick Manor, Wolverhampton

Worcestershire
Hagley Hall, Nr. Stourbridge,Worcs
H anbury Hall, Nr.Droitwich,Worcs
Spetchley Park, Nr. Worcester
The Picton Gardens at Old Coust Nurseries, Colwall Village

Walks & Nature Trails

Derbyshire
Carsington Water, Ashbourne
Gulliver's Kingdom, Matlock Edge
Longshaw Estate, Hathersage

Gloucestershire
Cotswold Water Park, South of Cirencester
Crickley Hill Country Park. Nr. Great Witcombe
Dean Heritage Centre, Nr. Cinderford
Great Western Railway Museum, Coleford
Forest of Dean Trails, starts at Cannop Ponds
Gloucester Guided Walks

Herefordfshire
City of Hereford Guided Walks
Croft Garden Centre, Nr. Leominster

The Heart of England

Kingsford Country Park, Wolverley
Symonds Yat Forest Trail, SW of
Ross-on-Wye

Leicestershire
Beacon Hill Country Park,
 Woodhouse Eaves
Bradgate Park, Newtown Linford
Burbage Common Visitors Centre
Melton Mowbray Country Park
Watermead Country Park, Syston
Rutland Water, Oakham

Northamptonshire
Barnwell Country Park, Oundle
Brigstock Country Park, Kettering
Daventry Country Park, Daventry
Pitsford Water, Brixworth
Sywell Country Park, Northampton

Nottinghamshire
Burnstump Country Park, Arnold
C lumber Park, Worksop
Colwick Park, Colwick
Portland Park & Visitor Centre,
 Kirkby-in-Ashfield
Rufford Country Park & Craft
 Centre
Rushcliffe Country Park,
 Ruddington
S herwood Pines Country Park,
 Edmonstowe

Shropshire
Broadway Tower Country Park
Cardingmill Valley, Long Mynd
Clee Hills, Cleobury Mortimer
Offa's Dyke, Clun Forest
Historic Hawkstone Park & Follies,
 Weston-under-Redcastle

Staffordshire
Cannock Chase Country Park
Codsall Nature Trail
Deep Hayes Country Park, Nr.
 Longsdon
Manifold Valley, Nr. Waterhouses
The Wildlife Sanctuary, Nr. Cheadle

Warwickshire
Crackley Wood , Kenilworth
Edge Hill, Nr. Kineton
Hatton Locks, Nr. Warwick
Ufton Fields Nature Reserve

West Midlands
Birmingham City Centre Canal
 Walk
Longmore Nature Trail
Wren's Nest National Nature
 Reserve, Dudley

**Worcester-
shire**
Malvern Hills
Walks & Trails
The North
Worcester-
shire Path
The Worces-
tershire Way

Derbyshire
Arkwrights's Cromford Mill,
 Matlock
Bolsover Castle, Bolsover
Blue John Museum, Ollernshaw
 Collection, Castleton
Hardwick Old Hall, Doe Lea
Natiuonal Trust Museum of Child
 hood, Sudbury Hall
National Tramway Museum, Crick
Peveril Castle, Castleton

Gloucestershire
Chedworth Roman Villa, Nr. Chel-
 tenham
Clearwell Caves, Nr. Coleford
Corinium Museum, Cirencester
Cotswold Motor Museum & Toy
 Collection, Bourton-on-the-Water
Gloucester Cathedral
Gloucester City Museum & Art Gall.
Gloucester Folk Museum
Holst Birthplace Museum, Cheltenham
Tewkesbury Abbey

Herefordshire
Goodrich Castle, Nr. Ross-on-Wye
Hereford Cathedral

Leicestershire
Ashby-de-la-Zouche Castle
Bradgate House, Newtown Linford
Stanford Hall, Lutterworth
Bosworth Battlefield Visitor Centre
 & Country Park
Donington Collection of Grand Prix
 Racing Cars, Castle Donington

Northamptonshire
Althorp House, Nr Northampton
Boughton House, Nr Kettering
The Canal Museum, Stoke Bruerne
Chichele College, Higham Ferrers
Lyveden New Bield, Oundle
Rushton Triangular Lodge, Rushton

Nottinghamshire
Holme Pierrepoint Hall, Nottingham
Newark Castle
Newstead Abbey, Linby
Brewhouse Yard Museum of Social
 History, Nottingham
DH Lawrence Birthplace Museum,
 Eastwood, Nottingham
N ottingham Castle Museum & Art
 Gallery

Shropshire
Acton Scott Historic Working Farm
Aerospace Museum, Cosford
Blists Hill Open Air Museum,
 Ironbridge
The Childhood & Costume Mu-
 seum, Bridgnorth
Coalbrookdale Furnace & Mu
 seum   of Iron
Ludlow Castle
Midland Motor Museum, Nr.
 Bridgnorth
Wroxeter Roman City, Nr. Shrewsbury

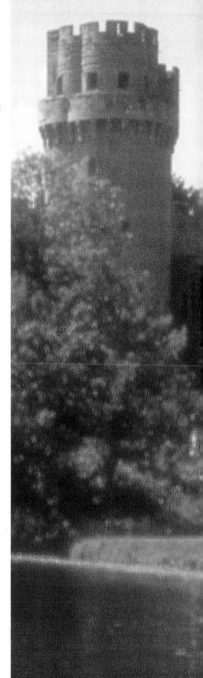

The Heart of England

Staffordshire
Bass Museum, Visitor Centre & Shire
  Horse Stables, Burton-on-Trent
The Brindley Mill & Museum, Leek
Gladstone Pottery Museum, Longton
Lichfield Cathedral
Samuel Johnson Birthplace Mu
  seum, Lichfield
Stafford Castle
Wall (Letocetum) Roman Site, Nr.
  Lichfield

Warwickshire
Anne Hathaway's Cottage, Shottery
James Gilbert's Rugby Football
  Museum, Rugby
Kenilworth Castle
Shakespeare's Birthplace, Stratford-
  upon-Avon
The Shakespeare Countryside
  Museum & Mary Arden's House,
  Wilmcote
Warwick Castle

West Midlands
Bantock House Museum, Wolver
  hampton
Birmingham Cathedral
Birmingham Museum & Art Gallery
Birmingham Museum of Science &
  Industry
Black Country Museum, Dudley
Broadfield House Glass Museum,
  Kingswinford
Coventry Cathedral
Jerome K Jerome's Birthplace Mu
  seum, Nr Walsall
The Lock Museum, Willenhall
Midland Air Museum, Coventry
Museum of British Road Transport,
  Coventry
National Motor Cycle Museum,
  Bickenhill
Walsall Leather Museum

Worcestershire
Avoncroft Museum of Buildings,
  Nr. Bromsgrove
Cotswold Teddy Bear Museum,
  Broadway
Elgar's Birthplace, Lower
  Broadheath
Hartlebury Castle State Rooms, Nr.
  Kidderminster
The Droitwich Spa Brine Baths
Worcester Cathedral
Worcester Royal Porcelain Dyson
  Perrins Museum

Entertainment Venues

Derbyshire
American Adventure, Ilkeston
Cauldwell's Mill & Craft Centre,
  Rowsley
Bentley Fields Open Farm, Longford
Denby Pottery Visitors Centre, Denby
Lathkill Dale Craft Centre, Bakewell
Royal Crown Derby Museum &
  Factory, Derby

Gloucestershire
Bibury Trout Farm
Birdland, Bourton-on-the Water
Cheltenham Hall of Fame, Race-
  course
Cotswold Woollen Weavers, Nr.
  Lechlade
Gloucester Docks
House of Tailor of Gloucester
Model Village, Bourton-on-the-Water
National Birds of Prey Centre, Newent
The Wildfowl & Wetland Trust
  Centre, Slimbridge

Herefordfshire
Cider Museum & King Offa Distillery
The Hop Pocket Farm, Bishop's Frome
The Jubilee Park, Symonds Yat West

Northamptonshire
Billing Aquadrome, Northampton
Wickstead Park, Kettering

Nottinghamshire
The Lace Centre, Nottingham
The Tales of Robin Hood, Nottingham
Newark Air Museum
Nottingham Industrial Museum
Patchings Farm Art Centre,
  Calverton
Sherwood Forest Visitor Centre &
  Country Park, Edwinstowe

Shropshire
Dinham House Exhibition Centre
The Domestic Fowl Tr't,Honeybourne
Lickey Hill Country Park
The Shrewsbury Quest, Shrewsbury
Twyford Country Centre, Nr.
  Evesham

Staffordshire
Alton Towers, Alton
Drayton Manor Family Theme Park
  & Zoo, Nr. Tamworth
Stoke-on-Trent - china factory tours

Warwickshire
Ashorne Hall Nicklodeon, Ashorne
  Hill
Heritage Motor Centre, Gaydon
Royal Shakespeare Theatre, Strat
  ford
Stratford open-top Bus Tours
Swan Theatre, Stratford
Twycross Zoo, Atherstone

West Midlands
Birmingham Jewellery Quarter
  Discovery Centre
Cadbury World, Bourneville, Bir-
  mingham
Cannon Hill Park, Edgbaston,
  Birmingham
Royal Doulton Crystal, Amblecote

Worcestershire
Severn Valley Railway, Bewdley to
  Bridgnorth
West Midlands Safari Park, Nr.
  Bewdley

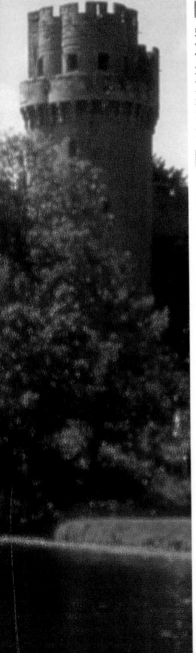

The Heart of England

DIARY OF EVENTS

February

5-7. Cheltenham Folk Festival. Folk Concerts & events. Town Hall Cheltenham, Glos
20-28 National Boat, Caravan & Leisure Show. National Exhibition Centre, Birmingham
16. Ashbourne Shrovetide Football, Ashbourne, Derbs

March

11-14. Crufts Dog Show. National Exhibition Centre, Birmingham
10-14 .Yonex All England Open Badminton Championships. National Indoor Arena, Birmingham.
16-18. Gold Cup National Hunt Week. Cheltenham Racecourse, Cheltenham, Glos
16-17. Careers Live. Careers Exhib'n. NEC, Birmingham, West Midlands
20. Midlands Grand National. Uttoxeter Racecourse, Staffs

April

2-5. Civil War Encampment The Commandery, Worcester
9-11. Cheltenham Jazz Festival, Gloucestershire.
24-25. Victor ian Extravaganza. Riverside Meadow, Stourport-on-Severn,Worcs.
30-May 3. Upton Folk Festival. Various venues, Upton-upon-Severn, Worcs.

May

1-2. National Classic Motor Show. NEC, Birmingham.
2. Cheese Rolling Parish Chch Randwick, Stroud, Glos.

6-9. Mitsubishi Motors Horse Trials. Badminton House Grounds, Badminton, Gloucestershire.
7-9. Malvern Spring Gardening Show. 3 Counties Showground, Malvern, Worcestershire.
8-15. 35th Buxton Antiques Fair, Buxton, Derbyshire.
8-9. Chatsworth Angling Fair. Chatsworth House & Gardens, Bakewell, Derbs.
9. National Vintage Communications Fair. NEC Birmingham.
10. Warwickshire v West Indies. One Day Match. Edgbaston Cricket Ground, Birmingham, West Midlands
13-16. National Dog Show. Perry Park Showground, Parry Barr, Birmingham.
21-22.. Shropshire & West Midland Agriculture Show. Shrewsbury Showground.
23-25. Leicester Early Music Festival. Castle Park, Leicester
29. Cricket World Cup. 12 teams compete. Edgbaston CG

June

6. Midland Counties Show. Uttoxeter Racecourse, Staffs
11-20. Leicester Int'l Chamber Music Festival. Various venues, Leicester, Leics.
15-17. Three Counties Show. 3 Counties Showground, Malvern, Worcs.
16. RAF Cosford Open Day. Aerospace Museum, Cosford, Shropshire
17. Cricket World Cup. Semi-final. Edgbaston Cricket Club, Birmingham.
29-July 7. Ludlow Festival. Ludlow Castle, Shropshire.
30-July 11. Warwick & Leamington Festival. Various venues,Warwicks.

July

2-11. HMV Birmingham Int'l Jazz Festival. Various

venues Birmingham,W Mids
3-18. **Cheltenham International Festival of Music.** Cheltenham Town Hall, Cheltenham, Glos.
5-8. **The Royal Show.** National Agricultural Centre, Stoneleigh, Warwicks.
9-11. **British Grand Prix.** Silverstone Racing Circuit, Northamptonshire
17-27. **Buxton International Festival,** Buxton, Derbyshire.

August

1-31. **Malvern Festival.** Malvern Theatres, Worcs
4-5. **169th Bakewell Show.** Bakewell, Derbyshire.
13-15*. **Balloon Festval,** Northampton.
14-24. **Ross-on-Wye Int'l Festival,** Ross-on-Wye, Herefordshire
13-15*. **British Open Horse Trials Championship.** Gatcombe Park, Minchin-Hampton, Glos.
15-20*. **Three Choirs Festival.** Worcester Cathedral, Worcestershire.
21-22. **Game Fair**. Ragley Hall, Alcester, Warwicks.

September

11-12. **15th Buxton Country Music Festival.** Octagon Pavilion Gardens, Buxton, Derbs
12. **Heart of England Judo Association Championships.** National Indoor Arena, Birmingham.
18-Oct.30. **Walsall Illuminations.** Walsall Arboretum, Walsall, West Midlands
23-25. **Burton-on-Trent Beer Festival.** Town Hall, Burton-on-Trent, Staffs.

October

7. **Nottingham Goose Fair.** Forest Recreation Ground, Nottingham.
8-24. **Cheltenham Festival**

of Literature. Cheltenham Town Hall, Gloucestershire.
10*. **Pearl World Conker Championships,** The Village Green, Ashton, Northants
20-1 Nov. **International British Motor Show.** National Exhibition Centre, Birmingham

November

4-14. **Int'l Motor Cycle Show,** NEC Birmingham.
10. Worcester Novices Chase, Worcester Racec'se.
13-14. **Murphy's Gold Cup Chase/Murphy's Draughtflow Hurdle.** Cheltenham Racecourse, Glos.
13-14. **National Classic Motor Show,** NEC Birmingham

December

11-12. **Christmas Craft Fair.** Pavilion Gardens, Buxton, Derbyshire

*Denotes provisional date
For further information contact:

TOURIST BOARD

The Heart of England Tourist Board, Larkhill Road, Worcester WR5 2EF. Tel: (01905) 763436.

Fotheringhay Church, Northants

The Heart of England

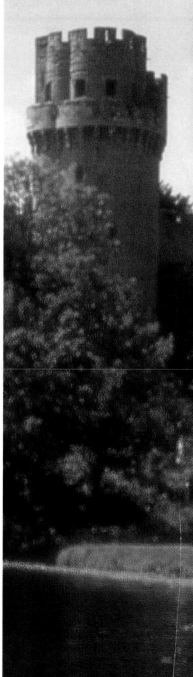

The Heart of England

Bibury

The Heart of England: a name that defines this lovely part of the world so much better than its geographical name: *The Midlands*. It is certainly at the very centre of England, with the advantage of fast motorway access from all parts of the UK, but, once off the major roads - whether you strike out north, south, east or west - you will quickly be deep into countryside of huge variety, from stark and dramatic moorlands in the north, to the gentler landscapes of the Cotswolds, dotted with dozens of picturesque tiny villages with "twinned" names such as Lower and Upper Slaughter, Little and Great Rissington, Temple Guiting and Guiting Power; the magnificent churches at Fairford, Cirencester and Chipping Campden, built by prosperous wool merchants of earlier days; and the relics of Roman settlements of even earlier days - all slumber in a timeless beauty. Some of Britain's best country house hotels are in this area and it is was the birthplace of SIGNPOST.

If you really want to escape to unknown places, head west to Herefordshire and the lovely Wye Valley, or to Shropshire - both counties are bordered by the Welsh Marches where England

Boscobel House, Shropshire

meets Wales - the scene of many past conflicts. But today all is peaceful - you can drive for miles without meeting another car, though undoubtedly the best way to experience the lovely views and fresh air is at a more leisurely pace, by cycle. You will pass through countryside that changes quickly from rich pastureland and small villages to wild hill land dotted with ancient castles and fortified manor houses. Here you will find few large hotels but any amount of country inns - often old black and white timbered buildings that have provided simple accommodation and food for centuries.

The Welsh border lands are perfect for walkers whether you want to tramp along Offa's Dyke, climb the mountains of Long Mynd or wander the wooded lanes of the Wrekin; Staffordshire too, in the northern part of the region, offers superb walking and cycling in the moorlands of the southern Peak district.

In Warwickshire Stratford-upon-Avon attracts huge numbers of visitors but retains the charm of a riverside market town. Experience a performance by the Royal Shakespeare Company at one of the three theatres in season (April-November) and visit the old timbered houses of Shakespeare's time.

The Heart of England has always played an important part in England's history: from the early border conflicts with the Welsh to the series of battles in the Civil War. This has left a heritage of great fortifications: the castles at Warwick, Kenilworth, Goodrich and Berkeley are especially worth a visit - and inevitably many homes of the aristocracy which display art and architecture of special interest.

The Wye Valley

Ragley Hall

the world's ceramic industry, demonstrate the traditional skills still used in china making, and the Gladstone Pottery Museum in Longton tells the story of British ceramics. At the Chatterley Whitfield Mining Museum, visitors can tour the coalface 700 feet underground. Shropshire's Ironbridge Gorge holds a complex of fascinating museums centred around the iron bridge over the river Severn, and the whole area at the Heart of England is criss-crossed by waterways. The canal system in Birmingham's city centre can be explored on a trip by long boat.

Ragley, near Stratford, and the home of the Marquess of Hertford, has a magnificent Great Hall decorated with some of the finest baroque plasterwork in England. Weston Park, the home of the Earls of Bradford, on the Staffordshire/Shropshire borders, is a superb Restoration house with a noted art collection; Hagley Hall, home of Lord Cobham, is another beautiful Palladian house with fine Italian plasterwork; and Sudeley Castle was the last home and burial place of Katherine Parr, the only one of Henry VIII's queens to outlive him.

These houses are all surrounded by acres of landscaped parkland and beautifully kept gardens. Garden enthusiasts should visit Hidcote and Kiftsgate in the Cotswolds, both of which are famous for their rose gardens; and also Hodnet Hall and Hergest Croft high up on the Hergest ridge looking towards Wales. Many of these gardens provide wonderfully atmospheric settings for out-of-doors performances of plays and music, notably at Sudeley and Ludlow, but also at several National Trust properties. There is also a great variety of festivals throughout the summer months (*see previous pages*), many of international repute: The Malvern Festival, the Cheltenham International Festivals of Music and Literature, the Ludlow Festival, the Buxton Festival, the Stratford Festival, the Lichfield Festival and the oldest musical festival of them all: the Three Choirs, held in 1998 in Gloucester, but rotating on a 3-year cycle to the cathedral cities of Hereford and Worcester.

The area holds many reminders of England's industrial history. In Staffordshire, the manufacturers of Stoke on Trent, centre of

Birmingham also offers important museum collections of fine and applied arts, historic buildings to study and explore, Botanical Gardens covering 10 acres as well as theatres, the new Indoor Arena and Symphony Hall with its resident symphony orchestra, and nearby the National Exhibition Centre. In the northeast of the area the most touristic county is Derbyshire, with its celebrated Peak District, recently portrayed to good advantage in the BBC's *Pride and Prejudice* serialisation. The 17th-century palladian Chatsworth, home of the Duke & Duchess of Devonshire, is one of the country's finest palaces. Nottingham is famous for its Museum of Costume and Castle Museum, whereas our home county of Northamptonshire boasts several stately homes and castles including Fotheringhay and Althorp, where there is now an exhibition, open July & August only, dedicated to the late Diana, Princess of Wales.

So the contrasts in the Heart of England are many, the choice is wide. Whatever your interest, there will be something to entertain and inspire you: walks in the Cotswolds, Malvern Hills or Derbyshire Dales, Shakespeare Country, Shropshire's Uplands, gardens, music or theatre and some of England's grandest stately homes and castles. All within one hour's drive of an area which was the powerhouse of the Industrial Revolution.

Riverside Country House Hotel

Ashford-in-the-Water, Nr. Bakewell,
Derbyshire DE45 1QE

Tel: (01629) 814275; Fax: (01629) 812873

The new owners of the Riverside are busy re-
furbishing bedrooms and public areas to
make this gem even more attractive. It nestles
by the river Wye in a quiet cul-de-sac with the
beauties of the Peak District National Park on
all sides and several classic stately homes:
Chatsworth, Haddon Hall and Hardwick Hall
near at hand. The country house, Georgian in
origin, stands in mature gardens in this quaint
unspoiled village of stone houses between
Bakewell and Buxton, a wonderful spot for
those seeking peace and quiet. Oak panelling
and crackling log fires in cooler weather welcome the visitor who is then shown to one of
the individually decorated and named bedrooms, some of which have four-posters. The
restaurant has 2 AA rosettes and an excellent
local reputation for seasonally available game
and fish from the neighbouring river. There is a
separate meeting / dining room for that important private party and the *Conservatory* buttery
is open from 10 am to 5 pm for lighter meals if
preferred. An excellent centre for touring the
Peak District or for relaxing in 'home-from-
home' comfort.

*Rates: Single room and breakfast from £95.00;
double room inc. breakfast from £115.00.* **Ⅴ**
Bargain breaks *- 2-day inclusive break (dinner,
b & b) from £175 per person.*

● *15 en suite bedrooms (10 double, 5 twin) all
with direct-dial telephone, hairdryer, laundry service, colour TV, tea/coffee making facilities, music/
radio/alarm clock, trouser press. All bedrooms
non-smoking.*
● *3-course dinner £33; lunch & special diets
available. Last orders 9.30 pm.*
● *Facilities for the disabled. Car parking for 30.*
● *Business services inc meeting room for 15.*
● *Fishing, riding, walking, shooting in the area.*
● *Open all year. All major credit cards accepted.*
**Matlock 9, Buxton 10, Chesterfield 12,
Ashbourne 17, Sheffield 18, London 86.**

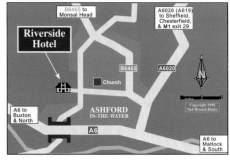

Biggin Hall

Biggin-by-Hartington,
Buxton, Derbyshire SK17 0DH
Tel: (01298) 84451;
Fax: (01298) 84681

Biggin Hall is an historic manor house of 17th century origin, situated 1000 ft above sea level in the Peak District National Park. The timeless nature of the peaks and valleys provides a perfect setting for a relaxing holiday. The Hall is Grade II listed and stands in its own grounds of some eight acres. There are eight bedrooms furnished with antiques in the main house (inc. one suite) and a further nine studio apartments in a bothy and barn in the grounds. Dinner is a daily changing menu of traditional home cooking with the emphasis on local ingredients and free range wholefoods. Guests will feel very much at home in this exceptionally welcoming, comfortable house. A superb centre for walking or touring in Derbyshire, with many historic houses within a 20 mile radius.

Rates: Double/twin room and breakfast from **V**
£49 (apartments); £59 (main house & bothy). Dinner, bed & breakfast from £35 pppn midweek (low) to £65 pppn weekend (high). **Bargain breaks:** *Ice-breaker specials - 2 nights midweek, dinner b & b from £70 pp to inc b&b, dinner, packed lunch, Glühwein.*

● *17 en suite bedrooms all with colour TV, hairdryer, tea/coffee making facilities.*
● *Table d'hôte dinner £14.50 @ 7 pm.*
● *Car parking for 20. 2 meeting rooms - cap 10/20*
● *Open all year. Visa, Mastercard, Switch accepted*
Ashbourne 9, Buxton 10, Leek 15, Derby 22, London 153

Underleigh House

Off Edale Road, Hope, Hope
Valley, Derbyshire S33 6RF
Tel: (01433) 621372; Fax:
(01433) 621324

What a discovery this was! Tucked away up a cul-de-sac off the Edale Road out of Hope, 800 ft high in the Peak District at the head of its own valley, lies Underleigh, the home of Tony and Barbara Singleton, which they have turned into a small family hotel. Views are of peaceful green fields over the valley to the hills beyond. The loudest noise is the Noe brook murmuring nearby. Bedrooms are individually styled and named: *Shatton, Brough, Derwent* etc and a teddy bear greets you on each bed! Breakfast and dinner are taken *'en famille'* with fresh menus each day - (Tony & Barbara used to run a Michelin / Egon Ronay acclaimed restaurant in Hope before 'retiring' to Underleigh!). For the bird watcher, cyclist or walker who likes the informality of a private house, this is paradise indeed.

Rates: Single room inc breakfast from £45; double from £66. Visa, Mastercard, Switch/Delta accepted.
Bargain Breaks: *Any two or more days, dinner b&b £94 per room per night. Open all year.* **V**

● *6 en suite bedrooms (inc 1 suite) with colour TV, direct dial telephone, tea/coffee making, hairdryer, music/radio/alarm clock. Non-smoker rooms avail.*
● *Table d'hôte dinner £17.50 @ 7.30 pm. Order by noon.* ● *No children under 12. No pets. Car parking for 6.* ● *Fishing, golf 3 miles; riding 10 m.*
Hathersage 6, Buxton & Sheffield 15, Derby 50, London 180

The Peacock Hotel

Rowsley, Nr Matlock, Derbyshire DE4 2EB
Tel: (01629) 733518; Fax: (01629) 732671

At the Peacock, part of the Jarvis Hotel Group, the welcome is warm and the unwinding process begins as soon as you walk in. This 17th-century house, set on the banks of the river Derwent, is furnished with antiques and many original features are preserved. The Peacock Bar with its oak beams and rough stone walls is a fine example and an excellent place to enjoy a pre-dinner drink after a busy day visiting the sights of Derbyshire. The restaurants provide a perfect setting for a delicious dinner or lunch, where the menus focus on modern British cooking using a variety of fresh, local ingredients. Some of the individual bedrooms have four-posters or half-testers and most are grouped around central landings, lending a country house atmosphere. A nice touch for families is board games and books / videos placed at strategic points. The many attractions in the neighbourhood include historic houses such as Chatsworth, Haddon Hall and the Heights of Abraham; yet understandably the hotel's speciality is fishing and packages are available which include tuition. In 1998 the long serving manager, Pat Gillson, who has made such a stamp on the hotel and is almost as much of an institution as the Peacock itself, retired but happily remains in the area.

Rates: Single room inc. breakfast from £75; double room with breakfast from £85.
Leisure breaks: *Min 2-night stay to include room, breakfast & dinner £140 per room per night; VIP Break - 2 nights £300 for two persons.*

● *16 en suite bedrooms all with direct dial telephone, colour TV, hairdryer, laundry/valet service, tea/coffee making facilities, room service.*
● *Table d'hôte 3-course dinner £198.75/lunch £12.95; special diets available. Last orders 9 pm.*
● *Two meeting rooms, capacity 30 theatre-style or 12 & 8 board meeting. Car parking for 40 cars.*
● *Walking. Fishing. Golf, shooting available nearby.*
● *Open all year. All major credit cards accepted.*

Chesterfield 11, Sheffield 16, Derby 23, Nottingham 30, M1 (exit 28 south, 29 north) 20 minutes, London 148.

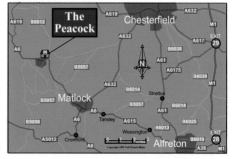

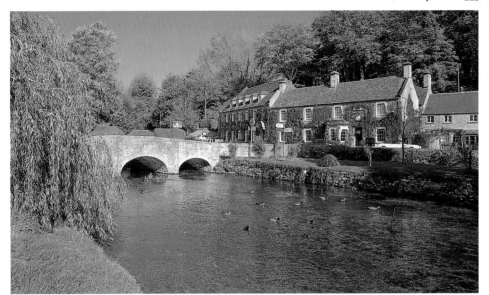

The Swan Hotel

Bibury, Gloucestershire GL7 5NW
Tel: (01285) 740695; Fax: (01285) 740473

William Morris called Bibury the prettiest village in England. The Swan hotel is proud to be at its heart. Summer or Winter the village has so much charm with the river Coln running past the front of the hotel and through the village. Indeed the hotel has its own beat on the river. The Swan Hotel is enchanting - privately owned, efficiently run and managed by very friendly staff. It has elegance yet the feeling of being welcomed into a private home. A choice of formal or informal dining is on offer - I actually sat outside in glorious sunshine on the terrace full of flowers and sampled the Bibury-reared trout which is to be heartily recommended. The bedrooms are wonderful - all individually decorated in luxurious style with good sized bathrooms. The Swan is a marvellous retreat for relaxation and perfectly placed for visiting all the interesting towns and villages of the Cotswolds - Rosemary Verey's garden at Barnsley is five miles away; the Roman Villa at Chedworth ten. I very much look forward to returning here myself and feel sure that readers will thank Signpost for this newly recommended addition to our hotel collection.

Rates: Double/twin room inc. breakfast from £150; family room from £250.
Cotswold Breaks: *Min 2-night stay, 4-course dinner, b & b, VAT from £180 per room per night*

● *18 en suite bedrooms, all with direct dial telephone, colour TV + satellite, hairdryer, laundry/valet service, 24-hr room service, trouser press, tea/coffee making. Non-smoker bedrooms available.*
● *A la carte dinner £32.00; lunch, special diets available. Last orders 9.30 pm.*
● *Two Conference rooms. Car parking for 50+.*
● *Fishing. Cirencester Leisure Centre 7 miles. Golf, shooting, riding nearby.*
● *Open all year. Amex, Visa, Mastercard, JCB credit cards accepted.*

Cirencester 7, Burford 10, Kemble 10, Stow-on-the-Wold 14, Cheltenham 17, London 96.

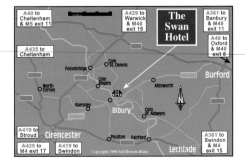

Hotel on the Park

Evesham Road, Cheltenham,
Gloucestershire GL52 2AH
Tel: (01242) 518898; Fax: (01242) 511526
E-mail: hotel@epinet.co.uk
Internet: http://www.i2i.net/hotelonthepark.htm

*Rates: Single room and continental breakfast
from £76.50; small deluxe double £92.50; superior
double/twin from £102.50; junior suite £122.50;
four-poster room £152.50.* **V**
*Bargain breaks: 2 nights/ 2 people sharing,
dinner, bed & breakfast from £67.50 per person
per night.*

On the Park is the most superb town house
hotel in the beautiful Spa town of Cheltenham. This elegant Regency house has been
caringly restored and refurbished and offers
luxurious accommodation in a very homely
atmosphere. The hotel is under the personal
supervision of its owner and proprietor
Darryl Gregory and you can be assured of a
friendly welcome and efficient staff.
The bedrooms are beautifully appointed, and all
have the most luxurious bathrooms, antique
furniture, paintings and every little comfort
for today's guest. The recent extension includes
four new bedrooms of which three are suites, a
library, a reception area and cloakrooms. The
restaurant is an important feature of this hotel.
It is a very stylish room with a most unusual
décor and lots of fresh flowers. Dinner was excellent and beautifully presented, and there is a
selection of wines to complement every meal.
Situated less than $1/2$ a mile from the main entrance to the famous Cheltenham Racecourse
this elegant Regency house is a good base for
exploring the Cotswolds.

● *12 en suite bedrooms (including 3 suites), all
with direct dial telephone and TV, room service.*
● *Last orders for dinner 9.30p.m.; special diets.*
● *Children over 8 years welcome; dogs by ar-
rangement.*
● *Golf and riding two miles; tennis one mile.*
● *Open all year. All major credit cards accepted.*

**M5 2, Stratford-upon-Avon 30, Birmingham
49, Bath 56., London 96.**

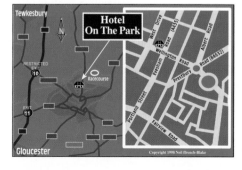

Tudor Farmhouse Hotel & Restaurant

Clearwell, Nr. Coleford, Gloucestershire GL16 8JS
Tel: (01594) 833046; Fax: (01594) 837093

What a wonderful find! Nestling in the small village of Clearwell, almost touching the border with Wales, this is a haven of warmth and charm. You can be sure to find a friendly welcome from new owners Colin and Linda Gray, whether you are looking to relax for a few days, are on business or simply want to tour this wonderful area. the cuisine is outstanding, with two menus to choose from, both with a good accompanying wine list. On the night I stayed I enjoyed an excellent dinner of local salmon and scallops, with an abundance of fresh vegetables. You will ceratinly not leave the table hungry! The actual house was built in the 13th century and features oak beams and original wall panelling. A large roughstone fireplace roars in the lounge in winter months. Some of the bedrooms are reached via an original oak spiral staircase, two have four-posters and others are located in cider makers' cottages and barns. Clearwell Caves are nearby where Midsummer and Halloween Balls are held. Make sure to book early so as not to miss out!

Rates: Single room inc. breakfast from £48.50; Ⓥ *double from £60.00; Corporate Business Rate from £62.50 to include dinner,bed & b'fast &VAT* **Bargain Breaks:** *2 days inc dinner, b & b from £80 (standard room) to £89 (luxury) per room per night.*

● *26 bedrooms (inc 2 four-posters), all en suite with colour TV, direct-dial telephone, hairdryer, laundry/valet service, tea/coffee making facilities.*
● *Table d'hôte dinner £21.95; traditional bar lunch available; special diets available. Last orders 9.30 pm.*
● *Business services inc 2 meeting rooms 20/20.*
● *Golf 3 miles. Car parking for 20.*
● *Open all year; all major credit cards accepted.*

Monmouth 6, Chepstow 9, Ross-on-Wye 14, Gloucester 22, Birmingham 55, London 125.

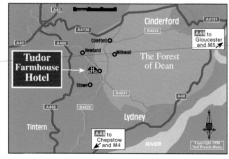

HEART OF ENGLAND

Washbourne Court Hotel

Lower Slaughter, Gloucestershire GL54 2HS
Tel: (01451) 822143; Fax: (01451) 821045

What a wonderful surprise to discover Washbourne Court Hotel in the heart of this beautiful little Cotswold village! The 400-year old Court was transformed two years ago into a luxury country hotel, whilst retaining all its original charm and character. Modern luxuries harmonise with traditional beamed ceilings, stone flag floors and mullioned windows. During the summer, guests can enjoy lunch or drinks on the terrace by the river Eye - a truly charming setting with wild birds in a natural habitat. In the Winter, guests can relax in front of real log fires. The beautiful dining room offers mouth watering menus of high quality English cuisine, using local produce whenever possible. The bedrooms are all beautifully and individually decorated. Bathrooms have fluffy bathrobes and many little extras; some with double showers or jacuzzis. In the grounds there are four Cottage Suites with private lounges. Washbourne Court is the ideal place for an away-from-it-all break, with many historic towns and villages to explore in the neighbourhood.

Rates: Single occupancy, dinner bed & breakfast from £135; double room, dinner b &b from £180.
Bargain breaks: *Double room two people dinner, b&b £140 per night, any two consecutive nights.*

● *28 en suite bedrooms (inc. 4 suites), all with colour TV, direct-dial telephone, hairdryer, laundry/valet service, 24-hour room/meal service, radio/alarm clock. Car parking for 40 cars.*
● *3-course dinner inc in room price. A la carte, lunch and special diets available. Last orders 9.30.*
● *Tennis. Golf 7 miles; riding 5 miles.*
● *Business services inc. 3 meeting rooms, cap. 20.*
● *Open all year. All major credit cards inc Switch accepted.*

Stow-on-the-Wold 3, Burford 11, Cheltenham 15, Cirencester 17, London 87.

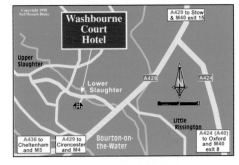

Burleigh Court Hotel

Burleigh, Minchinhampton, Stroud,
Gloucestershire GL5 2PF
Tel: (01453) 883804; Fax: (01453) 886870

Try as I might to avoid hotel brochure hyper-bole, the phrase *hidden gem* could not be more appropriate for Burleigh Court. It lies off the beaten track near the pretty village of Minchinhampton and set in $3^1/2$ acres of beautiful gardens with the most outstanding views of the South Cotswolds. It is a privately owned hotel under the personal supervision of Ian Hall, the proprietor, who believes that happy and friendly staff are the key to run-ning a successful hotel. Burleigh Court is impressive and sophisticated and yet has the feeling and welcome of a family home. The dining room is elegant and offers a delicious menu with an extensive wine list. Fresh, local produce is used, complemented by herbs from the hotel's private herb garden. The bar is friendly and relaxing with panelled walls and scattered sofas and chairs. Bedrooms are individually decorated and the coach house has some wonderful family rooms leading onto the garden and the Victorian plunge pool. With its log fires in winter and fresh flowers in summer, this is certainly a hotel for all seasons.

Rates: Single room with breakfast from £72.50; double £100.   **V**
Bargain breaks: Double room two people dinner, b&b £140 per night, weekends included.

● *17 en suite bedrooms (inc. 1 suite), all with colour TV, direct-dial telephone, laundry/valet service, tea/coffee making facilities, radio/alarm clock. Non smoker and disabled bedrooms available.*
● *Table d'hôte dinner £22.50. Lunch (hot or cold buffet) available. Special diets available. Last orders 9 pm.*
● *Outdoor swimming pool, putting lawn. Golf, riding, tennis nearby.*
● *Business services inc. meeting room for 16*
● *Open all year. Diners, Mastercard & Visa accepted.*
Stroud 5, Gloucester 11, Cheltenham 13, Bristol 26, Oxford 27, London 116

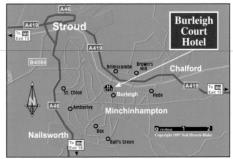

HEART OF ENGLAND

The Grapevine Hotel

Sheep Street, Stow-on-the-Wold,
Gloucestershire GL54 1AU
Tel: (01451) 830344; Fax: (01451) 832278
E-mail: enquiries@vines.co.uk
Internet: http://www.vines.co.uk/

This award-winning gem of a hotel is set in
the centre of Stow-on-the-Wold, renowned for
its antique shops and galleries, mellow Cotswold stone houses and its wonderful position
in the rolling hills of the Cotswolds. Bourton-
on-the-Water is just four miles away. Much of
the Grapevine's undoubted success lies with
the staff, a loyal and happy team superbly led
by Peter Dann, professional and energetic
General Manager of the hotel. Bedrooms are
beautifully decorated, some in the lovely old
17th Century building, others across the
courtyard in the garden rooms. All have every
modern facility and are well appointed and
comfortable. I enjoyed a superbly presented
dinner in the relaxed atmosphere of the romantic conservatory restaurant which is
crowned by a magnificent historic vine.
 The staff alone would guarantee a wonderful
stay at the Grapevine and coupled with realis-
tic prices, I can highly recommend it.

*Rates: Single room including breakfast from
£87.00; double room from £134.00.* **V**
Leisure Breaks *are available for any two nights;
d,b&b from £72.00 pppn on the basis of two people sharing a twin/double room.*

● *22 en suite bedrooms with colour TV; direct-
dial telephone; hairdryer; laundry/valet service;
tea/coffee-making facilities. Room service until
23.30.*
● *Last orders for dinner 21.30.*
● *Golf by arrangement. Riding, clay shooting
nearby; jogging track. Own tennis court 1½ miles.*
● *Meeting room with capacity for 30 (+ boardroom 20). Full secretarial and AV services.*
● *Parking 23 cars. Car rental can be arranged.
Safe deposit in reception.*
● *Open all year. Excellent Christmas/New Year
programmes. All major credit cards accepted.*

**Moreton-in-Marsh 5, Cheltenham 18, Cirencester 18,
Oxford 23, Birmingham Airport 40, London 84.**

Hare and Hounds

Westonbirt, Nr. Tetbury, Gloucestershire GL8 8QL
Tel: (01666) 880233; Fax: (01666) 880241

This most attractive Cotswold stone Country
House has been owned by the Price family for
over forty years, and the two brothers, Martin
and Jeremy, now run the hotel. The house, set
in ten acres of garden and woodland, stands
well back from the A433 which runs from the
A40 near Burford towards Bath and Bristol.
There are beautiful fresh flowers everywhere,
which add a lovely personal touch to this
homely hotel. The spacious lounges are comfortable and relaxing, with views of the garden, and in the winter there are welcoming
log fires as well as full central heating. The
bedrooms are attractive and well furnished,
with some particularly pleasant rooms in the
adjacent garden cottage, including two on the
ground floor. The restaurant offers a good
choice of varied and original dishes as well as
à la carte. There is also Jack Hare's bar which
serves excellent hot and cold food at lunchtime and evenings. Westonbirt is the site of
Britain's most famous arboretum and one of
the country's best-known girls' schools, as
well as the Hare & Hounds !

Rates: *Single room from £75.00, doubles from
£85.00. Dinner from £18.50*   **V**
Bargain breaks: *2 nights inc d,b&b January-
December 1999 - from £120.*

● *30 en suite bedrooms, all with colour TV, radio
and direct dial telephone.*
● *Restaurant; snacks; diets available*
● *Tennis; squash; snooker; croquet in summer;
table tennis; golf one mile.*
● *Children welcome; dogs welcome; drying room;
conference rooms; large garden*
● *Open All Year. Member of Best Western Hotels.*
● *Major Credit Cards accepted.*

**Cirencester 13, Severn Wild Fowl Trust 15,
Bath 19, Gloucester 22, Bristol 25, Cheltenham 26, Birmingham 78, London 100.**

HEART OF ENGLAND

The Compass Inn

Tormarton, Nr. Badminton, Gloucestershire GL9 1JB
Tel: (01454) 218242; Fax: (01454) 218741

Any visitor using the M4 to the West Country or Wales will pass within a few minutes of the Compass Inn, yet this 18th century coaching inn sits in six acres of its own land in the middle of the country. It derived its name from the fact that a previous owner decorated the inn with chandlery from Bristol although all that remains of this today is a pair of ship's lanterns in the Long Bar and wooden ships' beams in the bars. Only 75 minutes from Heathrow, it is yet ideally placed for visiting Bath, Bristol, Wells and the Cotswolds. In addition the Severn Road Bridge gives easy access to the Wye Valley and the "secret" Royal Forest of Dean. Numerous leisure activities can be arranged locally including clay pigeon shooting at the famous Ladywood Shooting School, hot air ballooning over Bath, riding at Dyrham where the rider will get closer to deer than ever he or she could on foot. Both restaurants and bars are open all day and serve good pub food. What a pleasant end to the day to sit in the orangery beneath a canopy of grapes from 20-year old vines! There are five conference rooms which provide facilities for a variety of functions.

Rates: Single room inc. breakfast from £77; Ⓥ
double room with breakfast from £96.50.
Bargain Breaks: Summer Getaway Breaks - 2/3 days from £59.50 per person per day, dinner b & b; Winter & Spring Getaway Breaks from £49.50 pppn

● *26 en suite bedrooms with radio, TV + satellite, direct-dial telephone, hairdryer, trouser press, tea/ coffee making facilities. Car parking for 100.*
● *Table d'hôte dinner £17.20. A la carte, lunch and special diets available; last orders 9.30 pm.*
● *Clay pigeon shooting, riding, hot air ballooning nearby.*
● *Business services inc. 3 meeting rooms for 60.*
● *Open all year. All major credit cards accepted.*

M4 (Junction 18) 1¹/₂, Bath 11, Chippenham 11, Bristol 15, Stroud 20, London 102.

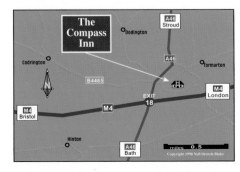

The Swan at Hay Hotel

Church Street, Hay-on-Wye,
Hereford HR3 5DQ
Tel: (01497) 821188; Fax:
(01497) 821424

Built round the old coaching yard this charming hotel in Hay-on-Wye is personally run by Rosemary and Colin Vaughan. The Swan's popularity is confirmed by many guests returning year after year. Well situated on the Welsh border, the hotel is ideally placed for excursions to view the Mappa Mundi at Hereford, the crystal factory at Rhayder, Blaenavon's Big Pit or the spectacular dams in the Elan Valley. There is also excellent local fishing on the Wye. Hay itself is a charming medieval town, famous for antique shops and antiquarian book shops which have won it the name of "the town of books". A stroll in the spacious flower garden of the hotel where you can enjoy a pre-dinner apéritif is a joy. The Cygnet restaurant offers à la carte menus beautifully cooked using fresh local ingredients. Bar meals are served in the Mallard Room, or you can join the locals in Drakes Bar. There are eighteen comfortable bedrooms with colour TV and all are individually furnished with some having special touches such as a canopied bed. It is a pleasure to return to this friendly hotel after a day of exploring the wonderful surrounding area.

Rates: *Single room including breakfast from* **V** *£50.00. Double room with breakfast from £65.00.*
Leisure Breaks: *Swan Special Breaks from £48.00 pppn incl. table d'hôte dinner, bed and breakfast. Special Winter Breaks.*

● *18 en suite bedrooms with radio, colour TV, direct dial telephone, hairdryer, trouser press, laundry service, tea/coffee making facilities, safety deposit box.*
● *Last dinner orders 21.30 hrs. Special diets available. Car parking.*
● *Billiards/snooker, lawn croquet. Fishing, golf, watersports, shooting, massage - by arrangement nearby. Ballooning by arrangement 25 miles*
● *Full business services include three conference rooms with total capacity for 160 guests.*
● *Open all year. All credit cards accepted.*

Brecon16, Hereford 21, Birmingham 51, Cardiff 56 , London 154 .

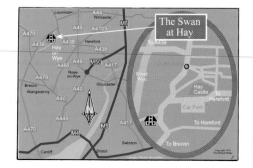

Stapleford Park

Nr. Melton Mowbray, Leicestershire
LE14 2EF
Tel: (01572) 787522; Fax: (01572) 787651

Casual luxury at its very best is how Stapleford has been described and, with its character and sumptuous comforts, it is one of the finest country house hotels in the world. Across acres of parkland, a tree lined avenue, through the arched stable block you reach the mellow facade of this Stately Home with every architectural style since the 16th Century. The public rooms reflect the majesty of the house: high ceilings, mahogany panelling, open fires and unique features such as a *trompe d'oeil* and a 450 year old vaulted kitchen. Meals are taken here and in the ornately carved Grinling Gibbons dining room which serves an outstanding cuisine conveying traditional but unpretentious British country cooking. The bedrooms have been individually created by famous designers and more unexpectedly by names such as Tiffany and Wedgwood, and they are unashamedly luxurious, offering simply everything including splendid marble bathrooms. A four bedroom cottage is also available nearby. All conventional leisure activities are possible here, and of course more exotic pursuits such as carriage driving and falcony. Stapleford is ideally situated for exploring England's finest heritage from York or Lincoln to Stratford. A stay here is unforgettable, combining as it does the grand style of bygone centuries with present day luxury, whilst the attentive service instils the feeling of home with none of its worries.

Room rate from £180.

● *51 en suite bedrooms with radio,CD player & colour TV; direct-dial telephone; hairdryer, trouser press, laundry service.*
● *Last orders for dinner 21.30 hrs weekdays, 22.00 hrs weekends. Special diets available.*
● *Swimming pool and full Health Spa facilities, billiards, croquet, jogging track, riding, shooting, tennis, falconry, golf academy.*
● *All business services including nine meeting rooms with capacity up to 260 in largest room.*
● *Airport pick-up. Car rental can be arranged. Facilities for the disabled. Ample car parking.*
● *Open all year. All major credit cards accepted.*

Leicester 15, Loughborough 15, Grantham 16, Kettering 29, London 104.

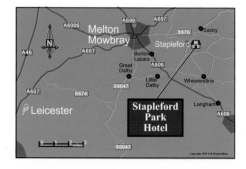

Fawsley Hall Hotel

Fawsley, Nr. Daventry,
Northamptonshire
NN11 3BA
Tel: (01327) 892000;
Fax: (01327) 892001

Fawsley Hall opened as an hotel in July 1998. It sits in 2000 acres of quiet parkland where sheep graze beside the 14th-century ironstone church, beyond which stretch lakes landscaped by Capability Brown. The Hall has three distinct styles of architecture: the original Tudor rooms form the core of the house including the wonderful panelled Great Hall and 8 authentically furnished bedrooms. This part of the house includes the Queen Elizabeth Chamber, where the Tudor monarch is reputed to have stayed. There are then 14 Georgian rooms and suites with large windows and high ceilings and 8 Victorian rooms. All have nice touches like a decanter of sherry to welcome you, big screen TVs, power showers and telephone extensions in bathrooms. The restaurant, hewn out of the original Elizabethan kitchen, is under the supervision of chef Tim Johnson and Nic Ladenis acts as a consultant. Cuisine is international with the emphasis on fresh game and fish. Fawsley is well situated for visits to Althorp, Sulgrave Manor, Silverstone and Towcester and is accessible to Oxford, Stratford-upon-Avon and Warwick. It is the perfect place to pamper yourself for that promised weekend, midweek or short break.
(See also front cover photograph)

Rates: *Double/twin inc. breakfast from £160.*
Bargain Breaks: *Two cons. weekdays £475 for the room (two people) inc dinner, lunch, VAT & service; three days £700; four days £950.* **V**

● *30 en suite bedrooms inc 2 suites & 10 four-posters, all with colour TV + satellite, direct-dial telephone, hairdryer, laundry/valet service, 24-hr room/meal service, music/radio/alarm clock, safety deposit box. Two non-smoker rooms. Two rooms suitable for disabled. Car parking for 100.*
● *2-course table d'hôte dinner £26.50/3 course £32.50. Lunch £16.50(2)/£20.50(3).Special diets available.*
● *Fishing, tennis. Golf 3 miles, riding & shooting 5m.*
● *6 meeting rooms - capacity 120. Weddings a speciality.* ● *Open all year. All major credit cards accepted.*

Daventry 3, Northampton 10, Banbury 13, Stratford 30, Oxford 36, London 86

The Windmill at Badby

Main Street, Badby, Nr.
Daventry, Northamptonshire
NN11 6AN.Tel: (01327)
702363; Fax: (01327) 311521

We were pleased to find The
Windmill in our home county of
Northamptonshire - an area not
over-endowed with Signpost-
profile hotels. It is a homely
village inn with a popular and
imaginative restaurant. Specialities include *Barbarie Duck Breast*
and *Chargrilled Cajun Chicken* and
there is always a selection of 'Fresh Specials',
Grills and a sensible childrens' menu. The bar
serves cask-conditioned ales. Décor is bright;
bedrooms are economically laid out with individual names like the *Fawsley Room* and there is
one family or honeymoon room - *The Windmill
Room*. Badby is in excellent walking and cycling
country (both The Knightley Way and The Nene
Way start here) and local places to visit include
Althorp, Sulgrave Manor, Silverstone Circuit,
Warwick and Stratford-upon-Avon.

Rates: Single inc. breakfast from £49; double
from £69. **Bargain Breaks:** Summer Weekend
Breaks from £89 per room for two nights/£133.50
for three nights. Dinner to be taken in hotel.   [V]

● *8 rooms, all with colour TV + satellite, direct-
dial telephone, hairdryer, laundry service, tea/coffee
making, trouser press, music/radio/alarm clock.*
● *A la carte restaurant open lunch & dinner.
Special diets avail. Last orders 9.30 pm. Parking 25.*
● *Meeting room to 40. Airport pickup on demand.*
● *Open all year. Visa, Mastercard, Amex accepted*
Daventry 3, Northampton 10, Banbury 13, Stratford 30, London 86

Yeung Sing Hotel & Restaurant

Market Street, Bingham,
Nr Nottingham NG13 8AB
Tel: (01949) 831831; Fax: (01949) 838833

We were recommended the Yeung Sing (formerly the *Bingham Court Hotel)* by no less a cook
than Imogen Skirving (see opposite) and were
pleased both to dine here and to be able to welcome our first Chinese Restaurant & Hotel to
Signpost this year. With the spreading popularity of Asian cuisine, we felt we should reflect
our readers' changing tastes. Anyone working
in nearby Nottingham might consider Yeung
Sing as a good base. Bedrooms are clean and
neat with private bathrooms, but it is the Cantonese cuisine downstairs which will encour-
age guests to return again and again. Specialities include *Fresh Lobster Fondue, Aromatic Duck*
and seafood-filled bacon rolls. Yeung Sing can
cater for 150 covers and is also popular for
weddings and business receptions.

Rates: Single inc. breakfast from £43; double/
twin from £56.   [V]

● *15 en suite bedrooms, all with colour TV,
direct-dial telephone, tea/coffee making, hairdryer.*
● *Cantonese dining from £15 per head; last orders
10 pm. Vegetarian options. Open Sunday lunch.*
● *Meeting room for up to 50. Car parking for 33.*
● *Open all year exc Xmas/Boxing Day. All major
credit cards accepted.*

**Nottingham 4, Newark 19, Grantham 20,
Leicester 26, London 127.**

Langar Hall

Langar, Nottinghamshire NG13 9HG
Tel: (01949) 860559; Fax: (01949) 861045

I always love my visits to Langar Hall. Although close to Nottingham, it is beautifully situated overlooking the Vale of Belvoir - a lovely country house, built in 1837, standing beside an early English church, with glorious views over the gardens, moat and parkland. The Hall is the family home of Imogen Skirving, where her father used to entertain famous cricketers of the 1930's. The public rooms are delightful. The charming proprietor and her excellent team make every effort for their guests' happiness. Together with her chef Toby Garratt, Imogen works to produce excellent, reasonably priced à la carte menus of French and English food which include such dishes as char-grilled tuna steak with balsamic vinaigrette, local lamb, turbot, steak and chips with bernaise sauce or lobster. One room has recently been extended to accommodate small conferences and private dinner parties. All the bedrooms are charming and uniquely furnished, and one has a four-poster bed. This is a truly lovely place to stay, with a peaceful and relaxing atmosphere.

Rates: *Single room and breakfast from £75;* **V**
double room and breakfast from £100; suite from £150.
Weekend breaks - *room and breakfast 2-night stay for 2 people from £150.*

● *10 en suite bedrooms, all with direct dial telephones, TV; room service; baby listening.*
● *Weekday table d'hôte dinner menu £15; à la carte menus £15-30; lunch from £10; last orders 9.30 p.m.*
● *Children welcome; dogs by arrangement. (£10)*
● *Own coarse fishing - bring your own rod; golf four miles. Hunting can be arranged.*
● *Open All year. Mastercard, Visa and Amex Credit Cards accepted.*
● *Licensed to hold marriages; exclusive house party booking; conferences 20 max.*

Nottingham 12, London 120, York 90.

Old England Hotel, Sutton-on-Trent
Nottinghamshire

JUST OFF THE GREAT NORTH
ROAD BETWEEN NEWARK AND EAST RETFORD
8 Miles from Newark and 12 miles from East Retford.
(For position see map on page 14, square C.2).

*The power of heredity, overcoming all kinds of difficulties, firmly
establishes this new hotel in pleasant and peaceful surroundings.*

THIS pleasant hotel, hidden in a quiet hamlet two minutes' run to the east of the Great North Road, is the practical result of a real romance in hotel keeping and affords striking proof of the power of heredity. Its owner started life in Newark as an errand boy, though his grandfather and great grandfather had been inn keepers. In a short time he became first partner and then proprietor of the business in Newark, and then felt an astonishing urge to run an hotel and cater especially for tourists. In the face of

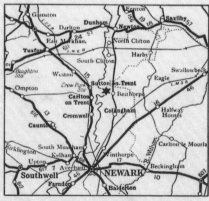

From a "Geographia" map.

The Old England

Sutton-on-Trent, Nr. Newark, Nottinghamshire NG23 6QA
Tel: (01636) 821216; Fax: (01636) 822347

The Old England is a real home from home. The Pike family have run the hotel since we first published Signpost and, more than 58 years later, we are still pleased to recommend it. This most attractive country house is situated in a large very well kept garden, which must be a haven of peace on a fine day. The house is continually being updated by its owners. All bedrooms have their own private bathrooms and are cheerful, cosy and well furnished. Those of you who appreciate good furniture, will be delighted with the beautifully polished antique tables and chairs in the dining room, and the many other interesting pieces and lovely old china throughout the hotel. The food, supervised by the Pike family, is really good British fare, such as steak, roasts and poached Scotch salmon, and always plenty of it. Later, I was assured by regular diners at the hotel that their high standard of food never varies. If you are travelling north or south, you can be assured of a very warm welcome at this lovely hotel.

Rates: Single room and breakfast from £47.50; double from £65.00 including VAT. **V**
Midweek breaks: £42.00 per person per night (min. stay two nights), including dinner, bed, breakfast & VAT.

● *10 en suite bedrooms (1 ground floor), all with TV; room service.*
● *Last orders for dinner 9. 00p.m.; special diets.*
● *Children welcome; dogs accepted; conferences max. 45.*
● *Grass tennis court; shooting/fishing four miles; golf eight miles.*
● *Open all year; Amex, Mastercard and Visa credit cards accepted.*

Newark 8, East Retford 12, Lincoln 24, Leicester 41, London 128.

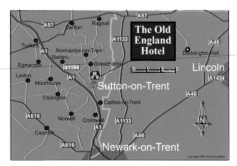

HEART OF ENGLAND

Stratford Victoria

Arden Street, Stratford-upon-Avon,
Warwickshire CV37 6QQ
Tel: (01789) 271000; Fax: (01789) 271001

I highly recommend this luxurious new hotel
in the centre of Stratford. Opened in 1996, it is
a welcome addition to the room stock in the
town and gives excellent value for money.
It is privately owned and the attitude of such
a highly motivated and loyal staff, I have
always found, rubs off to give the visitor a
warm and personal welcome. The Victoria
Restaurant and Bar will tempt you with snacks
throughout the day or main meals from the
carvery and grill menus. Purpose-built conference suites and board rooms seating up to 140
have all modern facilities and full back-up
from the hotel's conference office. There is a
well-equipped gym to work off those extra
calories gained in the restaurants! Bedrooms
are generously proportioned and for special
occasions there are Premier Rooms, a four-
poster room or the luxury suite. There are also
family rooms, interconnecting rooms and
rooms for the disabled. The hotel is very well
run and a great centre for visiting the heart of
Shakespeare country. It is within walking
distance of the Theatre Royal and the Town
Centre and adjacent to the Railway Station.

*Rates: Single room and breakfast from £79.00;
double inc. breakfast from £99.00.* **V**
Bargain Breaks: *Two nights, dinner b & b from
£62.50 per person per night, based on 2 people
sharing. 4-poster rooms/suites avail. at a suppl't.*

● *102 en suite bedrooms, all with colour TV +
satellite, direct-dial telephone, hairdryer, laundry service, tea/coffee making facilities, trouser
press. Non-smoking and rooms for disabled
available. Car parking for 104 cars.*
● *Table d'hote £19.50; à la carte, lunch & special
diets available. Last orders for dinner 10.00 p.m.*
● *Business services inc 6 meeting rooms to 140*
● *Fitness centre/gym, jacuzzi/whirlpool.*
● *Open all year. All major credit cards accepted*

**Warwick 8, Banbury 20, Birmingham 23,
Oxford 39, London 93.**

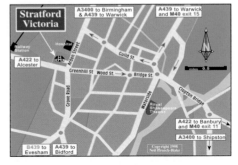

Dormy House Hotel

Willersey Hill, Broadway,
Worcestershire WR12 7LF
Tel: (01386) 852711; Fax: (01386) 858636
E-mail: reservations@dormyhouse.co.uk

It has always been a great joy for me to visit the Dormy House Hotel. The standards are high, yet the hotel is so welcoming and friendly. The hotel is under the personal management of Ingrid Philip-Sorensen, whose style and taste are impeccable and who cares for her staff as much as for her guests. All 49 bedrooms are beautifully and individually decorated with all modern luxuries and the public rooms are cosy with fresh flowers and a roaring log fire. There is *Tapestries* restaurant which offers really exciting menus, changed regularly, and the *Barn Owl* Bar, which is great fun for less formal dining. A nice touch is the provision of a pair of 'public spectacles' for those having difficulty with the small print of the menu! The building is a beautifully converted 17th century farmhouse with spectacular views over the Cotswold escarpment. Broadway golf course is adjacent. Previous guests receive the hotel's newsletter *Dormy Days* which details special events throughout the year: New Year's Eve, Opera Evening, Easter, Jazz Brunch, Summer Ball, Special August and sumptuous Champagne Dinners.

Rates: Single room with breakfast from £71. **V**
Double room including breakfast from £142.
Champagne Weekend breaks *Fri/Sat incl.*
room, table d'hôte dinner, full English breakfast,
fresh flowers and champagne. **Carefree Break** *-*
any 2 nights Sun-Thurs as above less flowers/
champagne. Please enquire for prices.

● *49 en suite bedrooms with radio & TV, direct-dial telephone, hairdryer, trouser press, laundry service; tea/coffee making facilities, safety deposit box.*
● *Last orders for dinner 21.30 hrs. Special diets.*
● *8 meeting rooms - capacity 170. Car parking 80.*
● *Billiards, croquet, putting, gym, sauna/steam, indoor games on site. Jogging trail, riding, boating, shooting, tennis & fishing by arrangement.*
● *Open all year exc. Xmas/Boxing Day. All major credit cards accepted.*

Broadway 2, Cheltenham, Stratford-upon-Avon 15, Birmingham Airport 40, London 95

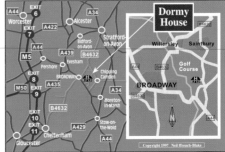

Cumbria - English Lakeland

In this beautiful corner of England, there is beauty in breathtaking variety - in the famous Lake District, loved by so many who come back again and again to its inspirational magic, brilliant blue lakes and craggy mountain tops.

There are other kinds of beauty to be enjoyed too. The central Lake District with its mountains, lakes and woods is so well known and loved that there is a tendency to forget that the rest of Cumbria contains some of the most varied and attractive landscape in Britain. In the east of the county, the lovely peaceful Eden Valley is sheltered by the towering hills of the Pennines, and everywhere are dotted charming little red sandstone villages. Further north, the border lands are flatter, with forests and lush green fields patterned by the typically English hedges and lanes. Cumbria's long coastline is itself full of variety. There are rocky cliffs with myriad sea birds, sandy estuaries, miles of sun-trapping sand dunes and friendly harbours, and everywhere something interesting to see, from reminders of our Roman occupation to the Flookburgh shrimp fishermen who go fishing, not in boats, but on tractors!

Wherever you choose to stay in Cumbria, you will not be far away from beautiful scenery: and whatever kind of accommodation you would like, Cumbria has it, from gracious country house hotels to country inns and bed-and-breakfasts. Don't think that summer is the only time when Cumbria is beautiful. In autumn the deciduous woodlands and bracken-covered hillsides glow with colour. In winter, the mountain tops stand in dazzling magnificence against blue skies. In spring, you can discover the delights of the magical, constantly changing light and joy of finding carpets of wild flowers. This is really the best time of the year to go walking or climbing - spending each day in the crisp fresh air to return in the evening with a healthy appetite to enjoy a delicious Cumbrian meal by the fireside in a cosy pub or friendly hotel.

There are many holidays in Lakeland which offer both activity and instruction in a range of sports - walking, climbing, orienteering, potholing, cycling, riding, golf, sailing, sailboarding, water-ski-ing, canoeing and fishing. A good way to absorb the beauty of this unique area is to plan your own personal route on foot or on cycle. *The Cumbria Cycle Way*, designed to avoid all the cyclist's prob-

Above: Coniston Water. **Below:** *Chester town centre*

lems like main roads and precipitate hills takes a circular route 250 miles (400 kms) long around this beautiful county. There are also good, cheap public transport services, and, where the big coaches cannot go, *Mountain Goat* minibuses run, even over the steepest mountain passes.

For a change from the great outdoors, there is a wealth of historic houses to visit, including a uniquely constructed thatched farmhouse, stately homes that have seen centuries of gracious living and the small cottages where famous writers have lived. Other houses are important because of their architecture, like the round house on Belle Isle, or majestic Hutton-in-the-Forest, which has a central tower dating from the 14th century, surrounded by later additions. The Cumbrian climate is ideal for gardens and the area is famous for the rhododendrons and azaleas which grow in abundance.

You will find out more about the secrets of this ancient kingdom by watching, or even joining in, some of its old customs, some of which are unique to Cumbria. There are many traditional agricultural shows displaying the essence of the English countryside - spiced in Cumbria with local specialities like *hound trailing*, which is like hunting but without the fox, and *fell races* - crazy lung-bursting ascents of the nearest hill, followed by a bone-bruising descent! For further information, contact the Cumbria Tourist Board, address on page 135.

133

The North West

Historic Houses, Gardens & Parks

Cheshire
Arley Hall & Gardens, Nr. Great
 Budworth
Bridgemere Garden World, Nr.
 Nantwich
Brookside Garden Centre, Poynton
Cholmondeley Castle Gardens
Dunham Massey, Nr. Altrincham
Gawsworth Hall Nr. Macclesfield
Little Moreton Hall, Nr. Nantwich
Ness Gardens Neston
Stapeley Water Gardens, Nantwich
Tatton Park, Knutsford

Tatton Park

Cumbria
Acorn Bank Garden, Nr. Temple
 Sowerby
Brantwood House, Coniston
Dalemain Histonc House & Gar
 dens, Nr. Pooley Bridge
Graythwaite Hall Gardens, Newby
 Bridge
Holker Hall & Gardens, Cark-in-
 Cartmel
Hutton-in-the-Forest, 6 miles from
 Penrith
Larch Cottage Nurseries, Melkinthorpe
Levens Hall & Topiary Garden, Nr.
 Kendal
Lingholme Gardens, Linghholme,
 Keswick
Mirehouse, Underskiddaw
Sizergh Castle, Nr. Kendal

Lancashire
All in One Garden Centre,
 Middleston
Astley Hall & Park, Nr. Chorley
Catforth Gardens & Nursery, Nr
 Preston
Gawthorpe Hall, Burley
Leighton Hall, Carnforth
Rufford Old Hall, Ormskirk
Williamson Park, Lancaster

Merseyside
Croxteth Hall & Country Park, Nr.
 Liverpool
Speke Hall, Liverpool

Walks & Nature Trails

Cheshire
Jodrell Bank Science Ctre & Arboretum,
 Nr. Holmes Chapel
Styal Country Park
Walk the Walls, Chester
Wirral Peninsula

Cumbria
Cark to Cartmel Village
Dodd Wood
Dunnerdale Forest Nature Trail
Grange-over-Sands to Hampsfell
Grizedale Forest Park Visitor Centre
 Hawkshead
Numerous fell walks and trails
 throughout Cumbria
Ulverston Town Trail

Lancashire
Carnforth Canal Circuit, from
 Camforth Railwayto Bolton-le-Sands
Pendle Way Walk at Pendle
 Heritage Centre, Nelson
The Weaver's Shuttle, around
 Pendle

Historical Sites & Museums

Cheshire
The Boat Museum, Ellesmere Port
Chester Cathedral
Experience Catalyst, Widnes
Macclesfield Silk Museum
Peckforton Castle, Nr. Tarporley
Quarry Bank Mill, Styal

Cumbria
Abbot Hall Art Gallery, Kendal
Appleby Castle, Appleby-in-
 Westmoreland
Birdoswald Roman Fort, Brampton
Brough Castle, Kirkby Stephen
Brougham Castle, Nr. Penrith
Carlisle Castle
Cartmel Priory
The Cumberland Pencil Museum &
 Exhibition Centre, Keswick
Dove Cottage, Grasmere
Furness Abbey, Barrow-in-Furness
Heron Corn Mill & Museum of
 Papermaking,
Milnthorpe Laurel & Hardy Museum,
 Ulverston
Museum of Natural History, Kendal
Penrith Museum
Rydal Mount, Nr. Ambleside
Stott Park Bobbin Mill, Newby Lake
Wordsworth Museum, Grasmere

Greater Manchester
Castlefield Urban Heritage Park,
 Manchester
Manchester Cathedral
Manchester United Football Museum

Newton, Forest of Bowland

The North West

Museum of Science & Industry, Manchester

Lancashire
Lancaster Castle, Lancaster

Merseyside
Liverpool Museum
Merseyside Maritime Museum, Albert Dock, Liverpool Museum of Liverpool Life, Pier Head
Pilkington Glass Museum, St Helens

Entertainment Venues

Cheshire
Cheshire Candle Workshops, Burwardsley
Chester Zoo, Upton-by-Chester
Gulliver's World, Warrington
Port Sunlight Visitor Centre, Wirral
Wetlands & Wildfowl Trust Centre, Martin Mere

Cumbria
Cumbria Crystal, Ulverston
Fell Foot Park, Newby Bridge
Lake District National Park Visitor Centre, Windermere Lakeland Bird of Prey Centre, Lowther
Ravenglass & Eskdale Railway, Ravenglass
Sellafield Visitors' Centre
South Lakes Wild Animal Park, Dalton-in-Furness
Ullswater Cruises
Webb's Garden Centre, Kendal
Windermere Lake Cruises
World of Beatrix Potter, Bowness-on-Windermere

Greater Manchester/Lancashire
Alexandra Craft Centre, Saddleworth
Blackpool Tower & Pleasure Beach
Butterfly World, Bolton
Camelot Theme Park, Chorley
Frontierland, Morecambe Bay
Granada Studio Tours, Manchster
Lakeland Wildlife Oasis, Nr. Camforth
Life Centre, Blackpool
Noel Edmonds' World of Crinkley Bottom, Morecambe Sea

Merseyside
The Beatles Story, Albert Dock, Liverpool
Knowsley Safari Park, Prescot
Pleasureland Amusement Park, Southport
The Tate Gallery at the Albert Dock, Liverpool

February

7. **Wordsworth Winter School.** The Wordsworth Trust, Dove Cottage, Grasmere, Cumbria.
25. **Chinese New Year Celebrations**. In and around Chinatown, Liverpool.
27. **Horse Racing: The Greenall Grand National Trial Chase**. Haydock Park Racecourse, Newton-le-Willows, Merseyside.

March

7. **Ambleside Daffodil & Spring Flower Show.** Old Junior School, Ambleside.
27. **English Lakes Hotels Coniston 14.** John Ruskin School, Coniston, Cumbria.

April

1. **Martell Grand National Race,** Aintree Racecourse, Merseyside.
2. **Lancashire Easter Maritime Festival**. Lancaster & Morecambe, Lancs.
23. **Lancashire Food Festival** Accrington Town Hall, Accrington, Lancs.

May

1. **Crowther Homes Swinton Hurdle**. Haydock Park, Merseyside.
8. **The Bardon Speed Hill Climb**. Barbon Manor, Kirkby Lonsdale, Cumbria
10/12. **Cricket World Cup 1999**. Scotland v Lancashire/Pakistan v Lancashire. Old Trafford Cricket Ground, Manchester.
15. **Lancashire Clog Dancing**

Festival. Accrington Town Centre, Lancashire.
22-25. **Chester Folk Festival.** The Morris Dancer, Chester Rd, Tarporley, Cheshire.
23-31. **Coniston Water Festival,** Cumbria
26. **Cartmel Steeplechases.** Cartmel, Cumbria.
29. **Tote Credit Silver Bowl.** Haydock Park, Mersyside
30. **Cricket World Cup 1999** West Indies V Australia. Old Trafford, Manchester.
31. **Kendal Medieval Market.** Market Place, Kendal.

June

1-12. **Isle of Man TT Motor Festival.** Motorcycle Racing. Various venues, Isle of Man
4. **Holker Garden Festival,** Holker Hall & Gardens, Cark in Cartmel, Cumbria.
5. **John of Gaunt Stakes.** Haydock Park Racecourse, Merseyside.
16. **Cricket World Cup 1999** Semi-finals. Old Trafford Cricket Ground, Manchester
22-23. **Cheshire County Show 1999.**The Showground, Tabley, Cheshire.

July

3.**Whitehaven Carnival & Gala Fair.** Whitehaven, Cumbria
3. **Letherby & Christopher Lancashire Oaks.** Haydock Park, Merseyside
10-17. **Wigan Jazz Festival.** Various venues, Wigan, Lancs
17. **Cumberland County Show.** Rickerby Park, Carlisle, Cumbria.
23-25. **Cumbria Steam Gathering.** Cark Airfield, Flookburgh, Cumbria.
25-Aug 2. **Lake Windermere Music Festival.** Bowness-on-Windermere, Cumbria
30-31. **Royal Lancashire Show.** Astley Park, Chorley.
30-31. **St Helens Show,** Sherdley Park, St Helens, Lancs.

August

1-13. **Lake District Summer Music Int'l Festival & Summer School.** Concerts/Classes Various venues, Cumbria.
1-15. **Wordsworth Summer Conference.** Dove Cottage, Grasmere, Cumbria.
1. **Cockermouth Agricultural Show,** Cockermouth, Cumbria
5-6. **Lake District Sheepdog Trials.** Hill Fm, Kendal, Cumbria
6-8. **Ambleside Great Summer Flower Show & Craft Fair.** Ambleside, Cumbria
6-8. **Lowther Horse Driving Trials & Country Fair.** Lowther Castle, Lowther, Cumbria
19-21 **Southport Flower Show** Victoria Park, Southport,Lancs
23-24. **Crewe Carnival.** Queens Park, Crewe, Cheshire
26-31. **International Beatles Week.** Cavern Club & other venues, City Centre, Liverpool
26. **Cartmel Steeplechases.** Cartmel, Cumbria.
28. **Isle of Man Int'l Jazz Festival.** Various venues, Isle of Man.
30. **Silloth Carnival**. Silloth-on-Solway, Cumbria.

September

3-Nov 8. **Blackpool Illuminations.** Talbot Square, Blackpool Lancashire. Illuminations from 7 p.m. nightly.
4. **Kirkby Lonsdale Victorian Fair.** Kirkby Lonsdale, Cumbria
4. **Stanley Leisure Sprint Cup.** Haydock Park Racecourse, St Helens, Lancashire.
5-7. **Crewe & Nantwich Folk Festival.** Various venues, Nantwich, Cheshire
9.**Westmoreland County Show.** Westmoreland Showfield, Crooklands, Cumbria
10. **Kendal Gathering & Torchlight Procession.** Kendal, Cumbria.
12. **Doll's House & Miniature Fair.** Marine Hall, Fleetwood, Lancs.
18-24. **Egremont Crab Fair.**

(World Gurning Championships) Egremont, Cumbria.
25. **Eskdale Show.** Brotherilkeld Farm, Boot, Cumbria

October

18-24. **Windermere Power Boat Record Attempts** Lake Windermere, Cumbria.
25-Nov 12. **Open Exhibition.** Lower Court Gallery, Egremont, Cumbria.

November

7. **Cumbria Brass Band Assoc Annual Open Contest.**Whitehaven Civic Hall, Cumbria
12-21. **Euro Wirral Int'l Guitar Festival of Great Britain.** Various venues, Wirral, Ches.
18. **Biggest Liar in the World Competition.** Bridge Inn, Santon Bridge, Cumbria.
18-20***British National Dance Championships**. Empress Ballroom, Blackpool, Lancs.

*Denotes provisional date .
For further information contact:

TOURIST BOARDS

The Cumbria Tourist Board Ashleigh, Holly Road, Windermere, Cumbria LA23 2AQ. Tel: (015394) 44444

The North West Tourist Board Swan House, Swan Meadow Road, Wigan Pier, Wigan, Lancashire WN3 5BB. Tel: (01942) 821222

THE NORTH WEST

Higher Huxley Hall

Huxley, Chester CH3 9BZ
Tel: (01829) 781484; Fax: (01829) 781142
E-mail: info@huxleyhall.co.uk

This extraordinary manor house, part of
whose building dates from the 13th century,
offers the best of all worlds. Furnished mostly
with antiques in keeping with the mainly
Elizabethan house, it has exposed beams, log
fires when necessary and a traditional ambience. The best of modern conveniences have
been thoughtfully incorporated however to
add to the guest's comfort. The bathrooms, for
instance, have all modern amenities and the
bedrooms are delightfully bright and cheerful. The cuisine, which is mostly traditional, is
prepared from the finest local ingredients
where possible, some from the manor's own
gardens, and is simply delicious. Cheshire is
noted for its sporting facilities and from
Higher Huxley one can ride, play golf or polo,
go racing or swim in the hotel's own indoor
pool. Fishing can also be arranged locally. The
manor looks over the wooded Cheshire hills,
medieval Beeston Castle and the purple
Welsh mountains. The ancient city of Chester
is just seven miles away. All in all, a little gem
of a place.

*Rates: Single with breakfast from £40;
double with breakfast from £70.*
*Bargain breaks: Weekday breaks available -
details on application*

● *Residential licence. Three en suite bedrooms
with colour TV, direct-dial telephone, hairdryer, tea/
coffee making facilities, music/radio/alarm clock.*
● *Non-smoking hotel. Car parking for 10.*
● *5-course table d'hôte dinner £22.50.*
● *Croquet, indoor swimming pool; coarse fishing
nearby.*
● *Open all year. Major credit cards accepted*

**Chester 7, Wrexham 16, Liverpool 25,
Nantwich 17, Manchester 38, London 207.**

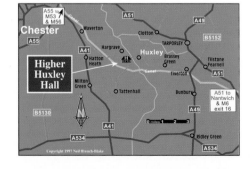

Hand Printed On Silk   Brocklehurst 1985

Sutton Hall

Bullocks Lane, Sutton, Nr.
Macclesfield, Cheshire SK11 0HE
Tel: (01260) 253211; Fax: (01260) 252538

If, like I do, you enjoy staying at an hotel of
character, then Sutton Hall is one of the
finest in which to indulge yourself. A
wealth of beams, log fires and four poster
beds are all in evidence, and the ales, conditioned in cask, are matched by the choice
of food from an excellent menu. As with
the inns of old, there is an atmosphere of
warmth, hospitality and good cheer. This,
married to such modern conveniences as
en suite bathrooms and colour TV, makes a
very happy amalgam of past and present.
To travel, even from afar, is well worth
while and this is made easy by the fact that
the M6 and Manchester Airport are less
than half an hour away. Also in the area
are many other famous old houses as well
as the scenic beauty of the Peak District.
The hotel is personally run by Mr. and Mrs.
Bradshaw.

*Rates: Room and breakfast from £75.00 single,
£45.00 double, per person, inclusive of VAT
and full English breakfast.*

● *10 en suite bedrooms, all with four poster
beds, colour TV, direct dial telephones, tea/
coffee maker; trouser press; full central heating.*
● *Late meals to 10 p.m.; diets available.*
● *Dogs welcome; conferences up to 20.*
● *Golf, tennis, riding nearby; Peak National
Park adjacent.*
● *Open all year. Most credit cards accepted.*

**Macclesfield 1, M6 (J18/19) ¹/₂ hour,
Manchester Airport ¹/₂ hour, London 240.**

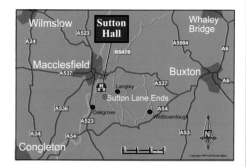

Rothay Manor Hotel

Rothay Bridge, Ambleside, Cumbria
LA22 OEH
Tel: (015394) 33605; Fax: (015394) 33607
E-mail: hotel@rothaym.demon.co.uk

*Rates: Double room and breakfast from £120.00
for 2 people; dinner, room and breakfast from
£155.00 for 2 people.*
Bargain breaks *November-March, midweek,
dinner, room & breakfast from £150 per night for
2 people; weekend break from £160 per night.*

If you believe, as I do, that one of the main
ingredients of civilised life is good food and
wines taken in comfortable surroundings,
then Rothay Manor is, without a doubt, one of
the finest venues in which to enjoy that life.
The hotel has been voted top of the list by a
publication on hotel breakfasts, and the excellence of the lunches and dinners complements
the sumptuous surroundings. Antiques and
fresh flowers are abundant, and the feeling of
warmth and well-being are everywhere. The
whole ambience is orchestrated by Nigel and
Stephen Nixon and their wives, and the reputation that they have gained for all round
excellence is more than justifiably deserved.
These impressions were echoed by many of
the other guests to whom I spoke, and even
from the elegant brochure, you too will begin
to feel the atmosphere of Rothay Manor. It
seems unnecessary to add that the surrounding mountains, lakes and the air of the Lake
District, make a superb backdrop and atmosphere in which to indulge these pleasures.

● *18 en suite bedrooms (2 for the disabled) all
with direct dial telephone and TV, room service;
baby listening.*
● *Last orders for dinner 9.00 p.m.; special diets.*
● *Children welcome; conferences max. 20.*
● *Free use of nearby leisure centre; tennis and
fishing ¹/₄ mile; sailing/boating ¹/₂ mile.*
● *Open all year; all major credit cards accepted.*

Kendal 13, Manchester 80, London 280.

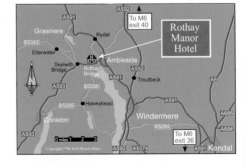

Wateredge Hotel

Borrans Road, Ambleside, Cumbria
LA22 OEP
Tel: (015394) 32332; Fax: (015394) 31878

It is not often that one comes across a hotel
that has excellent food, is immaculately and
comfortably furnished and decorated, and yet
is perfectly situated, but the Wateredge Hotel
is exactly that. With its gardens running down
to Lake Windermere, beautiful views from
the public rooms, delightful bedrooms and
delicious meals, it makes an idyllic venue for
a holiday in the Lake District. Not only is
there the peace and quiet of the hotel itself,
but there is the tranquillity of a stroll on the
nearby fells to be enjoyed. For those seeking a
more active time, there is boating and fishing
on the doorstep; there are sporting facilities of
all kinds, both indoor and out, in the immediate vicinity. In addition, Ambleside is a lively
and bustling town with everything that a
holiday maker or tourist could need. The
Wateredge is an unpretentious, "honest to
goodness" hotel which makes any visit to the
Lake District well worthwhile.

Rates: *Dinner, room and breakfast from £68.00
single, £114.00 double/twin.*
Bargain breaks: *3 day midweek & weekend breaks
from £162 per person including dinner, room and
breakfast.*

● *23 en suite bedrooms (5 ground floor), all with
radio, TV and telephone, complimentary morning
tea and coffee tray.*
● *TV lounge; full central heating; diets, children
over 7 welcome, dogs not allowed in public rooms
or suites; small conferences.*
● *Lake bathing; boat launching & mooring on private jetty; complimentary use of nearby leisure club*
● *Mastercard, Amex and Visa credit cards accepted. Closed mid-December to mid-January.*

Kendal 13, Keswick 17, Penrith 30, London 300.

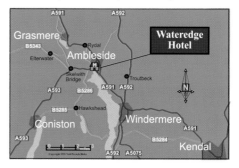

Appleby Manor Country House Hotel & Leisure Club

Roman Road, Appleby-in-Westmorland, Cumbria CA16 6JB
Tel: (017683) 51571; Fax: (017683) 52888
E-mail: appleby.manor@btinternet.com
Website: http://www.btinternet.com/appleby.manor

Appleby Manor stands high, commanding views of the historic little town, its romantic castle and the sweeping countryside and fells beyond. Within you will find relaxing and friendly courtesy, and most attractive and spacious public rooms. Facing south, the house gives shelter to its sunny gardens onto which some of the delightful rooms in the new wing have direct access. The spotlessly clean bedrooms are comfortable and furnished in keeping with the period of the house. The popular award-winning restaurant offers an international and imaginative selection of tasty dishes. The wine list offers a selection of wines from 20 countries and the bar stocks over seventy single-malt whiskies. There is plenty to see and do locally, with walks to suit all abilities. Appleby is ideally situated for touring the scenic Lake District, and the Borders Hadrian's Wall, the Roman Camps, the high Pennines and the Yorkshire Dales are all within easy motoring distance.

*Rates per person start at £49 for bed and breakfast, £59 for dinner, bed and breakfast; weekly rates from £354, including dinner, bed and breakfast. **Bargain breaks:** min. 2 nights from £59 pppn; also "Flying Falcon" breaks, 2 nights from £183 and the "Cloud Nine Experience" from £149 and "Hangover Breaks" from £145 - all inc. dinner, b & b & VAT.*

● *30 en suite bedrooms (10 ground floor; 5 four-posters), all with telephone, hairdryer, colour TV, satellite and video film channels.*
● *Last orders 9. 00 p.m; diets available.*
● *Children welcome; baby listening; dogs in coachhouse bedrooms only; conferences 30 max.*
● *Games room; snooker and pool; indoor heated swimming pool; jacuzzi; sauna, solarium, leisure centre, squash 1/2 mile, fishing locally; riding 13 miles; golf 2 miles.*
● *Hotel closed 3 days at Christmas only. All major credit cards accepted.*
M6 (junctions 38 & 40) 13, Penrith 13, Ullswater 15, Kendal 25, Keswick 31, Scotch Corner 37, London 272.

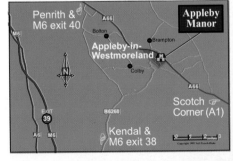

PARTNERS IN INSURANCE

Lakesure is the Exclusive Partner to
Signpost Recommended Hotels and offers
SAVINGS ON YOUR PREMIUMS

We understand the market and have developed a
number of schemes giving extremely wide cover at a
competitive price and with first class security.

We also offer a special basis of quoting each risk using
'OUR UNIQUE NO CLAIMS
BONUS AT INCEPTION'.

Call 01702 471135 or 471185 (Phone and fax)
Talk to Bruce Thompson for further details

WE KNOW OUR BUSINESS

THE NORTH WEST

The hotel from the deer park.

Armathwaite Hall Hotel, on Lake Bassenthwaite, Keswick

24 Miles from Carlisle, 8 miles from Keswick and 27 miles from Windermere.
(For position see map on page 10, square B.3).

Splendidly preserved baronial hall with its own deer and deer park standing in magnificent Lakeland scenery—All modern comforts—Amusements include rock climbing, fishing, boating, bathing, golf, squash rackets, tennis and dancing.

FIVE years ago it seemed as if this splendid mansion would be pulled down and sold as scrap. Fortunately its present owners, a well known Keswick family, came to the rescue and after spending thousands of pounds in equipping it with every modern comfort, opened it as an hotel.

As a place for a holiday its situation beside the lake is ideal and its facilities for sport unique. Then as a port of call on your way south from Scotland viâ Carlisle and the English lakes to Kendal it is a place to be remembered. Locally it is renowned for its good food and very hospitable atmosphere.

Here are some points that particularly impressed me. The baronial panelled hall decorated with trophies of the chase, the white coated waiters, spotless lavatories and bath rooms, fine modern bedrooms with excellent beds and baths, amusing collection of caricatures in the billiard room, the splendid ballroom and the library with its magnificent 16th century fire place. Bed and breakfast from 11/-.

Armathwaite Hall Hotel

Bassenthwaite Lake, Keswick,
Cumbria CA12 4RE
Tel: (017687) 76551; Fax: (017687) 76220

Few hotels are as beautifully situated as
Armathwaite Hall - one of the original stately
homes of England, set magnificently in 400
acres of deerpark and woodland, bordered by
the beauty of Bassenthwaite Lake and framed
by the dramatic vista of Skiddaw Mountain
and the surrounding fells. The Graves family,
who have owned and run Armathwaite Hall
for twenty years, know exactly how to pamper their guests. Cuisine is under the supervision of Masterchef Kevin Dowling. Style is
traditional English, with Cumbrian specialities and using local produce, and classical
French, but with a light touch. This is just a
prelude to all the activities available. Discreetly hidden is the magnificent 'Spa' Leisure
Club with indoor pool, gymnasium, beauty
salon etc. and in the grounds is a farm with
rare breeds and a BHS-approved Riding Centre. Fishing and boating are on the doorstep.
Armathwaite Hall is the perfect base from
which to enjoy the best of this lovely area.

Rates: single with breakfast £55; double with **V**
breakfast £110. **Breaks:** *Easter, Christmas/New
Year, Bank Holiday and other packages available.
Details on request.*

● *43 en suite bedrooms with colour TV + satellite,
telephone, hairdryer, laundry/valet service, tea/
coffee making facilities, 24-hr room/meal service,
radio/alarm clock, safety deposit box at reception,
trouser press.*
● *6-course table d'hôte dinner £34.95. Last orders
9.30 p.m. à la carte, lunch & special diets available*
● *Business services inc. 3 conference rooms to 100*
● *Billiards/snooker, croquet, fishing, indoor heated
swimming pool; jacuzzi; sauna, solarium, fitness
centre, equestrian centre, clay shooting, beauty the-
rapy, tennis, falconry on premises; golf $1^1/2$ miles.*
● *Open all year. Amex, Diners,Visa, Mastercard.*

Cockermouth 5, Keswick 5, Carlisle 25, London 295

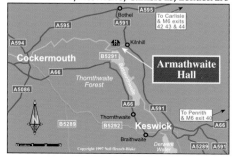

The Wild Boar Hotel, nr. Bowness on Windermere

ON THE ROAD FROM BOWNESS TO KENDAL
2½ Miles from Bowness and 6 miles from Kendal.
(For position see map on page 10, square B.4).

Commonsense and culture turn a wayside inn into a comfortable small hotel—A hospitable and inexpensive touring centre.

THERE is real romance about this place started a year or two ago by Malcolm Urquhart and his wife, then amateurs in hotel keeping. But they knew how a house should be run and so put hospitality, comfort, cleanliness, good plain food and supple beds in the front of their programme. The locals thought the scheme was crazy. Then when they saw rows of cars outside the place they wondered how they'd got there. "Must be a mistake", was the general opinion. But they were wrong, and to-day the place, the nearest hotel to the Windermere golf course, is a popular rendezvous.

A new wing has been built on the site of an old cock fighting pit from which you can see the lights of Morecambe. I stayed the night there and gave the place full marks for comfort and hospitality. There are modern bathrooms, running water in the bedrooms, bed lights, ash trays and matches and scores of detail comforts you don't meet everywhere. The afternoon teas and dinners and home-cured hams are particularly good. Bed and breakfast 9/-. Daily pension 12/- to 15/6.

A corner of the lounge with the dining room beyond.

The Wild Boar Hotel

Crook, Nr. Windermere,
Cumbria LA23 3NF
Tel: (015394) 45225; Fax: (015394) 42498
E-Mail: wildboar@elh.co.uk
Internet: http://www.elh.co.uk

A former Coaching Inn that, quite simply, offers you the chance to unwind and relax. Steeped in tradition, the hotel has retained its open log fires, low oak beams and spacious, comfortable lounges. Unique in character and atmosphere, the service is friendly but not too formal, attentive but not obtrusive. Dining is an essential element of a visit to the hotel. The AA rosette award winning restaurant, sculptured around a natural outcrop of rock, combines cuisine of classical dishes and delicate flavours. The house speciality, fresh wild boar, can be enjoyed with fine wines from the extensive cellar. Throughout the autumn and winter season, dinner dances are featured to the sound of the hotel's resident band.

From the hotel , Windermere Golf Club is just along the road and beyond are the shores of Lake Windermere with all its varying activities. Complimentary membership of the extensive Leisure Club at our sister hotel, Low Wood, provides all year round sporting facilities.

Rates: per person start at £43 for bed & full breakfast. Superior 4-poster rooms & suites are available at a supplement.
Bargain Breaks: Min. two nights from £53 pppn inc. dinner, bed & breakfast. Three night special saver terms available all year. **V**

● *34 en suite bedrooms & 2 suites, all with colour TV + satellite, direct-dial telephone, hairdryer, 48-hour laundry service, tea/coffee making facilities. Non-smoker bedrooms available.*
● *A la carte, speciality evening menu, with local produce. Last orders 10 pm. Light lunches available. Traditional lunch on Sundays.*
● *Business services inc. two meeting rooms - capacity 40. Car parking for 80. Car rental avilable.*
● *Fishing & sailing 3 miles. Fitness centre, jacuzzi, watersports, massage, sauna, squash, indoor swimming pool seven miles.*
● *Open all year. All major credit cards accepted.*
M6 (Jct 36 via A590/591 to Windermere, joining B5284) 11, Bowness 3, Golf Course 1, Kendal 6, Ambleside 7, London 275.

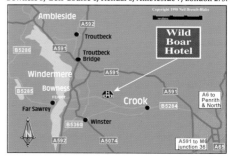

Graythwaite Manor Hotel

Grange-over-Sands, Cumbria LAll 7JE
Tel: (015395) 32001/33755;
Fax: (015395) 35549

What first impressed me here was the courtesy and thoroughness with which one of the owners showed me round. As a result of what I saw and felt, I returned a few days later for a night's lodging and this is what I found. A largish and substantial house, beautifully appointed and with every indication that the detailed comfort of visitors had been most conscientiously achieved. The armchairs were cosy enough to go to sleep in. The dining room, an imposing affair, displays cut glass chandeliers and some fine oil paintings. There was a choice from the à la carte or table d'hôte menus at dinner, both excellently cooked and served. I made a special note, too, of how pleasant and attentive the staff were, obviously taking their cue from the owners. Bedrooms, all with private baths fulfilled the expectation of the downstairs comfort and elegance. Faithful guests return year after year for Graythwaite and Grange are within easy reach of the Lake District.

Rates: Dinner, room and breakfast from £57.50 single, £115.00 twin.   **V**
Special breaks of two days or more available November to March; prices on request.

● *22 bedrooms (some ground floor), 20 with private bathrooms and all with telephone, TV, tea/ coffee making facilities, electric blankets.*
● *Drying room; small conferences.*
● *billiards; attractive gardens; golf locally, putting green; hard tennis court; riding nearby.*
● *Open all year. All major credit cards accepted.*

Lake District (Windermere) 15, Carlisle 58, Liverpool 76, London 261.

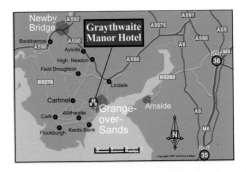

Netherwood Hotel

Grange-over-Sands, Cumbria LAll 6ET
Tel: (015395) 32552; Fax: (015395) 34121

Rates: Room and breakfast from £50 single, £100 double. **Winter breaks** *from 1st Nov. 1998-31st March 1999 (exc. Fridays & Saturdays): 2 nights £130; 3 nights £185. Prices per person include dinner, bed & breakfast and VAT.*

This imposing hotel, set in its own topiary gardens on a woodland slope, dominates the main road into Grange-over-Sands. The house dates back to 1893, and it retains all the original panelling, wood-carvings and fireplaces. However, modern conveniences also have their place here, and you will find a lift servicing the first floor bedrooms, and all the dining areas are air conditioned. There is a honeymoon suite with all its original furniture, to help you re-live the romance of days gone by, and there are ten new bedrooms, all non-smoking, furnished in harmony with the rest of the hotel. The food at the Netherwood is excellent, being prepared from the freshest ingredients with imagination and flair. It is easy to over-indulge in the dining room, but downstairs there is a heated swimming pool, spa bath, steam room and beauty salon where you can work off those extra inches gained, or simply relax after perhaps a tiring day touring this lovely area. The southern Lake District offers much for the nature lover and tourist alike, and the delights of Morecambe Bay and the Lune Valley are on the doorstep.

● *28 en suite bedrooms (1 for disabled); two pairs of intercommunicating bedrooms; all have radio, telephone, TV; night service; lift to 1st floor.*
● *Late meals, special diets; children welcome; baby listening; dogs allowed, conferences.*
● *Indoor heated swimming pool, spa bath, steam room, gymnasium, beauty area, parking for 160 cars, dancing, 11 acres of gardens; tennis 1/2 mile; squash, badminton, riding, shooting and fishing all five miles.*
● *Open all year. Major credit cards accepted.*

Lake District (Windermere) 5, Kendal 12, Keswick 41, Carlisle 58, Liverpool 82, London 262.

Michael's Nook Country House Hotel

Grasmere, Ambleside, Cumbria LA22 9RP
Tel: (015394) 35496; Fax: (015394) 35645
E-mail: m-nook@wordsworth.grasmere.co.uk

This hotel stands high up in a splendid, well-kept garden and overlooks the Vale of Grasmere. It is furnished with many antiques in the warm, country house manner. Some bedrooms contain pieces of furniture originally made for the house and in many rooms the built-in marble top washbasins have been retained. Fresh fruit and flowers are a feature of all rooms. The Oak Room, with its stone fireplace, handsome panelling and gilt furnishings, is available for small meetings and private functions. However the superb comfort is almost incidental to the food. Fresh fish, vegetables, fruit, poultry and meat are delivered daily. All dishes are beautifully prepared and presented. It is a joy to see the tables set for dinner with fine bone china and Stuart crystal. The menus are superb with an excellent choice of wines. I cannot praise this hotel enough. It is a must for any *Signposter* wishing to stay in the centre of the Lake District. Pride of Britain member.

Rates: From £85-£135 inc. breakfast, 5-course dinner & VAT. **V**
Breaks: 10% discount on stays of five+ nights. Midweek winter breaks. tariff on application.

● *12 double en suite bedrooms & 2 suites, with colour TV, direct-dial telephone, room service.*
● *Table d'hôte dinner £47.50; lunch & special diets available. Last orders 2030 hrs.*
● *3-acre garden, 10 acre woodland; indoor pool & health club at nearby* Wordsworth Hotel *(see following page). Sailing, boating, fishing locally. Free golf on weekdays.*
● *Conferences up to 12 people. No dogs.*
● *Open all year. Major credit cards accepted.*

Ambleside 4, Keswick 13, Kendal 17, London 271.

The Wordsworth Hotel

Grasmere, Ambleside,
Cumbria LA22 9SW
Tel: (015394) 35592; Fax: (015394) 35765
E-mail: Enquiry@wordsworth-grasmere.co.uk

Set in the centre of Grasmere, in 1¹/₂ acres of
landscaped gardens, this hotel offers all that is
best for a holiday in the Lakes. It is spacious,
airy and has all the modern amenities to be
expected by the discerning traveller. One
bedroom has retained its original Victorian
bathroom and is very much in demand, as the
shower facilities must be seen to be believed.
There are also three romantic four-poster
rooms, one of which is a suite. The public
rooms are tastefully furnished in keeping
with the period of the buildings, without the
gloomy atmosphere inherent in so many
Victorian hotels. The swimming pool has
large doors opening onto a patio and makes
an excellent place in which to relax after a few
days of walking, climbing or sightseeing. The
hotel is owned by Reg Gifford of Michael's
Nook Country House Hotel, so little more
need be said of the food here, other than that
the fame which he has gained as an hotelier is
more than justified. What could be better than
the fresh air of the Lake District and maybe a
little exercise, coupled with the cuisine of the
hotel's *Prelude* restaurant?

*Prices from £65 per person, inc. breakfast & VAT.
Christmas and New Year house parties. Winter
and other special offer **breaks** available throughout the year.*

● *35 en suite bedrooms (2 ground floor) and 2
suites, all with colour TV, telephone and full
central heating. Lift, night service.*
● *Last orders 9.00 p.m. Fri-Sat 9.30 p.m.; bar
meals; vegetarian diets.*
● *Children welcome, baby listening; no dogs;
conferences up to 100; games room; dancing by
arrangement.*
● *Indoor
heated swim-
ming pool;
sauna and
solarium; mini
gym; jacuzzi;
free golf on
weekdays;
squash, riding
and fishing
nearby.*
● *Open all
year. All major
credit cards
accepted.*
**Ambleside 4,
Keswick 13,
Kendal 17,
London 271.**

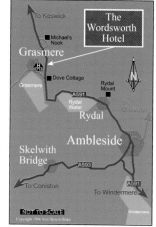

Dale Head Hall Lakeside Hotel

Thirlmere, Keswick, Cumbria CA12 4TN
Tel: (017687) 72478; Fax: (017687) 71070
E-Mail: enquiry@dale-head-hall. co.uk
Internet: http://www.dale-head-hall.co.uk

At the northern end of Thirlmere, you will find an hotel situated in one of the most idyllic positions in the Lake District. Set in a clearing on the shores of the lake, with Helvellyn rising majestically behind, you cannot help falling in love with Dale Head Hall. A small, yet luxurious hotel, this 16th century Hall is beautifully decorated in keeping with the age of the building. It exudes that intimate atmosphere of a true family home. The untiring enthusiasm, skill and innate sense of hospitality of the resident proprietors, Alan and Shirley Lowe, combine to make Dale Head Hall a very special place. Three red squirrels play on the lawn. The sun sets over the lake and fell, as I join fellow guests in the lounge for an aperitif, all in eager anticipation of yet another wonderful meal. The award-winning cuisine is truly superb, lovingly prepared by one of the most dedicated mother and daughter teams I know. They even grow their own vegetables, fruit, herbs and flowers in the Hall's Victorian kitchen garden. Dale Head Hall is in an ideal position for exploring the Lake District, with all the major attractions not far away. It comes highly recommended and represents some of the best value in Cumbria.

Rates: Room and breakfast from £37.50; dinner,room & breakfast from £65. Cumbria Tourist Board 4 Crown Highly Commended. **V**
Bargain Breaks: Logfire Winter Breaks available from 4.11.98-27.03.99 any 2 nights from £54. Spring Breaks available from 1.4.99-30.5.99 any two nights from £62.50. All are based upon dinner,b&b per person per night.

● *9 en suite bedrooms, all with direct dial telephone, room service, baby listening.*
● *Last orders for dinner 8.30p.m.; special diets.*
● *Children welcome.*
● *Sailing, boating, shooting, fishing, tennis, spa pool, gymnasium, squash courts. Golf five miles, riding seven miles.*
● *Open all year. All major credit cards accepted.*

Keswick 4, Grasmere 5, Penrith 16, London 285.

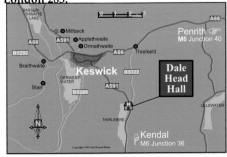

Stakis Keswick Lodore Hotel

Keswick, Cumbria CA12 5UX
Tel: (017687) 77285;
Fax: (017687) 77343

The Stakis Keswick Lodore Hotel, situated overlooking Derwent Water and at the foot of the famous Lodore Falls, is an hotel of international class and reputation. It caters superbly for all manner of guests and their families. One of the most impressive aspects is the way in which children are looked after by N.N.E.B. nurses, with their own playroom and kitchen, providing parents with a welcome rest. The public rooms are all bright and airy, the bedrooms are spacious and well appointed, and the whole hotel is beautifully decorated and cheerful. Many of the excellent dishes served are from original Swiss recipes, and the staff are all courteous and friendly. The gardens are a delight, and the immediate environs have the most imposing views, yet there is also a gentler beauty in the landscape. All the Lake District, with its sporting facilities, as well as its natural and historical features is easily accessible, so whether you are holidaying as a family or alone, there is something here to suit you. The hotel also has its own many and varied facilities for guests to enjoy.

Rates: Dinner, bed & breakfast from £66.00; **V** *weekly rates (including dinner) from £416.00.* **Bargain Breaks** *- for a minimum of 2 nights, holiday rate from £39.50 per person per night applies, to include dinner, bed & breakfast.*

Keswick 3¹/₂, Penrith 21, Carlisle 38, London 300.

● *75 bedrooms all with en suite bathroom, satellite TV and telephone; room and night service; baby listening; lift.*
● *Last orders 9.15 p.m.; bar lunches; special diets.*
● *Children welcome; registered nursery with NNEB trained nannies; conferences up to 80.*
● *Games room; outdoor/indoor heated swimming pool; leisure centre; sauna; beautician/hairdresser; gymnasium; sunbed; squash and tennis; sailing, boating and riding nearby; fishing by arrangement; free golf Mon-Fri (18 hole course), Sat-Sun £20 per person.*
● *Open all year. All major credit cards accepted.*

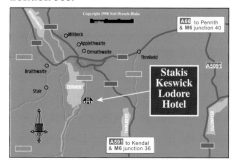

THE NORTH WEST

Scafell Hotel

Borrowdale, Nr. Keswick, Cumbria
CAl2 5XB
Tel: (017687) 77208; Fax: (017687) 77280

It is not surprising that the Scafell is becoming
one of Lakeland's leading hotels following its
recent improvements and the consistent ef-
forts of its management. Situated almost at
the head of the beautiful Borrowdale Valley,
its position is as outstanding as the service
and comfort which it provides for all its
guests. There is an excellent table d'hôte
menu and for those wishing to dine later, a
comprehensive à la carte supper menu. Both
menus are accompanied by a well balanced
wine list. Year after year guests return to walk
and climb for they know that they are going
to be comfortable and well looked after. For
the less energetic, there are cosy and homely
lounges. The bedrooms are comfortable and
attractively furnished, all of them having their
own private bathroom. Pleasant views are to
be had of the sheltered garden ringed by
mighty mountains on which internationally
famous climbers have learned their craft. Yes,
this is a home for the visitor seeking peace or
exercise and wishing to 'get away from it all'.

Rates: *Dinner, bed and breakfast from £48.00 to
£60.00.*
Midweek breaks *available : any two consecutive
nights Sunday-Thursday inclusive £79.00 per
person, dinner, bed and breakfast. Fell Break Week
-ends are available: Friday evening to Sunday
lunch and include all dinners, packed lunches,
breakfasts, afternoon tea and Sunday lunch - £118.00.*

● *24 en suite bedrooms (8 ground floor), all with
direct-dial telephone, tea/coffee making facilities,
TV; full central heating.*
● *Children welcome and dogs accepted; bar meals.*
● *Drying room; river bathing; boating; fishing;
pony trekking; tennis six miles; golf ten miles.*
● *Hotel open all year.*

**Keswick 6, Penrith 24, Carlisle 36, Kendal 36,
London 291.**

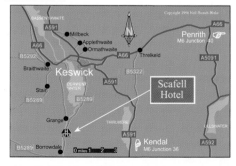

The Swan Hotel

Newby Bridge, Nr. Ulverston, Cumbria LA12 8NB
Tel: (015395) 31681; Fax: (015395) 31917

Set 'twixt the river and the lake in what must be one of the most superb situations in the Lake District, the Swan has all the facilities that a traveller or holiday maker could wish for. It has its own lovely marina, fishing in the river and is close to the steam railway at Newby Bridge; all this at the end of Lake Windermere. The hotel was originally a coaching inn but has now been completely modernised to provide every convenience. Special autumn breaks are offered and my only regret was that I could not stay longer to explore this lovely part of Cumbria. The Lonsdale Suite has a king size bed, luxurious drapes and craftsman-built mahogany furniture to luxury standard.

● *36 en suite bedrooms including shower, all with TV,radio, tea/coffee making facilities, hair-dryer and telephone; central heating.baby listening.*
● *Night service; late meals by arrangement; diets.*
● *Children welcome; residential conferences for up to 64; approved by the local authority for civil marriages.*
● *Fishing; marina; riding two miles; golf 6¹/₂ miles.*
● *Most credit cards accepted.*

Rates: Room and breakfast from £60.00 single Ⅴ *and £96.00 double.* **Breaks:** *Hotel open for 3-day Christmas Holiday Break and 1, 2 or 3 day New Year Break. 'Swan Breaks' - any two nights week ends only (Friday and Saturday or Saturday and Sunday) from £100 per person, dinner, bed and breakfast in double room with private bath. Spring to Autumn "Swan Break Superplus" - 4-day breaks - dinner, bed and breakfast, mini-cruise and "A Trip Down Memory Lane" from £200 per person.*

Ambleside 12, Kendal 15, M6 16, Kirkby Lonsdale 22, Manchester 83, London 267.

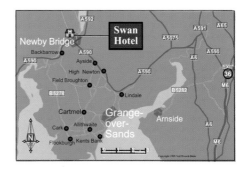

THE NORTH WEST

Our 51st season

In 1948 Francis' father, James Coulson, threw a copy of the Manchester Guardian on to his bed, and suggested that he looked to see if there were any properties on the market in the Lake District. There, to his amazement, he saw a small advertisement: "Family mansion on the edge of Lake Ullswater, with half a mile of lake edge and twelve acres of woodlands. Offers".

To cut a long story short, Francis came up to see this idyllic sounding place! Remember that just after the war there were no motorways, petrol was rationed, food was rationed, furniture required dockets and the Lake District was very unfashionable.

However, in October 1948 he arrived with very little capital, but the full support of his father and family. With the help of friends he was able to open Sharrow for guests at Easter 1949, with just a few rooms and a lot of faith!

Progress was slow but in a very short time Francis' baking became renowned and people were queuing up for the home made teas at two shillings and sixpence ($12^1/_2$ pence) each!!

In 1952 fate stepped in and Brian Sack met Francis and likewise fell in love with Sharrow. They complemented one another perfectly with Francis producing his superb food and Brian running the dining room and the office. They both have a love of people and their interests were identical.

In 1958 Sharrow was accepted into the Signpost Hotel Guide, *created by Mr Mc Minnies (*"weekly terms from nine and a half guineas - reduced in winter"). Gradually rooms were developed, twelve in the main house, four in the Lodge annexe, three in the cottage in the grounds, two in Thwaite cottage four miles away, and finally seven in Bank House, a converted 17th century farmhouse one mile away with a magnificent panoramic view of Ullswater.

And so, having reached our 51st season, nothing could have been achieved without the help and loyalty of so many people. Now we are trying to maintain the standards that are expected of us, as we are told that we have become a living legend!

Sharrow Bay Country House Hotel

Ullswater, Howtown, Nr. Penrith,
Cumbria CA10 2LZ
Tel: (017684) 86301 / 86483;
Fax: (017684) 86349

Away from the bustle of the holiday rush, in one of the most envied positions in the Lake District lies Sharrow Bay. The late Francis Coulson M.B.E. and Brian Sack M.B.E. must be congratulated on their 51st year of service to the gourmets of the world, providing the most exquisite food and wines in the most comfortable of atmospheres. The reputation of being the first Country House Hotel in this country and being the oldest British member of *Relais et Chateaux* collection is surely recommendation enough, but people who have stayed here will still describe in nothing but superlatives the home from home atmosphere that the owners have worked so hard to create and maintain. The décor is superb, the service impeccable and the overall effect is a tribute to these two brilliant hoteliers. Add to all this the beauty of the Lake and mountains and you have total perfection. I should add that there is now a beautiful converted farmhouse called Bank House, about a mile from Sharrow, which has seven superbly furnished bedrooms, all with private bathrooms and lake views . Breakfast is served in the magnificent Refectory dining room, which was converted from the seventeenth century barn. It has a striking Portland stone fireplace and over-mantle, which came from Warwick Castle. It also has incredible English silk damask curtains, old English furniture and a specially made carpet - a copy of one in the Royal Opera House. Lunch and dinner are served at Sharrow Bay. Some of the staff have been with the hotel for over 30 years, and Brian Sack with Nigel Lightburn, who is now managing director, will carry on Sharrow Bay's renowned traditions. Tariff on application.

● *26 bedrooms; 24 with private bath and/or shower, including 6 cottage suites, TV, radio, antiques, peace. Small conference facilities.*
● *Golf locally, lake bathing, boating, riding, fishing*
● *Closed end-November to end-February.*
Penrith 7, Keswick 20, Kendal 33, London 289

The Old Church Hotel

Old Church Bay, Watermillock,
Cumbria CA11 OJN
Tel: (017684) 86204; Fax: (017684) 86368
E-mail: info@oldchurch.co.uk
Website: http://www.oldchurch.co.uk

A long drive through meadowland to the
shores of Lake Ullswater (one of the less tour-
isty areas of the Lake District) brings you to
this delightful hotel. Its extensive lawns run
down to the lake and the surroundings are of
great beauty with magnificent views of lake
and mountain scenery. On entering the gracious hall, the visitor has his first impression
of the pleasures and comforts to come. The
bedrooms and public rooms are all beautifully
and decorated to create the ambience of a
country house of bygone days - the building
dates from 1734 and is on the site of a 12th
century church. The owners, Kevin and
Maureen Whitemore, ensure that the service
is discreetly impeccable, that the food is delicious and that the well-being of their guests
remains of primary concern. All the Lake
District's attractions are close by: climbing
and walking from the hotel and sailing and
boating on the doorstep. The less energetic can
just savour the air, good food and comfort.

*Rates: single room inc. breakfast from £65.00
double/twin inc. breakfast from £90.00* Ⓥ
Bargain Breaks: Rates on application.

● *10 en suite bedrooms, all with colour TV, direct-
dial telephone, hairdryer tea/coffee making facilities*
● *A la carte dinner from £20. Last order 8.00p.m.
(Closed Sunday evenings). Car parking for 20 cars*
● *Airport pick up and car rental by arrangement.*
● *Fishing. Sailing/boating, riding, watersports
four miles.*
● *Closed beginning of November to end-March.*
● *Mastercard, Amex, Visa credit cards accepted*

**M6 (Junction 40) 7, Penrith 7½, Ambleside
15, Keswick 17, Kendal 26, London 281.**

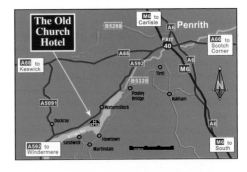

Cedar Manor Hotel

Ambleside Road, Windermere,
Cumbria LA23 1AX
Tel: (015394) 43192; Fax (015394) 45970

True lovers of the Lake District wishing to immerse themselves in everything that the beautiful area has to offer will naturally seek out a smaller, more intimate hotel. They need look no further than the Cedar Manor which is a traditional and very genuine Lakeland house, with some interesting architectural features, in a country garden setting. Moreover all that is within the hotel is a reflection of its peaceful and secluded location for it exudes an air of comfort, friendliness and quiet efficiency with the added bonus of immaculate decoration and elegant furnishings in the public rooms. The bedrooms too are very comfortable and some have lovely views towards Lake Windermere. The reputation of the restaurant had preceded it and is reflected in the many awards and accolades it has received from connoisseurs. The food was indeed excellent with fresh local produce and I enjoyed a roast leg of lamb Westmoreland style with Cumberland sausage stuffing and other trimmings. This homely country hotel, so close to Cumbria's beauties and not far from its many other attractions, is a place for the lover of good things in life. The Cedar Manor puts it another way: "Often sought, seldom found".

Rates: Single room including breakfast from £40.00. Double room with breakfast from £60.00.
Leisure Breaks: Christmas & New Year Pro grammes; Golf Breaks - throughout the year. Honeymoon Package. Details of all these are available upon request.

● *12 en suite bedrooms with radio & colour TV, direct-dial telephone, hairdryer, laundry service; tea/coffee making facilities.*
● *Last orders for dinner 20.30 hrs. Special diets available.*
● *Fishing, watersports, riding, tennis & golf - all nearby. Hotel offers free use of local leisure facilities. Car parking for 16 cars.*
● *Open all year. All credit cards accepted (except Amex and Diners).*

Kendal 8, Penrith 26, Lancaster 28, London 246.

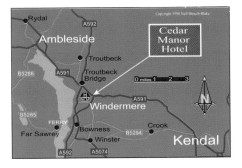

Langdale Chase Hotel, Windermere

BESIDE LAKE WINDERMERE

3½ Miles from Windermere and 2½ miles from Ambleside.
(*For position see map on page 10, square B.4*).

A picked position on one of England's loveliest lakes affords ever varying views of mountains, clouds and water—Country house charm with twentieth century comforts—Splendid facilities for boating, bathing, golf, tennis, putting and croquet.

THE man who chose this site knew well the peace and pleasure of an ever-changing view of water, mountains, cloud and sunlight. And having picked his site he built his house to take the full advantage of the view. It stands amid great trees above an expanse of lawn leading to the waters' edge, close to the road from Carlisle to the South viâ Windermere. On two sides are stone paved ballustrated terraces where on a summer's afternoon you read, smoke, talk and have your tea, soaking in that splendid view of the Langdales right across the lake. With equal care he built his rooms, gracious and spacious with deep windows commanding the same fine panorama. Zealous to miss nothing of the view he cunningly contrived extensions to his corner rooms to give him wider angles still and catch every moment of the setting sun.

To-day these rooms, fitted with every modern comfort and furnished with rare taste and quality, await the traveller. Some that I saw were let as bed-sitting rooms, their built-out corners with the view forming a charming retreat for working, reading or writing. Central heating, running water, excellent beds and

Langdale Chase Hotel

Windermere, Cumbria LA23 1LW
Tel: (015394) 32201; Fax: (015394) 32604

As the Langdale Chase is renowned for its excellence by connoisseurs all over the country and by all in the Lake District, just ask any 'local' and he or she will direct you to the gates on the Windermere to Ambleside Road. Then turn into the drive and note the stately trees and immaculately mown and edged lawns, and park in peace outside the front door. Note, too, the splendid lakeside view with the unique skyline of the Langdales in the distance. Inside, parts of the hotel suggest a baronial atmosphere; others are more modern, particularly the picture-windowed restaurant and conservatory which leads into the cocktail bar, with views of the gardens and lake. Food is properly understood here and served in a memorable setting. Some of the staff have been here a long time and may remember your name. Upstairs you'll be intrigued by some of the bedrooms which grow small offshoots into the turrets. A Lakeland stone bungalow annexe offers six superb en suite bedrooms, so that guests can have their own apartment with direct car access, whilst enjoying all the facilities of the hotel.

Rates: Room and breakfast from £55.00 per person, inclusive of VAT and service charges. **V**
Bargain breaks: 15% off for a three-night break, dinner, bed & breakfast.

● *29 en suite bedrooms (including 6 in annexe), all with telephone, colour TV, hairdryer, tea/coffee making facilities, 24-hour room/meal service.*
● *Table d'hôte dinner £18-25; à la carte, lunch & special diets available; last orders 9.30 pm.*
● *Two meeting rooms, cap. 20/10. Car parking - 30*
● *Croquet, fishing, indoor swimming pool, tennis. Gymnasium, watersports, massage/sauna, sailing/boating at Leisure Centre 500m; riding nearby.*
● *Open all year. Major credit cards accepted.*

Ambleside 2½, Windermere 3½, Kendal 8, London 283

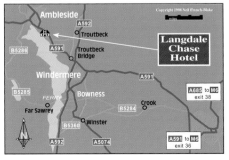

Lindeth Fell Country House Hotel

Bowness-on-Windermere, Cumbria
LA23 3JP
Tel: (015394) 43286; Fax: (015394) 47455

With superb views of Lake Windermere and set in seven acres of beautifully wooded and secluded grounds, Lindeth Fell is possibly the best situated of all Lakeland hotels. The house itself is superbly furnished and decorated with many antiques and original paintings. The gardens dazzle in spring and early summer with superb displays of rhododendrons, azaleas, shrubs and a new herbaceous border. The food, cooked under the personal supervision of Mrs Kennedy herself, is predominately English and is outstanding. Most guests are tempted to over indulge in these culinary delights but to counterbalance the hedonism, there is bowling, croquet and putting in the hotel grounds with golf one mile away and Windermere Marina just down the hill. Bowness and Windermere are close at hand and, for the more ambitious, there are lakes and rivers to be fished, mountains to be climbed and all the other outdoor pursuits that the Lake District has to offer.

Rates. Single room with breakfast £50; double room with breakfast from £100.
Winter Breaks. *8th Nov-31 Mar (exc. Xmas/ New Year) any 2 days from £50 pppn inc. dinner, room & breakfast.*

● *15 en suite bedrooms, all with colour TV + satellite, direct dial telephone, hairdryer, laundry/ valet service, music/radio/alarm clock, trouser press. Car parking for 20.*

● *2 lounges/2 dining rooms. 5-course table d'hôte dinner £19. Lunch & special diets available. Last orders for dinner 8. 30 p.m.*

● *Children welcome; dogs accepted in grounds; meetings to 12.*

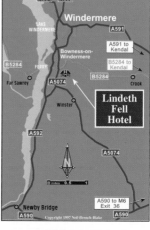

● *Croquet, fishing, pitch & putt, bowls. Riding, golf, sailing/boating nearby.*

● *Open all year. Visa & Mastercard accepted.*

Bowness 1, Kendal 7, Manchester 76, Newcastle 90, London 280.

Linthwaite House Hotel

Crook Road, Windermere, The Lake
District, Cumbria LA23 3JA
Tel: (015394) 88600; Fax: (015394) 88601
E-mail: admin@linthwaite.com

This hotel, situated on the B5284 Bowness to
Kendal road, only a mile or so from Bowness,
is surely the epitome of what every Signposter would like to find. It is set in 14 acres
of superbly kept grounds with magnificent
views of Lake Windermere and of every major peak in the Lake District. There is a well
stocked tarn (in which 5 lb trout have been
caught) and where one can while away the
day with a picnic. The golf practice area is
surrounded by lovely woodland walks. Naturally, within a very short distance are all the
other amenities that one expects in the area,
such as swimming, yachting and tennis. But
enough of outside activities! Inside the hotel
is immaculate, tastefully interior designed. A
feature is the use of old trunks and suitcases.
The food is superb and many of the guests
return to Linthwaite again and again. Surely
this speaks more eloquently than any words?
Any Signposter who visits here for the first
time will, like others, keep coming back to the
atmosphere of peace and tranquillity.

Rates: *Room and breakfast £75-£250.* 🆅
Romantic breaks *(minimum 2 nights) - including champagne in room on arrival, box of hand
made chocolates, canopied king size double bed
with lake view, breakfast and candlelit dinner.*

● *18 en suite bedrooms (5 ground floor), all with
direct dial telephone and satellite TV; room service*
● *Last orders for dinner 8.45 p.m., light lounge
lunches; special diets. No under 7s in restaurant
for dinner.* ● *Children welcome. Conferences to 20*
● *Sauna, solarium, spa pool, gymnasium and golf
one mile; mountain walking and riding three
miles; sailing/boating and water-skiing one mile;
golf practice hole par 3; own tarn brown trout.
Mountain bikes to hire at hotel.*
● *Open all year; all major credit cards accepted.*
**Bowness 1, Kendal 7, Manchester 76,
London 280.**

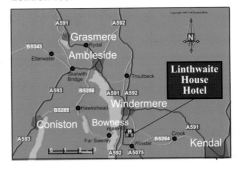

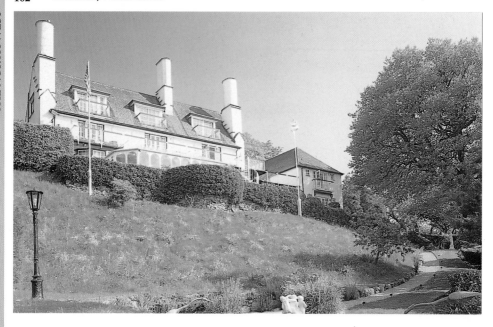

Miller Howe

Rayrigg Road, Windermere, Cumbria
LA23 1EY
Tel: (015394) 42536; Fax: (015394) 45664

Miller Howe stands in four and a half acres of
well-kept gardens on the shores of Lake
Windermere. Charles Garside has recently
taken over the hotel along with his brother
Iain, a lakeland hotelier of many years' experience and owner of the Fayrer Garden House
Hotel in Bowness. Their team offer a blend of
warm hospitality, a wonderful location, comfortable accommodation and impeccable food.
They have retained John Tovey, who built up
the reputation of the hotel for cuisine and
hospitality, as a consultant. All bedrooms
have private facilities, little extras in the bathroom and even board games including Scrab-
ble and Backgammon in case of inclement
weather! Staff pride themselves on maintain-
ing a warm, friendly and relaxing ambience to
match the serenity of views from bedrooms,
the internationally acclaimed restaurant
(named *Restaurant of the Year 1998* by Which
Good Food Guide), the conservatory and the
three elegant lounges. The Lakes are beautiful
at all times and the hotel offers special packages for guests all through the year.

*Rates: Per person inc dinner & breakfast & VAT
from £70.* **V**
Bargain Breaks. *3-night breaks per person inc
dinner, b & b from £189 (April & November);
£195 October. December Escape - 1-21st any
three nights for price of two; Christmas, New
Year and Valentine Breaks - prices on application.*

● *12 en suite bedrooms, all with colour TV, direct-dial telephone, hairdyer, laundry/valet service,
music/radio/alarm clock, trouser press.*
● *5-course table d'hôte dinner £32. A la carte, lunch &
special diets available. Orders: 7.30 for 8 pm.*
● *Business services inc. conferences max. 30.*
● *Fishing,
sauna/solarium,
sialing/boating,
riding locally.
Golf 2 miles;
watersports 1 m*
● *Dogs accepted
(in room only-£3
p night)
Car parking 40.*
● *Open 12 Feb-
1 Jan inc. Major
credit cards
accepted.*

**Ambleside 5,
Windermere 1,
Bowness 1,
Kendal 8,
London 283**

The Old Vicarage Country House Hotel

Witherslack, Cumbria LAll 6RS
Tel: (015395) 52381; Fax: (015395) 52373
E-Mail: hotel@old-vic.demon.co.uk

The Old Vicarage was recommended to me by one of the country's top hoteliers - and how right he was. For those wishing to visit the Lake District, to remain in perfect peace and seclusion and yet to sample the art of cooking and service at their best, then here is the venue in which to do so to perfection. The hotel is set in a particularly beautiful valley and it offers the finest of food prepared only from the freshest of ingredients. It is indeed a haven. The atmosphere is of unhurried simplicity but the thought and energy expended to achieve this ambience is, I am sure, immeasurable. Mr. and Mrs. Burrington-Brown and Mr. and Mrs. Reeve have set a standard that many hotels will strive to match but which few will attain. I look forward to visiting this unique hotel again, and especially to staying in the "Celebration Suite", one of the new bedrooms in the Orchard House, with its terraces overlooking unspoilt woodland.

Rates: Dinner, room and breakfast £70-90 per V *person, inc VAT & service. Celebration suite £100.* **Bargain breaks** *- near to the lakes, far from the crowds. Any two nights, midweek or weekends, fully inclusive from £60 per person, dinner, bed and breakfast per night.*

● *14 en suite bedrooms including 5 in the Orchard House, all with telephone, colour TV, full central heating.* ● *Dinner 7.00 p.m. until 8.30 p.m.; diets available. Non-residents dinner £29.50.* ● *Children by arrangement; dogs by arrangement.* ● *All weather tennis court for guests' use; sailing, golf, squash, badminton, riding, shooting, fishing all nearby.* ● *Open all year. Major credit cards accepted.* **M6 Junction 36 10 mins., Sea 4, Lake Windermere 6, Kendal 8, Lancaster 19, London 263.**

The Pines Hotel & Haworths Bistro

Clayton-le-Woods, Chorley,
Lancashire PR6 7ED
Tel: (01772) 338551; Fax: (01772) 629001

One of the pleasures of visiting this part of Lancashire is to stay at The Pines. It has always surprised me how M rs Duffin, the owner, has every year been able to add some new facility or to improve the hotel. With superbly comfortable public rooms, beautiful bedrooms with all the "extras",there is surely nothing more a discerning guest could want? The food is delicious, the wine list long and well chosen and Lancastrians from all over the county gather here to dine. Various suites are available for conferences or small meetings and one of them, the *Dixon Suite*, is in great demand for wedding receptions. An acre of beautiful garden provides a fitting backdrop for ensuing photographs! The hotel is ideally situated for the business traveller, being only minutes from the M6 and M61. For the holiday maker and North-South traveller, Blackpool and Lytham St Annes (for golf) are near at hand; the Pennines and South Lake District only an hour away and the entertainment and academic centre of Manchester 30 minutes down the motorway.

Rates: Single superior room inc. breakfast £70; double room inc. breakfast £80.   **V**
Bargain Breaks: *Cabaret weekend breaks available*

● *38 en suite bedrooms (inc 2 suites) all with colour TV, direct-dial telephone, hairdryer, laundry/valet service, tea/coffee making facilities, 24-hr room/meal service, trouser press. Non-smoker bedrooms and rooms for disabled available.*
● ***Haworths Bistro*** - *Lite Bites 10am-10pm; full Bistro menu 12-2 pm/6-10pm.* ***Crystal Room*** - *fine dining à la carte restaurant or can be hired privately for up to 24 people.* ***Cabaret Nights*** - *held throughout the year. Please telephone for full cabaret brochure.*
● *Open all year exc Dec 26.*
● *All major credit cards accepted.*

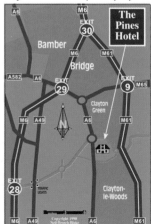

M6 (Junc. 8) 1,
Blackburn 10,
Bolton 10,
Southport 19,
Manchester 22,
London 203.

Chadwick Hotel

South Promenade, Lytham St Annes,
Lancashire FY8 1NP
Tel: (01253) 720061; Fax: (01253) 714455

I was most impressed with this hotel. It is owned and run by the Corbett family and every detail has been carefully thought out and provided. The staff are particularly charming and helpful and they immediately make you feel at home. The décor is bright and airy and all the rooms are well decorated and comfortable. Here are all the facilities of a large international hotel, but without the pomposity sometimes associated with them. There are rooms for the disabled; there is a health club with an indoor heated swimming pool, spa bath, solarium & gymnasium and the bedrooms have every convenience including in-house movies and satellite TV. The Chadwick Hotel's newly refurbished restaurant serves excellent food and has a good wine list. The Bugatti Bar features over 100 malt whiskies. The Chadwick is situated right on the sea front of this pretty town and there are particularly good rates for families with children and also for the keen golfer with many superb courses within a very short distance.

Rates: Double/twin room and breakfast from £30 per person, including VAT. **V**
Bargain breaks. Midwinter breaks with two persons sharing £38.50 for dinner, bed & breakfast. Alternatively our popular dinner dance and speciality weekends include entertainment on Friday and 7-course banquet with dancing on Saturday for £85.50 per person for the complete weekend.

● *75 en suite bedrooms (2 for the disabled), some with 4-poster beds, some with spa baths, all with direct dial telephone and TV; room service; baby listening; night service; 24-hour food service; lift.* ● *Last orders for dinner 8.30 p.m., bar meals; diets.* ● *Children welcome. Conferences max. 50.* ● *Childrens' soft adventure playroom; indoor heated swimming pool; leisure centre/gym; sauna; solarium; spa pool; sea fishing; golf ½ mile; sailing/ boating, tennis & squash courts 1 mile; riding 3 m.* ● *Open all year; all major credit cards accepted.*
Blackpool 7, Preston 14, Lancaster 30, London 224.

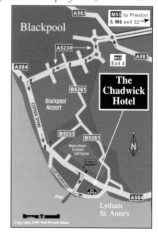

Le Meridien Victoria & Albert Hotel

Water Street, Manchester M3 4JQ
Tel: (0161) 832 1188; Fax: (0161) 834 2484

The luxurious four-star de luxe Le Meridien Victoria & Albert Manchester stands on the banks of the river Irwell. This beautiful listed building, with its mellowed brickwork and exposed beams creates a country house atmosphere in the city centre. It is a fabulous concept, well executed and representing the ultimate in comfort. The staff have been chosen from the best in this country and abroad and the overall result is an hotel which should be a yardstick to others in the category. For those wishing to hold a meeting or large conference in Manchester, the John Logie Baird suite is a modern purpose built conference venue which can split into four sound-proofed venues. The Baskerville Room, overlooking the river, can accommodate up to 60 guests. Elegant lunches and dinners are a speciality of the hotel. Under the guiding hand of executive chef Paul Patterson, each event turns into a gourmet delight. Otherwise two restaurants are available for guests: the *Sherlock Holmes* with two AA rosettes and *Cafe Maigret*, a warm and welcoming French brasserie. Whether on business or pleasure, Le Meridien Victoria and Albert is Manchester's premier venue.

*Rates: Single or double midweek room only from £160; **Special weekend rates** from £115 per night for a twin/double room including English breakfast and VAT.*

● *156 en suite bedrooms (2 for the disabled, 19 executive rooms, 8 lounge suites & 6 rooms in the Ladies' Wing), all fully air-conditioned and with direct dial telephone, tea/coffee making facilities and TV, trouser press, hairdryer, iron + board, 24-hour room service; night service; 2 lifts.*
● *Last orders for dinner Cafe Maigret 10.30 p.m., bar meals; special diets.*
● *Conferences 300 max; hotel shop.*
● *Indoor swimming pool 200 yards; leisure centre; sauna; solarium; small gym, complimentary use of leisure club nearby.*
● *Complimentary valet car parking for all residents.*
● *Open all year. Most major credit cards accepted.*

Piccadilly Station 1, M62 Motorway 2, M65 3, Manchester Airport 10, London 201.

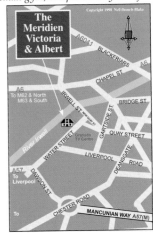

SIGNPOST'S RECOMMENDED BUSINESS TRANSFER AGENT

Yorkshire &
The North East

Historic Houses, Gardens & Parks

Cleveland
Burn Valley Gardens, Hartlepool
Fairy Dell, Middlesbrough
Ormesby Hall, Ormesby, Middlesbrough
Ward Jackson Park, Hartlepool

County Durham
Eggleston Hall Gardens, Eggleston
Hardwick Hall Country Park, Stockton-on-Tees
Houghall Gardens, Durham

East Riding of Yorkshire
Burton Agnes Hall, Driffield
Burton Constable Hall & Country Park, Nr. Hull
Sledmere House, Driffield

Northumberland
Alnwick Castle
Belsay Hall, Castle & Gardens, Belsay
Cragside House & Country Park, Rothbury
Hexham Herbs, Chollerford
Howick Hall Gardens, Alnwick
Hulne Park, Alnwick
Lady Waterford Hall, Berwick on-Tweed
Meldon Park, Morpeth
Otterburn Hall
Paxton House, Berwick on-Tweed
Seaton Delaval Hall, Blyth
Shaw Garden Centre Cramlington
Wallington House Walled Garden & Grounds, Morpeth

Tyne & Wear
Bessie Surtees House, Newcastle-upon-Tyne
Bolam Lake Country Park, Newcastle-upon-Tyne
Kirkley Hall Gardens, Ponteland
Rising Sun Country Park & Countryside Centre, Benton
Saltwell Park, Gateshead

Yorkshire - North, West & South
Allerton Park, Knaresborough
Beningbrough Hall, York
Bramham Park, Wetherby
Burnby Hall Gardens, Pocklington
Castle Howard, Coneysthorpe
Constable Burton Hall Gardens, Leyburn
Duncombe Park, Helmsley
East Riddlesden Hall, Keighley
Epworth Old Rectory, Doncaster
Fairfax House ,York
Golden Acre Park, Bramhope
Harewood House, Leeds
Harlow Carr Botanical Gardens, Harrogate
Japanese Garden, Horsforth
Kiplin Hall Richmond
Land Farm Garden, Hebden Bridge
Lotherton Hall, Leeds
Margaret Waudby Oriental Garden, Upper Poppleton Newburgh Priory, York

Newby Hall Gardens, Ripon
Normanby Hall, Scunthorpe
Nostell Priory, Wakefield
Nunnington Hall, York
Parceval Hall Gardens, Skipton
Ripley Castle, Harrogate
St Nicholas Gardens, Richmond
Sheffield Botanical Gardens
Sheriff Hutton Park, Nr. York
Stockfield Park, Wetherby
Sutton Park, Nr. York
Temple Newsam House, Leeds
Thorp Perrow Arboretum, Bedale

Walks & Nature Trails

Cleveland
Bilingham Beck Valley Country Park

County Durham
Allensford Park, Consett
Blackton Nature Reserve, Teesdale
Derwent Walk, Consett
Durham Coast, Peterlee
Hamsterley Forest, Bishop Auckland

East Riding of Yorkshire
Elsham Hall Country & Wildlife Park, Brigg
Humber Bridge Country Park, Hessle
Normanby Hall Country Park, Scunthorpe

Northumberland
Allen Banks Woods, Hexham
Bedlington Country Park
Carlisle Park & Castle Wood, Morpeth
Fontburn Nature Reserve
Hareshaw Dene, Bellingham, Hexham
Ingram National Park Visitor Centre
Northumberland Coast, Newton-by-the-Sea, Alnwick
Plessey Woods Country Park
Scotch Gill Wood Local Nature Reserve, Morpeth

Tyne & Wear
Derwent Walk Country Park, Rowlands Gill
The Leas & Marsden Rock, S.Shields
Thornley Woodlands Centre, Rowlands Gill

Yorkshire - North, West & South
Anglers Country Park, Wintersett
Barlow Common Nature Reserve, Selby
Bretton Country Park, Wakefield
Bridestones Moor, Pickering
Brimham Rocks, Harrogate
Cannon Hall Country Park, Barnsley
Chevin Forest Park, Otley
Dalby Forest Drive & Visitor Centre, Pickering
Hardcastle Crags, Hebden Bridge
Howstean Gorge, Pateley Bridge
Malham Tarn, Settle
Millington Wood Local Nature Reserve

Marston Moor, Huddersfield
Newmillerdam Country Park,
 Wakefield
Ogden Water, Halifax
Ravenscar Coastline, Scarborough
Rother Valley Country Park,
 Sheffield
Sutton Bank Nature Trail - between
 Helmsley & Thirsk
Ulley Country Park, Sheffield
Worsbrough Country Park, Barnsley

Historical Sites & Museums

Cleveland
Guisborough Priory, Guisborough
Gray Art Gallery & Museum,
 Hartlepool
Guisborough Museum, York
Saltburn Smugglers Heritage Centre
PSS Wingfield Castle, Hartlepool

County Durham
Barnard Castle
Beamish - The North of England
 Open Air Museum
Durham Cathedral
Durham Castle
Raby Castle, Staindrop

East Riding of Yorkshire
Burton Agnes Manor House,
 Driffield
Maister House, Hull
Wilberforce House, Hull

Northumberland
Aydon Castle
Bamburgh Castle
Berwick Castle, Berwick on-Tweed
Brinkburn Priory, Longframlington
Chesters Roman Fort, Hexham
Chillingham Castle
Dunstanburgh Castle
Edlingham Castle
Etal Castle, Etal, Cornhill-on-Tweed
Grace Darling's Museum, Bamburgh
Hadrian's Wall
Hexham Abbey
House of Hardy Museum &
 Country Store, Alnwick
Lindisfarne Castle, Holy Island,
 Berwick-on-Tweed
Marine Life Centre & Fishing
 Museum, Seahouses
Norham Castle, Berwick-on-Tweed
Prudhoe Castle
Warkworth Castle
Wine & Spirit Museum & Victorian
 Chemist Shop, Berwick-on-Tweed

Tyne & Wear
Castle Keep, Newcastle-upon-Tyne
Hatton Gallery, Newcastle-u-Tyne
The Laing Art Gallery, Newcastle-
 upon-Tyne
Newbum Hall Motor Museum,
 Newcastle-upon-Tyne
The Shipley Art Gallery, Gateshead
South Shields Museum, South
 Shields

Yorkshire North, West & South
Aldborough Roman Town, Nr.
 Borougbridge
Assembly Rooms, York
BardenTower, Bolton Abhey
Barley Hall, York
Beverley Minster, Beverley
Bishops House, Sheffield
Bolling Hall, Bradford
Bolton Castle, Leyburn
Borthwick Institute of Historical
 Research, York
Bronte Parsonage Museum, Haworth
Captain Cook Memorial Museum,
 Whitby
Clifford's Tower, York
Dales Countryside Museum, Hawes
Eureka! The Museum for Children,
 Halifax
Fountains Abbey a Studley Royal,
 Ripon
Fulneck Moravian Settlement &
 Museum, Nr. Pudsey
Gainsthorpe Deserted Medieval
 Village
Georgian Theatre Royal &
 Museum, Richmond
Jervaulx Abbey, Ripon
Jorvik Viking Centre & Brass
 Rubbing Centre, York
Kirstall Abbey, Leeds
King's Manor, York
Marmion Tower, Ripon
Mount Grace Priory, Northallerton
National Museum of Photography,
 Film & Television, Bradford
National Railway Museum, York
Red House, Gomerad
Rievalulx Abbey, Rievaulx
Sion Hill Hall & Birds of Prey
 Centre, Kirkby Wiske
Skipton Castle, Skipton
The Old Smithy & Heritage Centre,
 Owston Ferry
Tetleys Brewery Wharf, Leeds
Treasurer's House, York
York Castle Museum, York
York Story, York
York Minster, York

Entertainment Venues

Cleveland
Botanic Centre, Middlesbrough
Cleveland Craft Centre,
 Middlesbrough
Margrove South Cleveland Heritage
 Centre, Boosbeck, Saltburn-by-Sea
Stewart Park, Middlesbrough

County Durham
Bowlees Visitor Centre, Middleton-
 in-Teesdale

East Riding of Yorkshire
Bondville Miniature Village, Sewerby
Fosse Hill Jet Ski Centre, Driffield
Humberside Ice Arena, Hull
Sewerby Hall, Park & Zoo,
 Bridlington

Yorkshire & The North East

Yorkshire &
The North East

Northumberland
Belford Craft Gallery
Tower Knowe Visitor Centre,
Kielder Water, Hexham

Tyne & Wear
Bowes Railway Centre, Gateshead
Predator Paintball, Newcastle-upon-Tyne

Yorkshire North, South & West
Catterick Indoor Ski Centre,
Catterick Garrison
Flamingo Land Family Funpark &
Zoo, Malton
Harrogate Ski Centre, Yorkshire
Showground
Hemsworth Water Park &
Playworld

Hornsea Pottery Leisure Park &
Freeport Shopping Village
Kinderland, Scarborough
Lighwater Valley Theme Park,
North Stainley
North of England Clay Target
Centre, Rufforth
Piece Hall, Halifax
Sheffield Ski Village, Sheffield
The Alan Ayckbourn Theatre in the
Round,Scarborough
Tockwith (Multi-Drive)Activity
Centre, Tockwith Thybergh
Country Park
Turkish Baths, Harrogate
Watersplash World, Scarborough
The World of Holograms,
Scarborough

DIARY OF EVENTS

January

To year 2000. **Leeds Centenary Tapestry.** Victoria Quarter, Briggate, Leeds, W Yorks
9. **Newton Chase**. Haydock Park Racecourse, N Yorks.

February

21.* **Jorvik Viking Festival.** Various venues, York. Viking themed - combat, feasts, fireworks, music etc.
27. **Greenalls Grand National Trial Chase**, Haydock Park.
28. **Northern Classic Restoration Show.** Flower Hall, Gt Yorks Showgr'd, Harrogate

March

6. **Middlesbrough Womens Festival.** Town Hall, Albert Rd, Middlesbrough.
6. **Grimthorpe Handicap Chase.**Doncaster Racecourse
5-21. **Bradford Film Festival.** National Museum of Photography, Pictureville, Bradford.
7. **National Classic Bike Show.** Gt Yorkshire Showground, Harrogate, N Yorks.
8-15. **North Lincs Music &**

Drama Festival. Var. Venues, Brigg, Humberside.
15-20. **Skipton Music Festival.** Town Hall, Skipton, North Yorkshire,
25-27. **Sporting Life Doncaster Mile/Worthington Spring Mile/Lincoln Handicap.** Doncaster Racecourse, South Yorks.
27. **Leeds Doll & Teddy Fair.** Civic Hall, Pudsey, West Yorkshire.

April

5. **Old Custom: World Coal Carrying Championship.** Royal Oak Public House, Ossett, West Yorkshire.
2-9. **Harrogate International Youth Music Festival.** Var. venues, Harrogate.
3-6. **York Model Railway Show.**York Racecourse,York
9-11. **Morpeth Northumbrian Gathering.** Concerts, crafts + , Morpeth, Northumbs
10-11. **Gateshead Spring Flowers Show.** Gateshead Cen Nurseries, Tyne & Wear.
17. **Thirsk Classic Trail**. Race meeting, Thirsk, N Yorks.
23-26. **Spring Flower Show.** Gt Yorkshire Showground, Harrogate, North Yorkshire.
24-26. **Leeds Art Fair.** Corn Exchange, Leeds, W Yorks.
30-May 9. **Bridlington Arts Festival.** Var. venues, Bridlington, ex-Humberside.

Yorkshire & The North East

May

8-22. **Sheffield Chamber Music Festival - Music of the Millenium.** Crucible Studio Theatre, Sheffield.
20/27. **1999 World Cup Full Match Schedule: Pakistan v Scotland/Australia v Bangladesh.** Durham Co Cricket Ground, Chester-le-Street, Co Durham.
23. **Cricket World Cup. Australia v Pakistan.** Yorkshire Co Cricket Club,Headingley, Nr Leeds,West Yorks.
28-June 6. **Scarborough Fayre.** Worldwide Morris & Folk Festival. Var. venues, Scarborough, North Yorks.
28-June 13. **Swaledale Festival.** Rural Arts Festival. Info from Thornborough Hall, Leyburn, N Yorks DL8 5AB.
29-31. **North Shields Fishuay Festival.** Town Centre, N.Shields, Tyne & Wear.
31. **Northumberland County Show.** (agricultural) Overdean Park, Craigton, Northumberland.

June

12-13*. **Durham Regatta.** River Wear, Durham.
19. **Ovingham Goose Fair.** Village Green, Ovingham, Northumbs. Village Fair.
June -July. **Bradford Festival.** Various venues, Bradford, West Yorkshire.
27-July 4. **Alnwick Medieval Fair.** Market Square, Alnwick, Northumberland.
18-July 3. **Grassington Festival.** Town Hall,Grassington, North Yorks.
1-31. **Hull International Festival.** Various venues, Hull, East Yorkshire.

July

3-Aug 8*. **C ookson Country Festival.** Var. venues, South Shields, Tyne & Wear.

9-11. **Whitley Bay Traditional Jazz Festival.** Park Hotel, Grand Parade, Tynemouth.
3-12.**York Early Music Festival.** Various venues, York, North Yorkshire.
17-18. **Durham County Show.** Lambton Park, Durham.
29-Aug 7. **1999 World Veteran Track & Field Championships.** Gateshead Stadium, Neilson Rd,Gateshead
30-Aug 1. **Gateshead Summer Flower Show.** Gateshead Nurseries,Lobley Hill, Gateshead, Tyne & Wear.

August

7-14. **Alnwick Int'l Music & Dance Festival.** Market Square, Alnwick,Northumbs
4-8. **Jazz on the Waterfront.** Hull Jazz Festival, various venues, Hull, E Yorkshire.
6-8. **Saltburn Int'l Festival.** Saltburn-by-the-Sea, Northumbs.
10-17*. **Leeds International Piano Competition.** Theatre Royal, Leeds, West Yorks.
17/18. **Juddmonte/Tote Ebor Stakes.** York Racecourse.
21/30. **St Wilfrid Handicap/ Champion Two Year Olds** Ripon Racecourse, N Yorks.

September

2-5.* **International Sea Shanty Festival.**The Marina & var. venues, Hull, E Yorks
4-5. **Classic Car Show.** Elsecar Heritage Centre, S Yorks
17-19. **Autumn Flower Show.** Gt Yorks Showgrd, Harrogate

October/November

8-16.10. **Hull Fair.** Walton St Fairground, Hull, E. Riding.
16.10. **Leeds Doll & Teddy Fair.** Civic Hall, Pudsey, West Yorks.
10-21.11*. **Hull Literature Festival,** various venues, Hull, E Yorks.

TOURIST BOARDS

For further information, contact:
Yorkshire & Humberside Tourist Board
312 Tadcaster Road
York YO2 2HF.
Tel: (01904) 707961

Northumbria Tourist Board
Aykley Heads, Durham DH1 5UX
Tel: (0191) 375 3000

Northumbria

Northumbria is an undiscovered holiday paradise, where the scenery is wild and beautiful, the beaches golden and unspoiled, and the natives friendly. The region is edged by the North Sea, four national parks and the vast Border Forest Park. Its eastern boundary with the sea is a stunning coastline - stretching 100 miles from Staithes on the border of Cleveland and North Yorkshire to Berwick-on-Tweed, England's most northerly town. In between you'll find as many holiday opportunities here as changes of scenery. There's a wonderful variety of seascapes, from Cleveland's towering cliffs to the shimmering white sands of Northumberland, where you can lose yourself in the dunes. Inland you will find the remarkable Hadrian's Wall, the National Park, hills, forests, waterfalls, castles, splendid churches and quaint towns and villages. Northumbria combines the fun of a seaside holiday with the relaxation of a break in the country.

History books come alive in Northumberland and exploring its heritage could take a lifetime. In the far north, Berwick-on-Tweed (fought over by the English and Scots for centuries) is steeped in history and has the finest preserved example of Elizabethan town walls in the country. The town is an ideal gateway to the Borders. Visitors can trace man's occupation of the region from prehistoric times to the Victorian age of invention. Prehistoric rock carvings, ancient hill forts, Roman remains, Saxon churches, Norman priories, medieval castles and a wealth of industrial archaeology can all be discovered here.

The region has a rich maritime heritage too. Imposing ruins, such as the gaunt remains of Dunstanburgh or fairy-tale Lindisfarne, are relics of a turbulent era when hordes of invaders landed on Northumberland's shores. Of course you don't have to explore castles and museums to capture the maritime flavour. Instead laze on a beach, fish from the end of the pier or take a trip from the fishing village of Seahouses, Northumberland, to the Farne Islands - a marvellous bird sanctuary and breeding ground of the Atlantic Grey Seal.

Lovers of the great outdoors will find Northumbria a paradise. In the National Park, where sheep outnumber people, the views will take your breath away. It is possible to enjoy the splendours of this area by car, but the remote hills are for the walker. Some of the wildest, highest and most beautiful scenery in England can be seen in the North Pennines. The noisiest thing in this peaceful refuge is the dramatic waterfall High Force! You'll pass through pretty villages such as Cotherstone in Teesdale, St John's Chapel in Weardale and Blanchland in Northumberland.

Holy Island. Photo - Northumbria Tourist Board

Searchers for activity will find the perfect base here also. Hike it, bike it, watch it - whatever your sport, you can do it in Northumbria. The countryside is ideal for pony trekking, walking, climbing, ballooning, orienteering, cycling, fishing, watersports and golf. Some hotels offer activity packages, such as golf or fishing weekends. More traditional local sports such as *hound trailing* and *Cumberland Wrestling* can be found at agricultural shows.

Naturally with so much countryside, agriculture is one of the region's most important industries. A super place to take children is Heatherslaw Mill, near Ford (a delightful model village), a restored water-driven corn mill and agricultural museum. If you were a fan of the television series *One Man and His Dog*, then the skill of shepherd and dog can be seen at sheepdog trials and country shows.

The ancient crafts and customs of Northumbria provide a fascinating insight into the character of this lovely region. It is said that fact can be stranger than fiction, and you'll have fun exploring some of the local myths, from the tiny island of Lindisfarne to the church in the pretty village of Kirknewton, close to the Cheviots, where the sculptured *Adoration of the Magi* depicts the Wise Men wearing kilts!

A less well known feature of the region is that is has one of the liveliest arts scenes outside London. The Theatre Royal, Newcastle, is the third home of the Royal Shakespeare Company and a venue for other major touring companies. Throughout the region you can enjoy first class entertainment from open air Shakespeare to costumed pageants; from the Royal Ballet to Rock N Roll, from Mozart to music hall.

Warkworth Castle. Photo - Northumbria Tourist Board

Wherever you go, from the traditional pub in a tiny village to a top class hotel, you'll always find a warm welcome. The region is well served by trunk roads, high speed trains and airports. Please contact the Northumbria Tourist Board, address on previous page, for details.

Waren House Hotel

Waren Mill, Belford, Northumberland
NE70 7EE
Tel: (01668) 214581; Fax: (01668) 214484
Internet: http://warenhousehotel.co.uk

After battling with the traffic on the A1, a sign points the way to Waren Mill. Follow two miles of peaceful roads and the tree-lined drive welcomes you to the house. Having been quietly shown to your room, perhaps you will complete the unwinding process by enjoying a hot tub in your superb bathroom. Throughout the hotel, the furnishings, mostly antiques and collectables, together with the immaculate and well chosen décor, exude a warm and friendly atmosphere. But this is not all for Waren House is a haven for the gastronome. Delicious repasts are tastefully presented, accompanied by a thoughtfully chosen wine list with a large selection of half bottles. Discreet service completes the air of peace and well-being. Anita and Peter Laverack are continually finding ways to improve this delightful hotel. The latest addition is a new wing for the business traveller. Here the quality of furnishing is equal to that of the main house but the rooms are simpler and more modern. The views from the hotel are some of the finest in the North-East. Waren House is a splendid centre from which to explore the rich diversity of local history and wildlife.

Rates: Single room and breakfast from £57.50; double room inc. breakfast from £115. **Ⅴ**
Bargain Breaks: 2 nights - 4-course dinner, room & breakfast from £149 per person standard room. For stay of 7+ nights, free upgrade standard→ superior/superior→suite.

● *10 en suite bedrooms (inc 2 suites), all with direct dial telephone, colour TV; hairdryer, tea/coffee making facilities, trouser press. Non-smoker bedrooms available. Car parking for 15.*
● *Table d'hôte dinner £25; special diets available. Last orders 2030.*
● *Business services inc meeting room to 20. Children over 14 welcome; dogs accepted; conferences (boardroom) 20 max/(theatre) 30 max.*
● *Sea/river bathing, watersports. Tennis and golf 2 miles; riding ¹/₂ mile.*
● *Open all year; major credit cards accepted.*

Berwick 14, Alnwick 14, Newcastle 45, London 350.

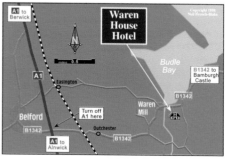

Aldwark Manor Hotel, Golf & Country Club

Aldwark, Nr. Alne, York YO6 2NF
Tel: (01347) 838146; Fax: (01347) 838867

Under new ownership, Aldwark Manor is a splendid 19th century country house hotel set in beautiful Yorkshire parkland and with its own 18-hole par 71 golf course. The 1671 yard course consists of two nine-hole loops linked by an 180-ft bridge over the river Ure. The residence was commissioned in 1865 by Lord Walsingham as a wedding present for his eldest daughter. With comfortable bedrooms, large well furnished public rooms and the Rendlesham restaurant in which good food and fine wines are assured, this is a place where for hedonistic relaxation. It is also a good centre for visiting the best sites of Yorkshire - Beningborough Hall, Newby Hall, Castle Howard, the fashionable spa town of Harrogate and one of the six racecourses which are nearby. Apart from the extensive grounds where I found it beneficial to walk after a gastronomic feast, the Vale of York, the Yorkshire Dales and North Yorks Moors are all within an easy drive and York city itself is only a few miles away.

Rates: Single room with breakfast from £55; double room with breakfast from £110.
Leisure Breaks: Golf Break mid-week £130 pp, weekend £150 2 nights+. Yorkshire Break midweek £95 pp/weekend £110 pp 2 nights+.

● *28 en suite bedrooms (inc one suite), all with direct-dial telephone, colour TV; hairdryer, laundry service, tea/coffee making facilities, 24-hour room service. Non-smoker bedrooms available.*
● *Last dinner orders 2130; lunch, bar meals, special diets available.*
● *Airport pickup by arrangement. Conferences to 80.*
● *Own 18-hole golf course. Fishing, riding by arrangement. Hair salon. Car parking for 80 cars.*
● *Open all year. All major credit cards accepted.*
Easingwold 3, Boroughbridge 7, Thirsk 12, York 14, London 212.

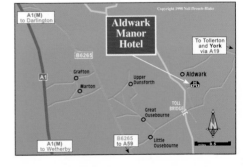

The Balmoral Hotel

Franklin Mount, Harrogate,
North Yorkshire HGl 5EJ
Tel: (01423) 508208; Fax: (01423) 530652
E-mail: info@balmoralhotel.co.uk
Internet: http://www.balmoralhotel.co.uk

What a delightful surprise it was to discover this superb hotel! It is situated in its own award winning gardens, away from the centre of town and yet within walking distance of all the amenities that Harrogate provides - conference centre, shops and wonderful surrounding countryside. The Balmoral is unique - beautifully furnished, mostly with antiques and tastefully decorated to create a warm, luxurious and welcoming atmosphere. The bedrooms are all individual, many having four poster beds and again are extremely comfortable with thoughtfully chosen décor. Everything that you could possibly need is provided and to stay in one of these rooms is an experience in luxury. The food in Villutoots Restaurant is not only imaginative but is prepared from the finest ingredients, cooked to perfection and served by friendly and attentive staff. E.T.B. ≈≈≈≈ Highly Commended.

Rates: Room and breakfast from £70.00 single, **V** *£85.00 double and weekly rates on application.* **Short breaks** *are also available throughout the year as are pampering and relaxing Spa breaks.*

● *20 en suite bedrooms (10 four poster rooms), all with direct dial telephone and TV; room service; baby listening; night porter.*
● *Last orders for dinner 10 p.m.; lunch 12-2; special diets available.*
● *Children welcome; dogs accepted.*
● *Solarium; indoor heated swimming pool and leisure facilities 100 yards away; 4 golf courses and riding stables nearby; tennis by arrangement*
● *Open all year; major credit cards accepted.*

Yorkshire Dales 15, Leeds/Bradford Airport 18, York 20, London 200.

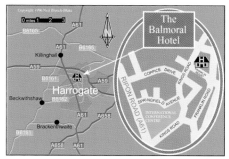

Stone House Hotel

Sedbusk, Hawes, North Yorkshire
DL8 3PT
Tel: (01969) 667571; Fax: (01969) 667720
E-mail: daleshotel@aol.com

A country house hotel should ideally provide
warmth and comfort, personal service, excellent food and outstanding surroundings. Here
at Stone House, you are cosseted by all this
and much more. The owners, the young and
forward looking Taplin family have a policy
of continuous updating and refurbishment
and take pride in their concern for the comfort
and welfare of their guests. They share their
own interests in such things as a collection of
Dinky Toys, antique thimbles and teapots
and they willingly guide people on what to
do and see in the vicinity. Their food, using
ingredients of the highest quality, is delicious
and accompanied by wines from a well chosen list. All this is provided in a lovely building situated high up in a secluded position
with spectacular views of the Pennines and
surrounded by an old English garden. Quiet
and secluded, Stone House is the perfect
centre for touring historic Wensleydale and
James Herriot country.

Rates: *Single room with breakfast from £35.* **V**
Double room including breakfast from £60.
Bargain Breaks: *Min 2-night stay October to
end-April approx. £49 per person per night.*

● *22 en suite bedrooms (inc. 5 suites), all with
radio & colour TV, direct-dial telephone, tea/coffee
making facilities, hairdryer, laundry service, safety
deposit box, trouser press. Disabled & non-smoker
bedrooms available. Car parking for 30.*
● *Table d'hôte dinner £17.50; special diets available; last orders 8 pm. Packed lunches on request.*
● *Billiards/snooker, croquet, tennis, walking. Fishing & riding locally. Conferences hire off-season.*
● *Open all year. Mastercard & Visa accepted.*

**Leyburn 16, Brough 21, Kendal 26, Skipton
36, London 250.**

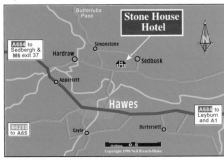

Feversham Arms Hotel

Helmsley, North Yorkshire YO6 5AG
Tel: (01439) 770766; Fax: (01439) 770346

Originally a coaching inn where candles and
beer were made and sold, this hotel has been
elegantly modernised and improved to a high
standard. The bedrooms, intimate rather than
large, are individually decorated and well
appointed with every modern convenience.
The reception rooms are relaxing and there is
an all-round friendly and welcoming atmosphere. The award winning candlelit Goya
restaurant displays a very comprehensive
menu including seafood, shellfish and some
game specialities and the awarded wine list is
excellent. The extensive bar snack menu includes shellfish specialities and, on a hot day,
a meal on the beautiful patio by the swimming pool is my idea of heaven. Helmsley is
an excellent centre for sporting activities, for
visiting historical buildings, abbeys and
stately homes and for exploring the unique
North York Moors National Park.

*Rates: Room & breakfast £55 single, £65 execu-
tive single, £80 twin/double, £90 four-poster or
suite. "**Bonanza Breaks**" available all year round.*

● *18 en suite bedrooms (6 ground floor, 5 four-
posters), all with hairdryer, trouser press, tea/
coffee making facilities, safe, radio, direct-dial
telephone, TV + satellite, full central heating.*
● *Last dinner orders 9 p.m.; bar snacks.*
● *Children welcome; baby listening; dogs wel-
come; conferences up to 30 (18 residential).*
● *Swimming pool; patio; tennis court and gar-
dens in hotel grounds; riding and golf nearby.*
● *Open all year (Check Christmas opening). Visa,
Amex, Mastercard and Diners cards accepted.*
Thirsk 14, York 20, Teeside Airport 35, London 222.

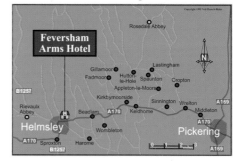

The Pheasant

Harome, Helmsley, N. Yorkshire YO62 5JG
Tel: (01439 771241; Fax: (01439) 771744

The Pheasant was recommended to me by
another hotelier of note in Yorkshire and how
right he was. Set in a pretty village, overlooking the village pond, it has been imaginatively
created from a group of buildings on two
sides of a courtyard. Inside, the log fires, the
antiques and the numerous beams lend an air
of warmth and comfort to the tastefully decorated rooms. Old fashioned in atmosphere the
hotel might be, but the best of all modern
amenities are also there. Mrs 'Tricia Binks
provides the most delicious food and many of
the ingredients come from the hotel's own
large garden and paddock. Holly Cottage is
also available - this is a charming, thatched
16th century cottage just 350 yards from the
hotel, with two double bedrooms and two
sitting rooms, all attractively furnished to the
same high standard as the hotel. It is serviced
by the hotel staff and meals are taken in the
hotel. A quiet and peaceful haven with a delightful atmosphere. Having said all this, The
Pheasant makes an ideal base from which to
explore this most beautiful part of England,
where there is so much to see and do.
  Rates: Dinner, room and breakfast from £57.50

*(1st Nov-mid-May); £59.50-£67.00 (high season)
per person per day including VAT.*

● *14 en suite bedrooms (1 ground floor), all with
telephone, colour TV, tea/coffee making facilities;
full central heating.*
● *Last orders 8.00 p.m; bar meals (lunch); diets.*
● *Children over 14 welcome; dogs by arrangement; conferences max. 12.*
● *Own heated indoor swimming pool; golf, tennis,
riding, fishing all nearby.*
● *Closed January and February. Major credit
cards accepted.*

**Helmsley 3, York 22, Scarborough 28, Leeds
48, Edinburgh 160, London 220.**

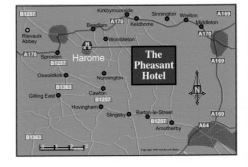

Lastingham Grange

Lastingham, Nr. Kirkbymoorside,
York YO62 6TH
Tel: (01751) 417345 / 417402;
Fax: (01751) 417358

You can discover this delightfully situated, elegant country house by leaving the A170 at Kirkbymoorside and making for Hutton-le-Hole. The Grange is stone-walled and built round a courtyard. It is set within 10 acres of well-kept gardens and fields, on the edge of the moors, in the historic village of Lastingham, a peaceful backwater in the heart of the National Park. Lastingham Grange is owned and personally run by Mr. and Mrs. Dennis Wood. The atmosphere, even during the height of the season, is unhurried and peaceful, the south-facing terrace providing a pleasant setting in which to relax and enjoy the beautiful rose garden, noted for the variety and rarity of its many flowering shrubs and trees. The spacious and homely lounge, with its open fire, and the comfortable bedrooms with their impressive views, are all tastefully furnished. The food is excellent - speedily and cheerfully served.

Rates: Room and breakfast from £79.00 single; £149.00 double. Short breaks available. **V**
Bargain breaks: Dinner, bed & breakfast from £94.50 for 2 days or more; £89.50 one week or more, per person per night.

● *12 en suite bedrooms, all with bath and shower; direct-dial telephone, trouser press, hairdryer.*
● *Table d'hôte dinner £25.50; lunch & special diets available; last orders 8.30 pm.*
● *Children welcome; baby listening in all rooms; drying room; diets.*
● *Golf five miles; riding four miles.*
● *Open March to the beginning of December.*
● *Credit cards not accepted.*

Malton 15, Scarborough 24, Thirsk 24, Whitby 26, York 33, London 232.

The Judges Lodging Hotel

9 Lendal, York, North Yorkshire
YO1 2AQ
Tel: (01904) 638733; Fax: (01904) 679947

Imagine yourself in York in the early 18th
century. You are arriving at your grand house
in the city centre. There is a glow from the
windows and the servants await you. Now,
retaining that ambience in your mind, transport yourself to the present day; add the comforts that we have all come to expect, and you
will begin to sense the flavour of a stay at The
Judges Lodging. The house has retained its
original plan and atmosphere, and yet has
been cleverly transformed into a small, warm
and intimate hotel. The furnishings and décor
are beautifully in keeping with the building.
There is a new brasserie and rooftop terrace,
serving delicious food with a wine list to suit
all palates and also a new residents' bar and
lounge. Now, when you visit York, you can
not only see all the historical sites, such as the
Minster, the Jorvik Viking Centre and the
National Railway Museum, but also stay in
one of the most historic houses in the city. A
good base for exploring the many houses and
abbeys in which Yorkshire abounds and the
wild, exciting Yorkshire Moors.

*Rates: Single room with breakfast from £75.00;
double from £100 inc. VAT.* **V**
Bargain Breaks: *Stay for 3 consecutive nights
(inc. a Sunday) and receive 3rd night's accomm.
at half price from November-February inclusive.*

● *15 en suite bedrooms with satellite TV, direct-
dial telephone, hairdryer, laundry service, radio/
alarm clock, tea/coffee making facilities.*
● *Dinner offer - guests may take a 15% discount
on food from the evening à la carte menu. Lunch,
diets available. Last orders 10 pm. Public bar,
residents's bar & lounge.*
● *Car parking. Children over 10 welcome.*
● *Open all year. All major credit cards + Switch.*
● *Boating 200 yds; 4 golf courses within 5 miles.*
**Leeds 24, Manchester 72, Edinburgh 192,
London 209.**

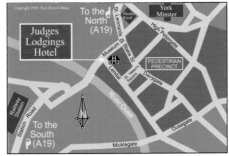

Wales

Llynnau Cregennen

Mid Wales is a land of dramatic contrasts in which youcan enjoy the considerable pleasures of both coast and countryside. It is an area of immense natural beauty with a wide variety of scenery, each season bringing its own particular enhancement. With well over half the Snowdonia National Park lying in Mid Wales, some of the beauty is unsurpassed.The region has high mountains with breathtaking views, large attractive lakes and rambling green hills.

There is no more relaxing way of enjoying nature's wonders than on horseback. Both the regular rider and novice will find superb pony trekking country. An alternative means of seeing the countryside is by taking a ride on one of the Great Little Trains. When various industries began to develop in Mid Wales, a need for transport arose. This demand was met by a network of small railways. There are five such narrow gauge railways, most of them dating back to the last century, operating in the region - now making Mid Wales a must for all steam enthusiasts. Throughout Mid Wales a network of well surfaced roads lead towards remote uplands, winding along the contours of the slopes. These are the Cambrian 'mountains, Wales' magnificent backbone, the upland region where hamlets and farms nestle into the folds of seemingly endless hills. In this area farming life is centred around a series of small towns which often stand at an important crossroads or a ford in the river. They are linked by splendidly scenic mountain roads or old drovers' ways along which cattle were once driven to market. Llanidoes, with its 16th century market hall built of stout timber, stands almost at the centre of Wales, and at the confluence of the Severn and Clywedog Rivers.

In Mid Wales life inland revolves around the historic market towns and the old spa centres, while the coastline is punctuated by small fishing villages and popular seaside resorts. The western districts are strongholds of Welsh culture where the language is in everyday use.

The west of the region has over a hundred miles of coastline. Expansive, sandy beaches, spectacular estuaries and rugged cliffs leading down to secluded coves make this an ideal area for a holiday. It is not surprising to discover that Mid Wales has always had a seafaring tradition. In bygone days schooners sailed all over the world from the little ports of Aberaeron, Aberdyfi, Aberystwyth, Barmouth and New Quay.

The harbours are still bustling and active but with a different type of craft.

To the East are the Welsh Marches with their traditional half-timbered black and white buildings. Despite being so close to England, the borderlands of Powys maintain much of their Welsh character and tradition. Many centuries ago this area was governed by the Marcher Lords on behalf of the king. Further back in time, Offa, an 8th century Saxon king, built a massive dyke to keep marauding Welsh forces out of his kingdom. Traces of these large earthworks can be seen along the border, forming the basis of the Offa's Dyke Trail, a long distance walkway of 168 miles. At Knighton a special Heritage Centre illustrates the significance of the Dyke.

The whole of Mid Wales has a colourful and exciting history and this is reflected in the many ancient buildings and other monuments which are to be seen. The struggle to keep Wales independent from the influence of numerous invaders has been a constant theme throughout history. This is evident in ruined castles such as Harlech Castle and Castell-y-Bere. Powys Castle, the home of "Clive of India" is on the other hand beautifully maintained, together with its outstanding gardens. Other popular attractions are the industries which reflect the Welsh rural life. These small industries such as woollen weaving in traditional patterns, pottery, and craft work, reflect a harmonious bond between people and environment which is typical of Mid Wales.

For those wishing to learn more
Ffestiniog Railway of the area's history there are a number of museums and interpretative centres in the region. Historical artifacts can be seen at displays in Llandrindod Wells, Llanidoes, Machynlleth, Aberystwyth, Tre'r Ddol, Newtown and Welshpool. At Llandrindod Wells a display on the *Spas of Wales* has been opened. There is also an opportunity to "take the water" in the original Pump Room, refurbished in the Edwardian style.

North Wales has been attracting holiday visitors for over two hundred years, - Wordsworth, Samuel Johnson, Turner, Nelson, George Burrows, Bismarck and Wellington have all come to the area. Nowadays we still attract artists, poets, politicians and sailors but the range of accommodation and attractions make North Wales a perfect venue, whatever your choice of holiday.

Our hotels, restaurants and inns are continually improving their standards and now compare with the best in Britain; added to this we have the unfair advantage of some of the most impressive scenery in the world. Snowdonia is justly famous for its magnificent mountains, lakes and forests, but the Hiraethog Mountains in the North East, the Berwyns, south of Llangollen and the beautiful river valleys of the Conwy, Clwyd, Dee and Glaslyn have a magic of their own. The variety of the scenery is what impresses first time visitors. Within six miles of Llandudno - our largest resort - you can find the peace of the Carneddau, one hundred square miles of beautiful mountain moorland, dotted with Neolithic trackways, standing stones, bronze age sites and beautiful lakes, without a single road crossing it (except the old Roman road from Caerhun to Carnarfon).

The past surrounds you in North Wales. You can trace the history of man in these parts from the Neolithic tombs of 6,000 years ago, to the Iron Age hill forts that were inhabited when the Roman legions came, then through the cells and abbeys of the early Celtic church to the Nonconformist chapels of the 19th century so admired by Sir John Betjeman.

The 12th century Welsh castles and 13th century castles of the Plantagenets reflect a more turbulent time, but what masterpieces of military architecture they left us - Conwy, Carnarfon, Rhuddlan, and Beaumaris are breathtaking in their size and splendour, while the Welsh keeps of Dolwyddelan, Dinas Bran and Dolbadarn will appeal to more romantic souls. Medieval towns such as Conwy and Ruthin, the splendid Elizabethan and Jacobean farmhouses and the tiny country cottages show the ordinary side of life in the 16th, 17th and 18th centuries. The Industrial Revolution brought changes to North Wales, most of which are now featured in our tourist trade. Slate was the major industry; now you can explore the slate caverns at Blaenau Ffestiniog or Glyn Ceiriog or see the Quarry Museum at Llanberis. Most of the Great Little Trains of Wales were first used to carry slate from the mines to the harbours, the one notable exception being the Snowdon Mountain Railway.

As soon as you cross the border into Wales, the look of the countryside changes, the road signs seem unpronounceable and you are met by warm hospitable people. The language, music and heritage of Wales add a special dimension to a holiday in our wonderful country. *Croeso* is the word for Welcome - you will hear it often.

Cardiff, Wales' capital is essentially a young city, even 'though its history dates back many centuries. The development of its docks during the Industrial Revolution for the export of Welsh iron and coal was the basis of its prosperity. Cardiff Castle is part Roman fort, part medieval castle and part 19th-century mansion. Its Chaucer Room has stained glass windows depicting The Canterbury Tales. Its Summer Smoking Room has a copper, brass and silver inlaid floor. The castle is the present home of the Welsh Assembly. The National Museum of Wales houses a wealth of exhibits, from impressionist paintings to examples of Swansea porcelain. To the East, near Newport is Caerleon. which was the site of the Roman fortress of Isca, built in AD75. Further East, on the Monmouth-Chepstow road is Tintern Abbey, one of the finest relics of Britain's monastic age. It was founded in the 12th century by Cistercian monks, rebuilt in the 13th-century and sacked by Henry VIII during the Dissolution of the Monasteries. Offa's Dyke, part of an 168-mile rampart built by King Offa of Mercia in the 8th century to keep the Welsh out, and now a noted walk, runs past Tintern's portals. To the northwest of Cardiff is the late 19th-century Castell Coch (Red Castle), a mixture of Victorian Gothic and fairytale styles. Well preserved is 13th-century Caerphilly Castle, with its famous leaning tower.

Further West, outside Port Talbot, the visitor comes to Margam Country Park, 850 acres including an Iron Age hill fort, a restored abbey church with windows by William Morris, Margram Stones Museum with stones and crosses dating from the 5th-11th centuries and the main house with its 327-ft long orangery.

Threecliff Bay

The Gower Peninsula, west of Swansea is a secluded world of its own, with limestone cliffs, remote bays and miles of golden sands. It is the 'Riviera' of South Wales. Sites not to miss here include the late 13th-century Weobley Castle, the ruins of Threecliff Bay and Gower Farm Museum with its 100-yr old farm memorabilia. Near Carmarthen is Dylan Thomas' village of Laugharne, in whose churchyard he is buried. The rugged Pembroke coast is guarded on its Western rim by Britain's smallest city - St David's, whose cathedral was founded by the eponymous saint in the 8th century, although the present building is believed to date from the 12th century.

Wales

Historic Houses, Gardens & Parks

Aberconwy & Colwyn
Chirk Castle, Bodelwyddan
Bodrhyddan Hall, Rhuddlan
Bodnant Garden, Tal-y-Cafn
Colwyn Leisure Centre

Anglesey
Plas Newydd, Llanfairpwll

Glamorgan
Castell Cochi, Tongwynlais, Cardiff
Cosmeston Lakes Country Park &
 Medieval Village
Dyffryn House & Gardens, St.
 Nicholas, Nr. Cardiff   Llanerch
Vineyard, Pendoylan

Gwynedd
Bryn Bras Castle, Llanrug, Nr.
 Llanberis
Parc Glynllifon, Nr. Caernarfon
'Y Stablau', Gwydyr Forest Park,
 Llanrwst

Monmouthshire
Bryn Bach Park, Tredegar
Caldicot Castle & Country Park, Nr.
 Newport
Llandegfedd Reservolr, Pontypool
Tredegar House, Newport

Neath & Port Talbot
Margam Park, Port Talbot

Pembrokeshire
Manor House Wildlife & Leisure
 Park, Tenby
Tudor Merchant's House, Quay Hill,
 Tenby

Wrexham
Erddig Hall, Wrexham

Walks & Nature Trails

Aberconwy & Colwyn
Llyn Brenig Visitor Centre, Corwen

Anglesey
Bryntirion Open Farm, Dwyran
South Stack Cliffs Reserve & Elfins
Tower Information Centre,Holyhead

Blaenau Gwent
Festival Park, Ebbw Vale

Carmarthenshire
Gelli Aur Countly Park, Llandeilo

Flintshire
Greenfield Valley Heritage Park,
 Holywell
Logger Heads Country Park, Nr
 Mold

Gwynedd
Coed-y-Brenin Forest Park & Visitor
 Centre, Ganllwyd, Dolgellau
The Greenwood Centre, Port
 Dinorwic

Parc Padarn, Llanberis
Tyn Llan Crafts & Farm Museum,
 Nr. Porthmadog

Merthyr Tydfil
Garwnant Visitor Centre, Cwm Taf

Neath & Port Talbot
Alan Forest Park & Countryside
 Centre, Port Talbot
Gnoll Country Park, Neath

Pembrokeshire
Bwlch Nant Yr Arian Forest Visitor
 Centre, Ponterwyd
Llysyfran Reservoir & Country
 Park, Nr. Haverfordwest
Pembrey Country Park, Pembrey

Powys
Brecon Beacons Mountain Centre,
 Nr. Libanus
Gigrin Farm & Nature Trail,
 Rhyader
Lake Vyrnwy RSPB Reserve &
 Information Centre
Ynys-Hir Reserve & Visitor Cenne,
 Machynlleth

Vale of Glamorgan
Bryngarw Country Park, Nr.
 Bridgend

Wrexham
Ty Mawr Country Park, Cefn Mawr

Historical Sites & Museums

Aberconwy & Colwyn
Bodelwyddan Castle
Carreg Cennen Castle, Trapp,
 Llangollen
Denbigh Castle
Valle Crucis Abbey, Llangollen

Cardiganshire
Museum of the Welsh Woollen
 Industry, Llandysul

Carmarthenshire
Castell Henllys Iron Age Hillfort,
 Crymych

Flintshire
Flint Castle & Twon Walls
Rhuddlan Castle, Nr. Rhyl

Glamorgan
Aberdulair Falls, Vale of Neath,
 Neath
Caerphilly Castle
Cardiff Castle
Castell Coch, Cardiff
Cefn Coed Colliery Museum,
 Crynant, Neath
National Museum of Wales
Welsh Folk Museum,Cardiff

Gwynedd
Beaumaris Castle
Caernarfon Castle
Conwy Castle

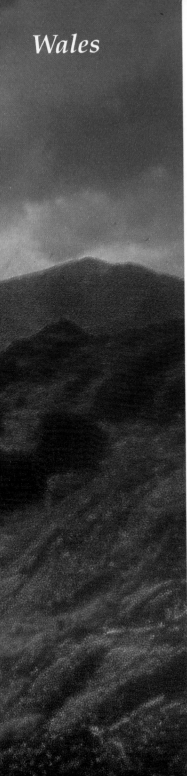

Wales

Cymer Abbey, Dolgellau
Dolbadarn Castle, Llanberis
Dolwyddelan Castle
Harlech Castle
Llanfair Slate Caverns, Nr. Harlech
The Lloyd George Museum,
 Llanystumdwy, Criccieth
Penrhyn Castle, Bangor

Monmouthshire
Chepstow Castle, Chepstow
The Nelson Museum & Local His
 tory Centre
Penhow Castle, Nr. Newport
Raglan Castle
Tintern Abbey, Tintern

Pembrokeshire
Castle Museum & Art Gallery,
 Haverfordwest
Kidwelly Castle
Manorbier Castle, Nr. Tenby
Milford Haven Museum, The
 Docks, Milford Haven
Picton Castle, Haverfordwest
Pembroke Castle
St Davids Bishop's Palace

Powys
Powys Castle & Museum,
 Welshpool
Tretower Court & Castle,
 Crickhowell

Entertainment Venues

Aberconwy & Colwyn
Felin Isaf Water Mill, Glan Conwy
Llyn Brenig Visitor Centre,
 Cerrigydrudion

Anglesey
Anglesey Bird World, Dwyran/Sea
 Zoo, Brynsiencyn

Cardiganshire
James Pringle Weavers of Llanfair
 P.G.
The Llywenog Silver-Lead Mines,
 Nr Aberystwyth

Flintshire
Afonwen Craft & Antique Centre,
 Nr. Mold

Gwynedd
Alice in Wonderland Visitor Centre,
 Llandudno
Butlins Starcoast World, Pwllheli
Ffestiniog Railway, Porthmadog
Maes Artro Tourist Village Llanbedr
Penmachno Woollen Mill, Nr.
 Betws-y-Coed
Portmeirion Village, Nr.
 Porthmadog
Sygun Copper Mine, Beddgelert
Snowdon Mountain Railway,
 Llamberis
Trefriw Woollen Mills, Trefriw
Welsh Gold, Dolgellau
Welsh Highland Railway,
 Porthmadog

Neath & Port Talbot
Margam Park, Port Talbot
Penscynor Wildlife Park, Cilfrew,
 Nr. Neath

Pembrokeshire
Oakwood Park Theme Park,
 Narberth

Powys
Dan-yr-Ogof Showcaves, Abercraf
Welshpool & Llanfair Light Railway
Welsh Whisky Visitor Centre,
 Brecon

Rhondda Cynnon Taf
Rhondda Heritage Park

DIARY OF EVENTS

*Denotes provisional date.

January

10 Dec-Feb 27*. **Welsh National Opera Spring Season** New Theatre, Cardiff.

February

26-28*. **Portmerion Antiques Fair,** Hercules Hall, Porthmeirion, Gwynedd.
26-27*. **Celtic Festival.** Rhondda Heritage Park, Trehafod.

March

1*. **St Davids Day Concert.** BBC Nat Orch of Wales, St David's Hall, Cardiff.

April

5. **Welsh Champion Hurdle.** Chepstow, Monmouthshire.

May

8/11/20. **Cricket World Cup Warm-up. Glamorgan v Australia/Glamorgan v Kenya/ Australia v New Zealand.** Glamorgan Co Cricket Grnd, Sophia Gardens, Cardiff.

June

3*. **Llangollen Choral Festival.** Royal Intl Pavilion, Llangollen. N Wales largest massed male voice festival.
6-12. **Cardiff Singer of the World Competition.** St David's Hall, Cardiff
19-24*. **Three Peaks Yacht Race: Barmouth to Fort William.** The Quay, Barmouth, Gwynedd.
22-27*. **Int'l Animation Festival.** St David's Hall, Cardiff.
25-27*. **Gwylifan Welsh Folk & Dancing Festival.** Various locations in Cardiff and surrounding areas

July

6-11. **Llangollen International Music Eisteddfod.** The Pavilion, Llangollen, Denbighshire. 53rd festival.
19-22. **Royal Welsh Show.**
Showground, Llenelwedd, Builth Wells. Wales' Premier Agricultural Show.
21-28*. **Ian Rush International Soccer Tournament.** Playing Fields, Llanbadarn Fawr, Aberystwyth, Cardigans
24-31*. **Fishguard Music Festival.** Various venues.
31-Aug 7. **National Eisteddfod of Wales.** Sir Ffon, Anglesey.

August

1*.**Gower Agricultural Show.** Fairwood Airport, Swansea
1*. **Brecon County Show.** The Showground, Brecon.
6-8*. **Brecon Jazz Festival.** Var's venues, Brecon, Powys.
7*. **Chepstow Agricultural Show.** Howick, Nr Chepstow, Monmouthshire.
12-13*. **United Counties Show,** Carmarthen.
14-22*. **Llandrindod Wells Victoria Festival.** Various venues in and around Llandrindod Wells, Powys
17-19*. **Pembrokeshire County Show.** Showground, Haverfordwest.

September

3-12* **Barmouth Arts Festival** Dragon Theatre, Barm'th 25th annual arts festival.

October

1. **50th South Wales Miners' Eisteddfod.** Grand Pavilion, Porthcawl, S Glam
2. **Free Hurdle Race Meeting.** Chepstow, Monmouths
30-Nov 1. **38th Portmeirion Antiques Fair.**Hercules Hall Portmeirion, Gwynedd

November

1-23 Dec. **Rugby World Cup Festival.** In & around Cardiff City Centre.
6. **Rugby Union World Cup Final.** New National Stadium, Cardiff, S Glamorgan.
6. **Tote Silver Trophy Hurdle.** Chepstow, Monmouths
12-21. **Welsh International Film Festival.** Various venues in Aberystwyth,Cards.

December

28. **Coral Welsh National Chase.**Chepstow,Monmouths.

For further information contact:
Wales Tourist Board
Brunel House, 2 Fitzalan Road, Cardiff CF2 lUY.
Tel: 01222 499909

Pembrokeshire Hotels - Haverfordwest

Stone Hall

Welsh Hook, Wolfscastle, Haverfordwest, Pembrokeshire SA62 5NS. Tel: (01348) 840212; Fax: (01348) 840815

Built around a 600-yr old manor house, Stone Hall is surrounded by 10 acres of gardens and woodland in stunning countryside. The style is a blend of elegance and country cottage. Hosts Alan and Martine Watson share their home with their guests and their many cats! There are no telephones in bedrooms, which is refreshing, but lovely antiques and pictures. Cuisine is French-orientated and breakfast is taken around a communal table. A happy retreat where you will enjoy being pampered.

Rates: Single inc breakfast from £48; double from £70. Major credit cards accepted. Open all year. Ⓥ
Bargain Breaks: 2-days dinner, b&b from £102 pp

● *5 rooms, all en suite, with TV, hairdryer, tea/ coffee making.* ● *Meeting room 30. Car parking 50.*
● *Fishing 300 yds. Golf, riding 3/6 miles respectively*

St. Mellons Country Club, Monmouth
(*At the Blue Horizon*).

ADJOINING THE MAIN CARDIFF-NEWPORT ROAD
6 Miles from Cardiff and 6 miles from Newport.
(For position see map on page 17, *square H.2).*

Georgian country house in beautiful 200 acre estate with 18-hole golf course and aeroplane landing ground in course of construction— Hard and grass tennis courts, indoor heated swimming bath, riding, outdoor games, delightful ballroom and residential accommodation. Permanent club dance band and cabarets frequently broadcast by the B.B.C.

THIS country club is well known owing to its week-end radio broadcasts of cabarets and the familiar signature tune "Beyond the Blue Horizon". Originally named the "Blue Horizon" because of the wonderful view of the Devon coast and channel, this fine Georgian house is a popular rendezvous and on Saturday evenings dinner dances and cabaret entertainments are given with such well known names as Ronald Frankau, Jean de Casalis, Stanelli and Leonard Henry figuring as entertainers.

Besides the attractive ballroom and dining room there are a large and modernised cocktail bar and a cosy oak panelled lounge dating from 1710. A card room, table tennis room and residents' lounge add to the amenities of the place. Hot and cold water is laid on in most of the bedrooms, several of which command delightful views. There is a variety of amusements for members. The indoor heated swimming pool where galas

View of the club from the lawn which looks over the Bristol Channel.

St Mellons Hotel

Castleton, Nr. Newport, Gwent CF3 8XR
Tel: (01633) 680355; Fax: (01633) 680399

Formerly an Edwardian gentlemen's club set in beautiful gardens, the St Mellons Hotel is a blend of many of the best things in life. There is a splendid leisure complex and all bedrooms and suites are thoughtfully presented, and tastefully decorated. Equally attractive bedrooms known as the Garden Rooms are immediately adjacent to the hotel. The Llanarthen Restaurant offers interesting and sensibly priced menus, featuring English, Welsh and International cuisine. Lighter meals may be enjoyed on the terrace or in the cocktail lounge. Functions of all types can be accommodated in the Ballroom, St Mellons Room, the Adams Room and the self-contained Terrace Suite. Conferences are extremely well catered for. I was delighted to find that Cardiff's allure as a shopping centre had not dimmed since my last visit and that parking was still cheap and easy. The Cardiff area is rich in treasures including Tredegar House, Caerphilly Castle, the Rhondda Heritage Park and the Big Pit Mine. St Mellon's is away from the city's bustle yet near enough for business and leisure visitors to enjoy the city's many amenities and attractions.

Rates: Single room and breakfast from £80; double room inc. breakfast from £90.   V
Weekend breaks: Two nights inc. a Saturday £190 per couple including 3-course tdh dinner, b&b, VAT and use of adjoining Leisure Complex.

● *41 en suite bedrooms, all with telephone, colour TV, clock radio, hairdryer, laundry/valet service, tea/coffee making facilities, trouser press. Disabled facilities.*
● *Table d'hôte & à la carte dining room; lunch & special diets available; last orders 21.30.*
● *Business services inc 7 meeting rooms, capacity 10-150. Car parking for 150. Beauty salon.*
● *Fitness centre/gym, jacuzzi/whirlpool, massage, solarium, squash, indoor swimming pool, tennis.*
● *Open all year. Major credit cards accepted.*

Cardiff 5, Newport 8, Caerphilly 8, Swansea 45 , Bristol 41, London 150.

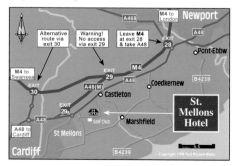

Trefeddian Hotel

Aberdovey (Aberdyfi), LL35 OSB
Tel: (01654) 767213; Fax: (01654) 767777

The Trefeddian Hotel stands in its own
grounds, away from the main road, and is one
mile from the middle of Aberdovey, a village
with many attractions and which is becoming
a centre where everyone, particularly the
young, can pursue many outdoor activities.
For example, supervision and special instruction can be arranged for sailing. The directors,
Mr & Mrs John Cave and Mr Peter Cave, are
responsible for the running of this first class
family hotel, which has all the amenities to
make a splendid holiday. The lounges are spacious, relaxing and peaceful and have recently
been beautifully refurbished. The bedrooms,
wih views of Cardigan Bay, are comfortable
and elegantly decorated. The menus offer a
good choice of interesting and nicely presented dishes, complemented by a well chosen wine list. The Trefeddian is in the immediate vicinity of a four-mile stretch of sandy
beach and overlooks the golf course with the
ever changing view of the sea beyond. The
courtesy and efficiency of the staff create a
happy atmosphere.

Rates: Single room and breakfast from £54; Ⅴ
double room inc. breakfast from £108.
Bargain breaks: Spring and Autumn breaks
from late February to end-April & all November =
quoted tariff less 5%. Also no single room sur-
charge at these times.

● *46 en suite bedrooms, all with telephone, colour TV,*
clock radio, hairdryer, laundry/valet service, safety
deposit box, tea/coffee making facilities. Non-smoker
and disabled bedrooms available. Car parking for 50.
● *5-course table d'hôte dinner £16.95; children's*
menu, lunch & special diets avail; last orders 8.30.
● *Billiards/snooker, indoor games, pitch & putt,*
watersports, solarium, sailing/boating, clay shoot-
ing, indoor swimming pool, tennis, children's play
area. Fishing & riding nearby.
● *Open March- Jan. Major credit cards accepted.*
Machynlleth 11, Talylynn & Cader Idris 14,
Barmouth 34, Dolgellau 24, London 215.

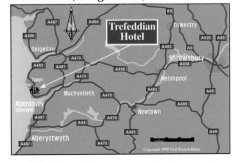

Bontddu Hall Hotel

Bontddu, Nr. Dolgellau, Gwynedd
LL40 2SU
Tel: (01341) 430661; Fax: (01341) 430284

Bontddu Hall, wonderfully situated in 14 acres of landscaped grounds, overlooks fine views of the Mawddach Estuary and famous Cader Idris range of mountains. The unspoilt charm of this attractive Victorian mansion has always made it a favourite of mine, and the owners Margaretta and Michael Ball know what is good. You will enjoy excellent food from an interesting country house evening dinner menu, dishes are varied and nicely served. Salmon and lobster are a speciality when available. A special carvery lunch is served on Sundays and an appetizing brasserie menu on other days. The furniture, pictures, colour schemes and flowers are all reminiscent of a country house and the hotel has been completely refurbished. All rooms are very comfortable and the "Princess of Wales" Bar extends a warm welcome. Nearly all bedrooms are with estuary and mountain views. In the Lodge, above the main drive are some additional rooms with balconies and exceptional views. I can only recommend a visit and you will want to come again and again.

Rates: *Room and breakfast from £62.50 (single), £100-£115 (double/twin), inclusive of VAT. Weekly demi-pension £450 per person; four-poster suites for romantics £150.* **V**
Bargain breaks: *Any two consecutive nights half board from £140-£150 per person inc. service & VAT. Extra nights pro rata.*

● *20 en suite bedrooms, all with telephone, colour TV, clock radio, hairdryer, tea/coffee making facilities; central heating; night service to midnight.*
● *Late meals to 9.30p.m.; diets; children welcome; dogs welcome.*
● *Sea bathing, golf and riding all five miles; gold mine nearby.*
● *Access, Amex, Diners & Visa credit cards accepted. Open March to December.*
Barmouth 5, Dolgellau 5, Aberystwyth 35, Caernarfon 50, Birmingham 110, London 235.

Borthwnog Hall Country House Hotel & Restaurant

Bontddu, Dolgellau, Gwynedd LL40 2TT
Tel: (01341) 430271; Fax (01341) 430682
E-mail:borthwnoghall@enterprise.net
Internet: http://homepages.enterprise.net/
borthwnoghall

Idyllically poised on the shores of the Mawddach estuary with views stretching six miles to the coast, this gem of a hotel dates from the late 17th Century. Six hundred feet of peaceful gardens with many unusual plant varieties run alongside the water, and this also provides for a good mix of woodland and estuary birdlife. Based here you are well placed to enjoy the many wonderful walks for which the Mawddach area is famous. Bedrooms, some with superb views of the Cader range of mountains, are pretty, spacious and comfortable with beautiful furniture and fabrics. The personalities of your hosts, Derek and Vicki Hawes are reflected in the abundance of interesting and original antiques and objets d'art. Within the hotel there is also an Art Gallery with an excellent range of paintings, pottery and other works of art. The intimate and characterful restaurant offers both table d'hôte and à la carte menus on which you will find some unusual dishes comple-

mented with excellent wines. Borthwnog has been described as a "little gem" and, with the highest accolades from the AA & RAC, I too can highly recommend it to any Signposter.

Rates: *Double room rate including breakfast from £45.00.* **Bargain Breaks**: *Standard short breaks from £49.00 per person per day with additional promotional breaks off season. Weekly breaks from £335.00. Please enquire.* **V**

● *Three en suite bedrooms with radio, colour TV and direct-dial telephone, hairdryer; tea/coffee making facilities.*
● *Last orders for dinner 20.15 hrs. Parking 8 cars.*
● *Art gallery in hotel. Golf and riding nearby.*
● *Open all year. Mastercard, Visa, Amex accepted.*

Dolgellau 4, Barmouth 6, Aberystwyth 38, Caernarfon 42, Birmingham 110, London 235.

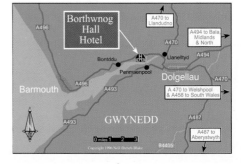

PRINCIPALITY
International

GROUP HANDLING-TOUR OPERATORS....

Your experts in England, Wales, Scotland and
Ireland for individual travel and tailor-made
groups. We shall be pleased to send you
our brochures for:

COUNTESS WELCOME HOLIDAYS
Our one price voucher programme in all
four countries.

WALKING HOLIDAYS in the National
Parks of Wales, the Highlands of Scotland
and the West Coast of Ireland.

CYCLING TOURS in Wales and Ireland.

GOLFING A LA CARTE HOLIDAYS.

CULTURAL and HERITAGE TOURS
in England, Wales and Ireland.

PRINCIPALITY INTERNATIONAL
**ST. BRIDES HILL, SAUNDERSFOOT,
PEMBROKESHIRE, WALES.
SA69 9NH**
Tel:+44 (0) 1834 812304
Fax:+44 (0) 1834 813303

TOLL FREE FAX from USA & CANADA
800 646 1620

Glen-Yr-Afon House

Pontypool Road, Usk, Monmouthshire
NP5 1SY
Tel: (01291) 672302 / 673202;
Fax: (01291) 672597

One of the first things that the visitor will notice about the Glen-Yr-Afon is the friendliness and efficiency of owners Jan and Peter Clarke who believe in a "hands on" approach. This is reflected in their staff who cheerfully anticipate the guests' every need. Only five minutes' walk from the pleasant market town of Usk, the hotel is situated on the Pontypool road with an agreeable river walk opposite. An excellent base from which to explore South Wales and only half an hour from the motorway. Glen-Yr-Afon is an imposing and elegant Victorian house retaining many original features, yet sympathetically updated by Jan and Peter. 26 elegantly decorated bedrooms boast bathrooms with wonderfully large baths. The newly refurbished bridal suite again reflects the impeccable taste of the owners who are celebrating 25 years at the hotel this year. The oak-panelled restaurant offers an excellent choice of à la carte or table d'hôte menus, imaginatively presented with generous helpings and a well-chosen wine list. Business people and wedding parties are well cared for with a function suite seating 140, whilst the charming library is the venue for anniversaries, dinner parties and smaller functions for up to 20 people.

Rates: Single room including breakfast from £53 + VAT. Double room with breakfast from £65+VAT.
Leisure Breaks: Any two days sharing room, dinner, bed & breakfast per person £85.

● *26 en suite bedrooms with satellite TV, radio, direct-dial telephone, laundry service, non-smoker bedrooms, tea/coffee making facilities.*
● *Last orders for dinner 21.00. Special diets available.*
● *Croquet, fishing, golf, gliding, grass skiing - nearby.*
● *Full business services and 2 conference rooms for total of 120 guests. AV equipment available.*
● *Car parking for 100 cars. Facilities for disabled.*
● *Open all year. Most credit cards accepted.*

Newport 10, Monmouth 13, Cardiff 22, Bristol 30, Gloucester 39, London 136 .

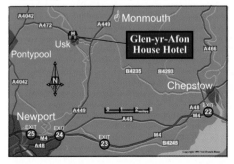

St Brides Hotel

St Brides Hill, Saundersfoot,
Pembrokeshire SA69 9NH
Tel: (01834) 812304; Fax: (01834) 813303
e-mail: ianbell@cipality.u-net.com

What a lovely surprise on my first visit to
Pembrokeshire to discover St Brides Hotel!
It is impressively situated in its own grounds
overlooking Carmarthen Bay and the harbour
and sandy beach of Saundersfoot. It is a privately owned and family run hotel offering
personal and friendly service. The bedrooms
are all individually designed. The Commo-
dore Restaurant, with lovely views overlooking the bay, serves varied and interesting
menus, according to season, with locally
caught fish, Angle Bay lobsters and
Saundersfoot crabs being a speciality. Dinner
dances are held most Saturday evenings.
History surrounds the hotel and there is
plenty to see in the area - ancient castles
which defended Pembrokeshire, the nearby
medieval walled town of Tenby, elegant and
majestic churches and cathedrals and notori-
ous inlets where Vikings landed and smugglers plied their trade. I look forward to returning to St Brides.

*Rates: Single room with breakfast from £65;
double room with breakfast from £90.*
Bargain breaks: *Weekends away to include
dinner, bed & breakfast Fri & Sat nights £69-£99
per person. Midweek 'Shuttle' Breaks £99 per person.*

● *43 en suite bedrooms with colour TV + Satellite, direct-dial telephone, hairdryer, minibar, tea/
coffee making facilities, radio.*
● *Non-smoker bedrooms; car parking (70) & rental.*
● *Table d'hôte dinner £18.50; lunch, à la carte and
diets available; last orders 21.15.*
● *Full business & conference facilities to 150.*
● *Outdoor
heated swim-
ming pool.
Fishing,
watersports,
boating/sailing
within $^1/_2$ mile;
squash 2 miles;
golf 3 miles.*
● *Open all year.
All major credit
cards accepted.*

**Pembroke 11,
Carmarthen 24,
Fishguard 30,
Cardigan 30,
London 235.**

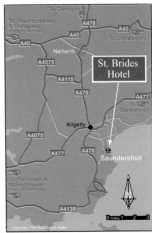

Warpool Court Hotel

St. Davids, Pembrokeshire SA62 6BN
Tel: (01437) 720300; Fax: (01437) 720676

The Warpool Court is in a wonderful position overlooking the wild Atlantic and within a few minutes' walk of the famous St. David's Cathedral. This splendid country house hotel, with its unique collection of antique tiles, has been recommended by Signpost for a long time. It is owned by Peter Trier and through his expertise you can be assured of good food, gracious living and a warm welcome. The colour schemes are soft and restful and the staff cheerful and efficient. The hotel has a high reputation for good food and a fine selection of well chosen wines. Four course table d'hôte menus are excellent and, whenever possible, local produce is used. Salmon is smoked on the premises, crab and lobster are caught at the nearby village of Solva. A vegetarian menu is also available. The lounge bar provides a relaxed atmosphere for diners, and the residents' lounge ensures peace and comfort. There are numerous outdoor activities available, the most popular being walking, bird watching and surfing.

Rates: Room and breakfast from £75 (single), £106 (twin/double) inclusive of VAT. **V**
'Country House Breaks' (2 nights out of season d,b&b from £69; 7 nights from £63 pppn). Full Christmas and New Year packages.

● *25 en suite bedrooms all with telephone, colour TV, baby listening, tea/coffee making facilities; family rooms; full central heating.*
● *Meals to 9.15 p.m.; diets; children welcome; dogs accepted.*
● *Table tennis, gymnasium and sauna, pool table, heated covered swimming pool (Apr-Oct), all weather tennis court, 9 hole golf course nearby (2 miles); sea bathing; sandy beaches; lovely walks.*
● *Major credit cards accepted. Open Feb-December inc*
Fishguard 16, Haverfordwest 16, Carmarthen 46, Severn Bridge 130, Birmingham 177, London 264

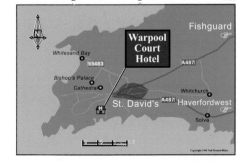

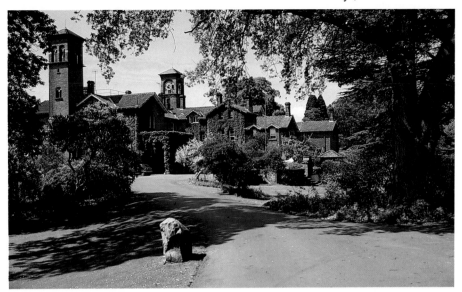

Gliffaes Country House Hotel

Crickhowell, Powys NP8 1RH
Tel: 0800 146719; Fax: (01874) 730463

Romantically situated in the lovely valley of the River Usk, Gliffaes is midway between the Black Mountains and the Brecon Beacons. 33 acres of grounds are planted with rare trees and shrubs, some dating from the nineteenth century. There is plenty to see and do in the area and the hotel has many leisure facilities. Over two miles of the river are reserved primarily for guests to fish for salmon and trout in the beautifully tranquil setting. The sitting room and the drawing room are most relaxing and French windows lead into an attractive and spacious sun room, which opens onto the terrace. The food at Gliffaes is excellent. Light lunch dishes may be ordered from the bar and home made afternoon tea is best described as a trencherman's dream! An extensive dinner menu includes plenty for vegetarians, using only the freshest ingredients and supported by a sensibly priced wine list. The bedrooms are priced according to size and views, all being comfortable and full of character. Having owned the hotel for 50 years, the Brabner family are experienced, charming and informal hosts, as a result of which many guests return year after year. Nick and Peta Brabner have now been joined by their daughter and son-in-law, making a third generation of the family at Gliffaes.

Rates: (from March 1999) Room & breakfast from £40.50 to £60 per person. **Bargain breaks:** *Short stay and weekly rates on application.* **V**

● *22 en suite bedrooms all with direct-dial telephone, colour TV, tea/coffee making facilities and baby listening.*
● *Children welcome; dogs (but not in hotel).*
● *Late meals by arrangement; diets.*
● *TV room; meeting rooms for small conferences (16) available.*
● *Salmon & trout fishing; tennis; putting & practice net; croquet; billiards. Golf, riding, shooting, sailing & boating all nearby.*
● *Open all year. Amex, Diners, Access & Visa accepted.*
Crickhowell 3½ miles, Abergavenny 10, London 160.

CELEBRATING 50 YEARS

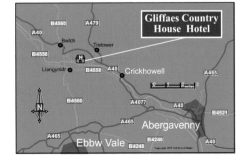

Scotland

Historic Houses, Gardens & Parks

Aberdeenshire
Castle Fraser & Garden, 4m N of Dunecht
Crathes Castle & Garden, Nr Banchory
Cruickshank Botanic Gardens, Aberdeen University
Darnside Herb Garden, Benholm by Johnshaven
DrumCastle & Garden, by Banchory
Duff House, Banff
Duthie Park & Winter Gardens, Aberdeen
Fasque, Fettercain
Fyvie Castle
Haddo House, Tarves
James Cocker & Sons, Rosegrowers, Aberdeen
Leith Hall & Garden, Kennethmont, Huntly
Pitmedden Garden & Museum of Farming by Ellon

Angus
Duntrune Demonstration Garden, Dundee
House of Dun, 3m W of Montrose

Argyll & Bute
Ardnaiseig Gardens, 22m E of Oban
Arduaine Garden, 20m S of Oban
Barguillean Garden, 3m W of Taynuilt
Brodick Castle, Garden & Country Park, Isle of Arran
Torosay Castle & Gardens, $1^1/_2$ m SSE of Craignure, Isle of Mull

City of Edinburgh
Dalmeny House, By South Queensferry
The Georgian House, Charlotte Sq., Edinburgh
Gladstone's Land, Royal Mile, Edinburgh
House of the Binns, l5m W of Edinburgh
Hopetoun House, W of South Queensferry
Inveresk Lodge Garden, 6m E of Edinburgh
Malleny Garden, Balerno, W of Edinburgh
Royal Botanic Gardens, Edinburgh

City of Glasgow
Greenbank Garden, Clarkston, Glasgow

Dumfries & Galloway
Drumlanrig Castle & Country Park, 3m N of Thornhill Galloway House Gardens, Garlieston
Maxwelton House, 13m NE of Dumfries
Meadowsweet Herb Garden, Castle Kennedy, Stranraer
Threave Garden, Castle Douglas

East Ayrshire
Dean Castle & Country Park, Kilmarnock

Fife
Balcaskie House & Gardens, 2m W of Pittenween
Cambo Gardens, 1m S of Kingsbarns
Earlshall Castle & Gardens, 1m E of Leuchars
Falkland Palace & Gardens, 11m N of Kirkcaldy
Hill of Tarvit Mansionhouse & Garden, 2m S of Cupar
Kellie Castle & Garden, 3m N of Pittenween
Sir Douglas Bader Garden for the Disabled, Duffus Park

Highland
The Achiltibuie Hydroponicum
Balmacara Estate & Lochalsh Woodland Garden, Kyle of Lochalsh
Dunrobin Castle, Gardens & Museum, Golspie, Sutherland
Dunvegan Castle, Isle of Skye
Inverewe Garden, by Poolewe
Oldwick Castle, Wick

Moray
Brodie Castle, 4m W of Forres

Perth & Kinross
Bell's Cherrybank Gardens, Perth
Blair's Castle, 7m NNW of Pitlochry
Branklyn Garden, Perth
Cluny House Gardens, $3^1/_2$ m from Aberfeldy
Edzell Castle & Garden, 6m N of Brechin
Magginch Castle Gardens, 10m E of Perth
Scone Palace, 2m NE of Perth

Scottish Borders
Bowhill, 3m W of Selkirk
Dawyck Botanic Garden, Stobo
Floors Castle, Kelso
Kailzie Gardens, 2m E of Peebles

Stirlingshire
Culcreuch Castle & Country Park, Fintry

South Ayrshire
Culzean Castle & Country Park, 4m W of Maybole

Scotland

West Lothian
Suntrap (Garden) Gogarbank, 6m W
of Edinburgh

Stirlingshire
Gartmorn Dam Country Park &
Nature Reserve, by Sauchie

Walks & Nature Trails

Aberdeenshire
Aden Country Park, Mintlaw
Braeloine Visitor Centre, Glen Tanar,
 by Aboyne
Bullers of Buchan, Cruden Bay
Forview Nature Reserve, Newburgh

Angus
Monikie Country Park, 10m N of
 Dundee

Argyll & Bute
Carsaig Arches, on shore 3m W of
 Carsaig, Isle of Mull
King's Cave, shore, 2m N of
 Blackwaterfoot
Lauder Forest Walks, 3m S of
 Strachur, Glenbranter
Puck's Glen, 5m W of Dunoon

Dumfries & Galloway
Caerlaverock National Nature
 Reserve, S of Dumfries

City of Edinburgh
Cammon Estate, NE off Queensferry
 Road, Edinburgh

East Ayrshire
Muirshiel Country Park, 9m SW of
 Paisley

East Lothian
John Muir Country Park, Dunbar

Fife
Scottish Deer Centre, £m W of
 Cupar

Highland
Abriachan Garden Nursery Walk,
 Loch Ness
Aultfearn Local Walk, Kiltarlity
Dalabil Glen, between Tarskavaig &
 Ostair, Isle of Skye
Falls of Foyers Woodland Walks
Farigaig Forest Trails
Forestry Walk, between Ardvasar &
 Aird of Sleat, Isle of Skye
Glen Affric Forest Walks
Plodda Falls Scenic Walk
Reelig Forest Walks, W of Inverness
The Trotternish Ridge, Isle of Skye

Perth & Kinross
Queen's View Centre, Loch Tummel,
 6m NW of Pitlochry
St Cyrus National Nature Reserve,
 Nether Warburton

Scottish Borders
Jedforest Deer & Farm Park,
 Camptown
Pease Dean, Nr. Cockburnspath

Historical Sites & Museums

Aberdeenshire
Aberdeen Maritime Museum -
 Provost Ross's House
Ballindalloch Castle
Balmoral Castle, Crathie
Braemar Highland Heritage Centre
Brodie Castle, Forres
Castle Fraser, Nr Inverurie
Colgarff Castle, Strathdon
Crathie Church, Crathie
Dallas Dhu Distillery, Forres
Kings College Chapel & Visitor
 Centre
Provost Skene's House, Aberdeen
St Michael's Cathedral, Old Aber-
 deen

Angus
Angus Folk Museum, Glamis
Arbroath Abbey
Barrie's Birthplace, Kirriemuir
Glamis Castle, 5m SW of Forfar

Argyll & Bute
Bonawe Iron Works, Nr Taynuilt
David Livingstone Centre, Blantyre
Doon Valley Heritage, 2m S of Patna
Duart Castle, Isle of Mull
Inverary Castle & Gardens
Kilmory Castle Gardens,
 Lochgilphead
The Old Byrem, Dervaig, Isle of
 Mull
Rothesay Castle, Isle of Bute
Souter Johnnie's Cottage,
 Kirkoswald

City of Edinburgh
Craigmillar Castle, 2.5m SE of
 Edinburgh
Edinburgh Castle
Palace of Holyrood House, Edin-
 burgh

City of Glasgow
The Tenement House, Garnethill

Dumfries & Galloway
Burns House, Dumfries
Caerlaverock Castle, 8m SE of
 Dumfries
Carlyle's Birthplace, Ecclefechan
Dumfries Museum & Camera
 Obscura, Dumfries
Maclellan's Castle, Kirkcudbright
Mill on the Fleet Heritage Centre,

Scotland

Gatehouse of Fleet New
Abbey Cornmill, 8m S
of Dumfries
Sweetheart Abbey, New
Abbey
Threave Castle, 3m E of
North   Berwick

East Ayrshire
Weaver's Cottage,
Kilbarchan, 12m   SW
of Glasgow

East Renfrewshire
Coats Observatory,
Paisley

East Lothian
Dirleton Castle & Garden, 7m W of
North Berwick
Preton Mill a Phmtassie Doocot,
23m E of Edinburgh
Tantallon Castle, 3m E of North
Berwick
The Heritage of Golf, Gullane

Fife
Aberdour Castle
Balgonie Castle, by
Markinch
Inchcolm Abbey
(via ferry from S
Queensferry)
St Andrew's Cathe-
dral
St Andrew's Castle

Highland
Castle Grant, Grantown-on-Spey
Cawdor Castle, 5m N of Nairn
Colbost Folk Musuem, Isle of Skye
Culloden Battlefield, 5m N of
Inverness
Dornoch Cathedral
Durness Visitor Centre
Eilean Donan Castle, 9m E of Kyle
of Lochalsh
Fort George, 10m W of Nairn
Giant MacAskill Museum,
Dunvegan, Isle of Skye
Glen Coe Visitor Centre, 17m S of
Fort William
Glenfinnan Monument, Lochaber,
18m W of Fort William
Hugh Miller's Cottage, Cromarty,
22m NE of Inverness
Leckmeln Shrubbery & Arboretum,
Nr Ullapool
Lochinver Visitor Centre
Piping Centre, Borreraig, Isle of
Skye
Skye Museum of Island Life,
Kilmuir, Isle of Skye
Urquart Castle on Loch Ness, Nr
Drumnadrochit

Moray
Elgin Cathedral

Perth & Kinross
Atholl Country Collection, Blair
Atholl

Black Watch regimental
Museum,
Balhousie Castle, Perth
Doune Castle, 8m S of
Callander
Killiekrankie Visitor
Centre, 3m N of Pitlochry
Loch Leven Castle, via
ferry from Kinross

Scottish Borders
Dryburgh Abbey, 5m SE
of Melrose
Robert Smail's Printing
Works, Innerleithen
Hermitage Castle 5m NE
of Newcastleton
Jedburgh Abbey
Jim Clark Memorial Trophy Room,
Duns
Melrose Abbey
Smallholm Tower, 6m W of Kelso

South Ayrshire
Bachelor's Club (re: Robert Burns),
Tarbolton
Burns Cottage &
Museum, 2m S of
Ayr

South Lanarkshire
Gladstone Court
Museum, Biggar
John Buchan Cen-
tre, 6m E of Biggar

Stirlingshire
Inchmahoune
Priory, Lake of Mentieth
National Wallace Monument, $1^1/2$ m
NNE of Stirling

West Dunbartonshire
Dumbarton Castle
The Hill House, Helensburgh

West Lothian
Linlithgow Palace
Blackness Castle, 4m NE of
Linlithgow

Entertainment Venues

Aberdeenshire
Alford Valley Railway, Alford
Fowlsheugh RSPB Seabird Colony
Glenshee Ski Centre, Cairnwell by
Braemar
Holyneuk Bird Park, Nr Macduff
Loch Muick & Lochnagar Wildlife
Reserve, Crimond
North East Falconry Centre, Cairnie,

Scotland

by Huntly
Peterhead Fish Market
Royal Lochnagar Distillery, Crathie
St Cyrus National Nature Reserve,
by Montrose
Storybook Glen, Maryculter
Ugie Fish House, Peterhead

Angus
Discovery Point, Dundee

Argyll & Bute
Ardnamurchan Natural History &
Visitor Centre, Nr. Glenborrowdale
Antartex Village, Balloch
Balloch Castle Country Park, at S
end of Loch Lomond
Glenbart Abbey Visitor Centre, 12m
NW of Campbeltown
Glenfinnart Deer Farm, Ardentinny
Inverawe Smokery, Bridge of Awe
Isle of Mull Wine Company,
Bunesan
Kelburn Country Centre, between
Lairgs & Fairlie
Mull Railway, Craignure
Mull Little Theatre, Dervaig
Tobermory Distillery Visitor Centre

City of Edinburgh
Camera Obscura, Castlehill
Edinburgh Clan Tartan Centre, Leith
Crabbie's Histonc Winery Tour,
Great Junction Street
Edinburgh Crystal Visitor Centre,
Penicuik
Kinloch Anderson Heritage Room,
Leith
National Gallery of Scotland, The
Mound
The Scottish Whisky Heritage
Centre, Royal Mile

Dumfries & Galloway
Old Blacksmith's Shop Centre,

Gretna Green
Robert Burns Centre, Dumfries

Fife
Deep sea World, North Queensferry

Highland
Aviemore Centre
Castle Grant, Grantown-on-Spey
Clan Donald Visitor Centre at
Armadale Castle
Dulsie Bridge
Glen Ord Distillery, Muir of Ord
Highland Folk Museum, Kingussie
Loch Ness Centre, Drumnadrochit
Made in Scotland Exhibition of
Crafts, Beauly
The Malt Whisky Trail, Speyside
Rothiemurchas Estate, Nr. Aviemore
Skye Oysters, Loch Harport
Speyside Heather Centre, Grantown
Strathspey Steam Railway, Nr.
Aviemore
Talisker Distillery, Loch Harport
Torridon Countryside Centre, 9m
SW of Aberdeen

North Lanarkshire
The Time Capsule, Monklands,
Coatbridge

Perth & Kinross
Beatrix Potter Garden & Exhibition,
Brinham
Caithness Glass (Perth),
Inveralmond
Crieff Visitors' Centre
Rob Roy & Trossachs Visitor Centre,
Callander

Scottish Borders
Borders Wool Centre Nr. Galashiels
Peter Anderson of Scotland Cash-
mere Woollens Mill & Museum,
Galashiels
St. Abb's Head, 2m N of
Coldingham

Stirlingshire
Bannockburn Heritage Centre, 2m S
of Stirling
Blair Drummond Safari & Leisure
Park
Village Glass, Bridge of Allan

Outdoors in Scotland

Scotland is synonymous with outdoor sports - golf, sailing, fishing, shooting and deer-stalking. Ideal country for field sports, it nurtured the game of golf - now at least four centuries old. It was the size of the Old Course at St. Andrews which dictated that golf everywhere should be played over nine holes or a multiple of nine.

The Royal and Ancient Club at St. Andrews is golf's ruling body and the democratic nature of the game is reflected in the great number of municipal courses and the low cost of playing.

Scotland has a large network of golf courses. The "Gold Coast" on the west between Troon and Turnberry on the Firth of Clyde has 20 courses in 20 miles. East-coast towns from the Borders to Caithness have fine breezy courses on undulating land among the dunes.

Whatever the origins of golf, Scotland is definitely the home of curling. The roaring game, as it is called from the hum of the polished stones gliding across the ice, was born on frozen Highland lochs.

Native enthusiasts made it a game of skill and exported it to Canada, Switzerland and other lands which now have curling traditions of their own. Most large Scottish towns and a few hotels have their artificial curling rinks, so it is no longer just a winter game.

To see the Scots at play, and enjoying a unique social occasion, go to Loch Leven or the Lake of Menteith after a prolonged January frost, when conditions permit a Grand Match, North versus South, to take place.

Scotland has four ski resorts - Aviemore, Glencoe, Glenshee and the Lecht. The large number of ski shops and instruction schools in Scotland mean snow business is becoming big business. The Cairngorm foothills around Aviemore are well provided with hotels, restaurants and bars with generous après-ski amenities. When conditions are right, some of the best skiing in Europe is to be found in the central Highlands of Scotland.

A fishing rod is part of a boy's heritage in Scotland and country buses are noted for the number of unscheduled stops they make at angling beats. More than three hundred Scottish rivers and numerous lochs are world famous for trout and salmon fishing. Apart from some private beats, fishing is very reasonably priced, occasionally free, and available (even on the celebrated Tweed, Tay or Spey rivers) with a permit from the local hotel, angling/tackle shop or fishing society.

In reservoirs, canals, some rivers and inland lochs, coarse fishing is cheaper, while sea angling from the shore is free on most parts of the coast. Another bonus is Scotland's *Fishing Heritage Trail* which offers touring motorists a choice of scenic and historic routes along the east coast from Eyemouth to Scrabster.

Highland Games staged throughout Scotland include more sporting and spectacular activities. Centuries ago, a Scottish king crossed a fallen enemy's sword with his own and danced a victory jig. That was the origin of the sword dance. The same king kept his soldiers fit by making them run up and down hills, and this is retained in many Highland Games. Ancient Picts improvising hunting dances, raised their arms and pointed their fingers, like antlers, and imitated the movements of a rutting stag. An early Highland fling, perhaps? Later feats of strength were devised by young clansmen: caber-tossing, shot-putting, hammer throwing.

Scotland's other open-air activities include pony trekking - a Highland invention, birdwatching, cycling, canoeing, mountaineering, rock-climbing, sailing and gliding. A sporting paradise, indeed.

Dumfries & Galloway

Turn left at Scotland and you will find yourself in Dumfries and Galloway, an area combining the grandeur of hill, forest and sweeping coastline with an especially mild climate, making it the perfect region for all kinds of holidays. It is ideal car touring country with quiet roads and a host of fascinating byways for you to explore; hill roads, shore roads, forest roads and farm roads ... and it won't take you long to get there. From England the main M6 motorway joins the A74 highway just north of Carlisle. Cross the border at Gretna and you're in Dumfries and Galloway.

While you don't need to leave the main roads to enjoy the area's scenic beauty, it is an ideal refuge for climbers and walkers, and for anyone who enjoys silence, space and solitude. Pony trekking is another excellent way of getting off the beaten track, and you don't need to be an experienced rider to enjoy travelling through the heart of the countryside.

Sparkling clear lochs and rivers and miles of attractive coast make fishing and water sports firm favourites throughout the year. The area offers variety for yachtsmen or anyone who enjoys messing about in boats. Visitors with a taste for exercise may wish to try water skiing, wind surfing or sub aqua. Others may prefer to find a quiet beach in one of the sheltered bays around the coast, soak up the sun and watch the rest of the family getting wet! The beaches offer safe bathing and swimming. The fisherman's paradise provides just the climate for a good day's sport, with game fishing for trout and salmon available at modest cost, and coarse fishing and sea angling growing in popularity every year. Dumfries and Galloway has a tremendous variety of golf courses, with glorious scenery included at no extra cost, and very moderate green fees.

The region's history is rich and fascinating, stretching back to the strange anonymous figures who have left their standing stones, chambered cairns and scattered relics to intrigue us. There are traces of Roman occupation, particularly in the east of the area and, even before St. Columba founded his abbey at Iona, St. Ninian had come to Scotland in the 4th century, making Whithorn a religious centre and place of pilgrimage, and the cradle of Christianity in Britain. The remains of this Priory are well worth a visit, as are other intriguing monuments. At Dundrennan Abbey Mary Queen of Scots spent her last night on Scottish soil before fleeing to England, captivity and execution. Sweetheart Abbey still stands as a memorial to a love story six hundred years old. Here in 1263 the grieving widow of John Balliol (together they founded the Oxford college) had her husband's heart built in over the high altar of the abbey, which became known as "Dulce Cor" - "Sweet Heart". In the spectacular

Galloway Forest Park stand two memorials to Robert the Bruce, who sheltered in the Galloway hills to pursue guerilla warfare against the English in the fourteenth century. Walk up Glen Trool to one of the Bruce Stones, which commemorates a battle on the hill, and enjoy the lovely view over the wooded banks of the loch. This was never an uneventful part of the world, even when free from wars. The imposing Caerlaverock, Threave and many other castles evoke the dangerous days when ruthless local families like the Douglases and Maxwells fought for domination of the area. The region's history is echoed in the continuing traditions of pageants and festivals. The Common Ridings in towns like Lockerbie and Annan revive times when it was necessary to patrol the boundaries of one's territory, to ward off rival families or English marauders.

The region's musical and literary heritage is similarly kept alive, and can be appreciated during the Arts Festival (May and early June). Scotland's most famous son, Rabbie Burns wrote many of his best-loved songs and poems when he lived in this area. Pay your respects at his house, now a curious museum, and then drink to his memory in his own "local", the still-flourishing Globe Inn. After many years of providing a haven for artists and craftspeople the region must now have more per mile than any other part of Scotland. Most are delighted to welcome visitors to watch them at work. You will find weavers, potters, glass-blowers, toy makers, textile printers, jewellers, woodturners, sculptors, and silk screen printers.

Accommodation is as varied as the scenery. Country house hotels, once private homes, are furnished to preserve their original character. Here you can enjoy a "house party" atmosphere in gracious surroundings, often with a range of leisure pursuits like fishing and golf available in the hotel's grounds or nearby. Dumfries and Galloway takes a pride in the friendliness of its people. Living out of the mainstream of today's hurry-scurry means that locals are happy to spare the time to make visitors feel at home.

DIARY OF EVENTS 1999

January

29 Dec-Jan 1. **Edinburgh's Hogmanay** - the world's largest winter festival.
22. **Scottish Borders National Chase.** Race meeting, Kelso, Scottish Borders.
25. **Robert Burns Day** - celebrations throughout Scotland for national poet.

February

6. **Rugby International.** Scotland v Wales, Murrayfield, Edinburgh.
22-27*.**Inverness Music Festival.** Var. venues, Inverness

March

5. **Hennessy Cognac Hurdle.** Kelso Racec'se, Borders.
6. **Scotland v Italy.** Rugby Int'l, Murrayfield, Edinburgh
20. **Rugby International.** Scotland v Ireland, Murrayfield, Edinburgh.

April

1-4. **Edinburgh Folk Festival.** Edinburgh, Lothian.
3-18. **Edinburgh International Science Festival.** Various venues.
6-9. **International Festival of Youth Rugby.** Various venues around Scotland.
17. **Scottish Grand National.** Ayr Racecourse.
29-3 May. **Isle of Bute Jazz Festival.** Var. venues, Bute.
30-May 2. **Highlands & Islands Music & Dance Festival.** Oban, Highland

May

20-30. **Perth Festival of the Arts,** Perth.
21-June 5. **4th Annual Highland Festival.** Thurso & various venues in Highlands
24/31. **1999 Cricket World Cup.** Scotland v Bangladesh/Scotland v New Zealand. Edinburgh.
28-June 6. **Dumfries & Galloway Arts Festival.** Var. venues throughout D & Gall

June

4-6. **Scotland's National Gardening Show.** Strathclyde Country Park, Glasgow
7-13. **Isle of Arran Folk Festival.** Var. venues, Isle of Arran
18-23. **St Magnus Festival,** Kirkwall, Orkney.
24-27. **Royal HighlandShow** Ingliston, Edinburgh.
25-July 4. **Glasgow International Jazz Festival.** Various venues, Glasgow.

July

July*. **12th Glasgow International Jazz Festival.** Various venues, Glasgow.
July*. **Hebridean Celtic Music Festival.** Var. venues, Stornoway. Isle of Lewis
3-4. **Game Conservancy Fair.** Perth, Perthshire.
7-10. **Loch Lomond PGA Golf Championship.** Luss, Dumbartonshire.
15-18. **Open Golf Championship.** Carnoustie, Fife.
30-Aug 2. **Cutty Sark Tall Ships Race.** Greenock, Inverclyde.
30-8 Aug. **Edinburgh International Jazz & Blues Festival.** Various venues.
31-Aug 1. **World Highland Games Championships.** Callander, Perthshire

August

6-28. **Edinburgh Military Tattoo.** Edinburgh Castle.
8-30. **Edinburgh Festival Fringe.** Various venues, Edinburgh.
14. **World Pipe Band Championship.** Glasgow.
15-29. **Edinburgh Int'l Film Festival.** Filmhouse Theatre.
15-Sept 4. **Edinburgh International Festival.** Prestigious multi-arts festival.

September

4. **Braemar Royal Highland Gathering.** Braemar, Aberdeenshire.
11. **RAF Battle of Britain International Airshow.** Leuchars, Fife.
4-5. **Golf: Walker Cup.** Nairn Golf Club, Highland
16-18. **Harry Rosebery Trophy/ Firth of Clyde Stakes, Ayr Gold Cup.** Ayr, S Ayrshire

October

2*. **October Musical Beerfest & Barbecue.** Gatehouse of Fleet, Dumfries-shire.
15-24. **Aberdeen Alternative Festival.** Music, dance, drama
25-31*. **International Scotch Whisky Festival,** Speyside & Edinburgh.

November

7. **Dunvegan Castle Firework Display.** Isle of Skye
24-30. **St Andrews Week.** Commemorations Scot landwide
*Denotes provisional date
For further details contact:
The Scottish Tourist Board, 23 Ravelston Terrace, Edinburgh EH4 3EU.
Tel: 0131 332 2433

Scotland

Ardoe House Hotel

Blairs, South Deeside Road,
Aberdeen AB12 5YP
Tel: (01224) 867355; Fax: (01224)
861283

Built in 1878 for a well known Aberdeen family, Ardoe House incorporates many features inspired by Balmoral Castle only 40 miles away. The magnificent wood panelled Grand Hall and staircase of the original house leads to a number of exclusive and unique bedrooms. Each one is different yet enjoys every modern facility. The cuisine should more than match your expectations, having recently been awarded two AA rosettes. The head chef caters for a variety of tastes as well as vegetarian options. There is a fine wine list specialising in good claret and New World vintages. Deeside is famous for its fishing and golf courses. The hotel's extensive conference and banqueting facilities and its proximity to Aberdeen make it an ideal venue for both business and pleasure and a good base from which to explore North East Scotland.

Rates: Mid-week from £80 single, £90 double. ☑
Lesiure Breaks: at weekends & certain mid-week dates accomm. from £130 per person 2-night stay inc dinner, b&b. Third night accom only free to Signpost readers on production of 1999 guide.
● *71 en suite bedrooms (inc 3 suites) all with colour TV + satellite, direct-dial telephone, hairdryer, laundry/valet service, tea/coffee making facilities, 24-hr room/meal service, music/radio/alarm, trouser press. Non-smoker & disabled rooms*
● *Restaurant. A la carte, lunch & special diets available; last orders 9.30. 4 meeting rooms to 400.*
● *Croquet. Fitness centre pool/tennis from mid-1999.*
Aberdeen 5 ,Braemar 30, Inverness 112, Edinburgh 125

Maryculter House

South Deeside Road, Maryculter,
Aberdeen AB12 5GB
Tel: (01224) 732124;
Fax: (01224) 733510

One of the most attractive small hotels I have stayed at, Maryculter, is situated on the banks of the river Dee, built on the site of a preceptory of the Knights Templar and dating from the 13th century. Many of the original features can still be traced inside the walled churchyard in the hotel grounds. The last owner of the property, Sir Cosmo Duff Gordon, in 1935 was one of the few male survivors of the Titanic. All 23 bedrooms are individually furnished. Dining areas include the Poachers Pocket for snacks, the Cocktail Bar, built above the cellars, and the main Priory Restaurant where the cuisine is traditional Scottish with French influences. Maryculter is an ideal hideaway for that special short break or longer holiday, being ideally situated for golf, shooting, fishing and country walks.

Rates: Single (room only) from £65; double ☑
from £90. Bargain Breaks: at weekends from £60 per person per night inc. breakfast & house dinner ★ *Sunday night accommodation complimentary to SIGNPOST readers.* ★

● *23 en suite bedrooms with colour TV + satellite, direct-dial telephone, hairdyer, laundry/valet service, music/radio/alarm, trouser press.*
● *4-course Table d'hôte dinner £31.50; lunch & special diets available; last orders 9 pm. AA   food*
● *Fishing, riding, shooting, golf nearby.*
● *Open all year. Major credit cards accepted.*
Aberdeen 8, Dundee 59, Edinburgh 122

Scotland

Balgonie Country House Hotel

Braemar Place, Ballater, Aberdeenshire AB35 5NQ
Tel & Fax: (013397) 55482

One of the most attractive small hotels it has been my pleasure to visit. The Edwardian-style country house is set in 4 acres of mature gardens, commanding superb views westward to Glen Muick and *Dark Lochnagar*. Each of the comfortable bedrooms is named after a fishing pool on the banks of the Dee. As befits a previous Caithness Glass / Taste of Scotland Prestige Award Winner, the two AA rosette dining-room is at the heart of the Balgonie experience. It offers the best of local produce: salmon from the river, game from the hill, beef from the field and seafood from the North Sea. In the heart of Royal Deeside, Balgonie is convenient for visiting Balmoral (open May-July) and as a centre for the famed Whisky and Castle trails as well as for walking, golf, fishing, shooting and ski-ing in winter.

Rates: Single inc breakfast from £65; double 🆅 *from £105. Visa, Amex, JCB, Diners, M'card.*

● *9 en suite bedrooms with colour TV, radio, direct-dial telephone, hairdryer, laundry service.*
● *4-course tdh dinner £28.50. Lunch & special diets available. Last orders 2100. Car parking 16*
● *Croquet. Golf & tennis 1 m. Riding, fishing 10 m*
● *Open February-December.*

Balmoral 7, Aberdeen 42, Perth 67, Edinburgh 111, London 483.

Thainstone House Hotel & Country Club

Inverurie, Aberdeenshire AB51 5NT
Tel: (01467) 621643; Fax: (01467) 625084

STB Highly Commended. Taste of Scotland.
AA ★★★★ RAC

Set in 40 acres of lush meadowland, the original Thainstone was burned by Jacobites in the 18th century. The Thainstone of today dates from the early 19th century and combines stately elegance with all the modern comforts of a luxurious 20th century hotel. A grand portal introduces you to the majestic galleried reception area on the way to your individually furnished bedroom which has nice extra touches like a decanter of sherry and Scottish shortcake awaiting you. The main restaurant *Simpsons* has two AA rosettes. In a sumptuous Georgian setting you can enjoy some of the most exciting menus in the North of Scotland. Situated between Inverness and Aberdeen, the hotel is well placed for visiting the North of Scotland's prehistoric stone circles, whisky distilleries and castles.

Rates: Single with breakfast from £80; double with breakfast from £95. 🆅
Bargain Breaks: weekends 2 nights dinner bed & breakfast £72 per person per night min. two-night stay inc. full use of Country Club.

● *48 en suite bedrooms all with colour TV+ satellite, telephone, hairdryer, laundry/valet service, tea/coffee making facilities, music/radio/alarm clock, trouser press. Non smoker bedrooms available.*
● *Table d'hôte £31.50; à la carte, lunch & special diets available; last orders 9.30 pm.* ◎◎ *Restaurant*
● *Business services inc. 5 meeting rooms to 350.*
● *Country Club with indoor pool, gym, jacuzzi/ sauna, jogging track. Golf, riding,fishing nearby.*
● *Open all year. All major credit cards accepted.*

Kintore 4, Aberdeen 14, Inverness 90, Edinburgh 147

Killiechronan House

Aros, Isle Of Mull, Argyll PA72 6JU
Tel: (01680) 300403; Fax: (01680) 300463

What more picturesque and quiet rural setting than at the head of Loch na Keal, on the west side of Mull? When I was there, a stag was leisurely cropping the grass in the garden, not the least worried by my photographing him. Killiechronan House is part of the beautiful 5000 acre Killiechronan Estate, with its own fishing and pony trekking facilities, and arrangements for stalking can easily be made. There are five miles of coastline along the north side of the Loch, and, of course miles of seldom used, single track roads. The hotel is easily accessible from the mainland, only 14 miles from the ferry terminal at Craignure, and forty minutes from Oban. The house was tastefully refurbished and redecorated in 1995, to the same standard as the Leroy family's other hotel at Oban (*page 207*). The warm and cosy décor of both the lounge and drawing room is most welcoming, with open log fires on colder days. In overall charge are Patrick and Margaret Freytag, the former a very experienced chef of traditional Scottish cuisine, using fresh local produce.

*Rates: Dinner, room and breakfast from £61.00 per person. **Minibreak** (min. 2 nights) from £54 per person. STB ⚜⚜⚜⚜ Four Crown. AA ◎◎ for food. A special weekly rate is available allowing consecutive nights to be spent at two of the Leroy hotels, with at least two nights being spent at Killiechronan.*

● *6 en suite bedrooms, all with direct dial telephone and radio.*
● *Last dinner orders 8. 00 p.m, special diets; dogs accepted.*
● *Sea bathing; sailing/ boating; pony trekking; shooting/fishing; stalking by arrangement; golf five miles.*
● *Hotel closed from October 31st-1st March. Mastercard, Visa, Amex & Switch accepted.*

Salen 2, Craignure 14, Tobermory 15, Iona 35, Edinburgh 130.

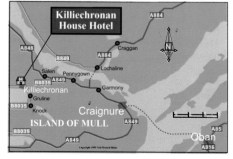

Scotland

Stonefield Castle Hotel

Tarbert, Loch Fyne, Argyll PA29 6YJ
Tel: (01880) 820836; Fax: (01880) 820929

Here is something unusual in the way of a holiday setting. Tastefully converted from a 19th century castle, once the home of the Campbells and overlooking Loch Fyne, Stonefield Castle is charmingly situated on a peninsula separating the Isles of Islay and Jura from Arran. It has panoramic views over the sea and its gardens are known for some of the finest rhododendrons in Britain, azaleas and other exotic shrubs that flourish in the mild west coast climate. Inside the castle, the rooms are spacious and comfortable. There is a large panelled cocktail bar, lounge-hall, library and drawing room. All the bedrooms are comfortably furnished, with those in the older part of the house being traditional, whilst rooms in the newer wing are of a more contemporary style. There are also several luxurious master bedrooms. The dining room, which enjoys stunning views, offers interesting table d'hôte menus, using local produce where possible. The accompanying wine list satisfies every taste and pocket. A snooker room and sauna suite are located within the hotel. Most traditional outdoor pursuits are available nearby and ferry trips to Arran, Gigha (gardens to see), Islay, Mull and Iona, together with the Mull of Kintyre are all within reach.

Rates: Dinner, bed and breakfast from £65-£75 per person, per night.   **V**
Bargain breaks: Very special offers of up to 30% off normal tariff available at certain times throughout the year.

● 33 bedrooms (32 en suite) all with direct dial telephone, colour TV, room service; lift.
● Table d'hôte and à la carte dining; bar lunch and special diets available.
● Children welcome; dogs can be accommodated by prior arrangement; conferences to 100 people.
● Snooker/billiards, sauna, solarium, sea bathing, fishing, sailing/boating; clay shooting, golf, riding nearby
● Open all year. All major credit cards accepted.

Lochgilphead 12, Inveraray 38, Campbeltown 38, Oban 51, Glasgow 95, London 500.

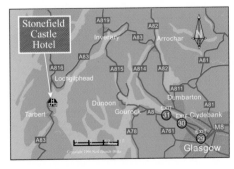

The Manor House

Gallanach Road, Oban, Argyll PA34 4LS
Tel: (01631) 562087; Fax: (01631) 563053

For peace and quiet within walking distance of
the bustle of Oban, I recommend the elegant
little Manor House Hotel. Built beside the sea
on the tip of the bay, it enjoys unrivalled views
over the harbour, the adjacent islands and the
mountains beyond. The hotel is owned by the
Leroy family, who also own Killiechronan
House on the Isle of Mull (*see page 205*), and is
supervised by their manager, Gabriel Wijker.
It provides a high standard of hospitality, service, comfort, and good food. The house is furnished in keeping with its dignity and age,
offering pretty, well appointed bedrooms and
an elegant drawing room. The parlour and
well furnished cocktail bar, with large windows overlooking the bay, make a pleasant
spot for an aperitif or bar lunch. The dining
room, which has an excellent reputation locally,
glows with silver in the candlelight. Chef Neil
O'Brien offers a tempting menu of Scottish and
continental cuisine, specializing in local fish
dishes and game in season. A good jumping off
point for fishing, exploring the scenic West
Coast, Mull or for visiting other islands and
places of interest.

*Rates: Dinner, room and breakfast per person
from £46 (low season) - £76 (high season) inc.
VAT. Weekly from £280(low season) to £462
(high season).*

● *11 en suite bedrooms, all with telephone, colour
TV and full central heating.*
● *Bar lunches; diets; AA Rosette for food.*
● *Sea bathing; sailing and boating ¹/₂ mile; indoor
heated swimming pool, sauna and solarium, golf,
each within 2 mile radius; helipad.*
● *Closed Monday & Tuesday from mid-November
to February (exc. Xmas/New Year); dogs allowed.*
● *Amex, Mastercard and Visa cards accepted.*
S.T.B. ～～～～ *Four Crown. AA* ☺☺ *for food.*
**Fort William 50, Glasgow 96, Dundee 116,
Inverness 118, Edinburgh 123, London 489.**

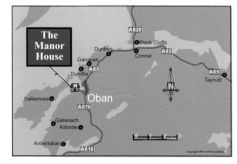

Scotland

Dungallan House Hotel

Gallanach Road, Oban, Argyll PA34 4PD
Tel: (01631) 563799; Fax: (01631) 566711

Superbly situated overlooking Oban Bay and
with magnificent views to the West and North,
Dungallan House has seen some changes since
building was started in 1868. It was originally
a stone built family home, then a rehabilita-
tion nursing home in the Great War. Called up
again in the 1939-1945 war, it was the head-
quarters of the Operational Signals Squadron
for the Flying Boat Base. Owners George and
Janice Stewart took over in 1995 and have insti-
tuted a major programme of refurbishment
since then. Janice presides in the kitchen and
her skill has been recognised by the award of
an AA rosette. She specialises in local produce,
particularly fish and shellfish. Oban is an excellent base for touring with Mull, Iona, Staffa and
Fort William all within a day's excursion.
Return in the evening to welcoming log fires,
fine cuisine, a good range of single malts and
the cosy, family atmosphere of the hotel.

● *13 bedrooms, 11 en suite, with colour TV,
hairdryer, laundry service. Car parking for 15.*
● *Table d'hôte dinner £25. A la carte, lunch (booked)
& special diets available. Last orders 2030.*
● *Sailing, sea/river bathing. Gym, fishing, golf
nearby. 2 meeting rooms 30/15. Closed Nov & Feb*

*Rates: Single room with breakfast from £40; double
inc. breakfast from £80.*   Ⅴ
Mastercard, Visa, Eurocard accepted.

Isle of Colonsay Hotel

Isle of Colonsay, Argyll PA61 7YP
Tel: (01951) 200316; Fax: (01951)
200353

One of the most beautifully remote
hotels in Britain, built in 1750 and a
listed historic building, Colonsay has
been carefully maintained and today
affords modern amenities that belie its
antiquity. The island is a paradise for
naturalists with 200 species of bird,
Atlantic Grey Seals and rare flora.
Archeologists will find artefacts from the pre-
Viking period. Most of the bedrooms are en
suite and there are larger family rooms and a
family bungalow. The hotel has ample public
areas, two bars and a separate building
incorporating a craft shop and coffee shop
where afternoon tea may be taken. Whatever
your interest, the mild winters and long light
summers add to the perfection of this tranquil
island. Your hosts, Claude (a Masterchef) and
Christine Reysenn are here to welcome you
and make your holiday as relaxing as possible.

*Rates: Low season from £75 per head inc. of
breakfast and 4-course tdh dinner; high season
from £85 inc breakfast and 4-course tdh.*   Ⅴ
Special rates for all stays of 3 nights and longer.

● *4 doubles, 1 single, 4 twins, 1 family room, 1
family bungalow, all with colour TV & tea/coffee
making facilities. Laundry service available.*
● *Special diets catered for.*
● *Open all year. Car parking. Ferry terminal pickup*
● *Fishing, golf, watersports, sailing, shooting all
nearby.* ● *Mastercard & Visa credit cards accepted.*
Mull 15, Argyll mainland 25, Oban-Colonsay by boat 2½ hours, Edinburgh 145.

Cairndale Hotel & Leisure Club

English Street, Dumfries DG1 2DF
Tel: (01387) 254111; Fax: (01387) 250555

The Cairndale Hotel has been owned by the Wallace family for 15 years and is now one of the premier hotels in Dumfries and indeed in the southwest of Scotland. Head chef Charlie Forrest oversees the main dining room and Sawney Beans Bar and Grill, ensuring that food is available throughout the day from both traditional table d'hôte and à la carte menus. 24 hour room service is also available and can be enjoyed in the Cocktail Bar / Reception area or delivered to your room. There are also light snacks available from early morning until late at night in the Forum Cafe Bar which overlooks the Leisure Club (open to residents). The hotel is in the middle of the historic town of Dumfries, close to forest parks, championship golf courses, seaside and wildlife parks and the fabulous countryside of south west Scotland and the Solway coast. The town is also well known for its local bard - Robert Burns. The hotel also offers conference facilities as well as holding functions and weddings throughout the year. With the acquisition of neighbouring Park House, another 19 bedrooms and conference facilities for 300+ guests will become available by end-1999. These and various other improvements ensure that the Cairndale's reputation continues to grow and that a large number of guests keep returning to sample its special brand of hospitality.

Rates: Single room inc. breakfast from £65- £95. Double room with breakfast from £85-£115. Ⓥ
Leisure Breaks: Various leisure breaks available including special rates for Young at Heart *(over 60s).Golf inclusive breaks from £52.50 db&b,pppn. Dinner dances (Sats;May-Oct) from £40 dinner, b&b per person. Conference rates: Day delegate from £20 pp. Residential rates from £65 per person.*

● *76 en suite bedrooms with satellite TV, radio, direct dial telephone, hairdryer, trouser press, laundry service, non-smoker bedrooms, tea/coffee making facilities, safety deposit box, minibar (some rooms).*
● *24-hour room service. Last dinner orders 21.30 hrs. Special diets available. Facilities for the disabled.*
● *Jacuzzi, sauna, indoor swimming pool, steam room, gym, toning tables. Golf nearby.*
● *Business services inc. 5 meeting rooms up to 200 capacity. AV equipment. Car rental. Parking for 60 cars. Open all year. Major credit cards accepted.*
● *New conference & banqueting facilities scheduled to open end-1999. For further details please contact Diane Waugh - Conference & Banqueting Office.*

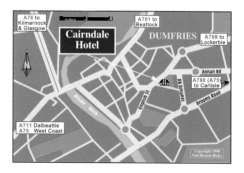

Scotland

Clonyard House Hotel
Colvend, Dalbeattie,Dumfries and
Galloway DG5 4QW
Tel: (01556) 630372; Fax: (01556) 630422

Once a Victorian country house, Clonyard is set in 7 acres of wooded grounds in a secluded position on the Solway coast, yet only 20 minutes from Dumfries. The accommodation offers a choice of traditional large first floor rooms or modern rooms in the Garden Wing, each with its own small patio. The 'Taste of Scotland' restaurant serves carefully produced dishes using local produce. Mild in Winter thanks to the warming Gulf Stream, there are six golf courses within 10 miles and salmon and trout fishing nearby in the river Urr. There is also excellent walking and cycling from the hotel and many castles and places of interest within a short drive.

Rates: Single room & breakfast from £40; double £70.
Bargain Breaks: 31 Oct-31 Mar dinner, b & b - £80
for 2 people per night. MC,Visa, Amex, JCB cards. Ⓥ
● *15 en suite bedrooms with telephone, radio/TV, hairdryer, laundry/valet service, tea/coffee making facilities. Facilities for disabled. Car parking 30. Open all year.*
● *Table d'hôte til 2100 £15; à la carte, lunch,diets avail*
Dumfries 14, Castle Douglas 6, Carlisle 47,Edinburgh 85

Queens Hotel
Annan Road, Lockerbie, Dumfries and
Galloway DG11 2RB
Tel: (01576) 202415; Fax: (01576) 203091

Conveniently situated just off the M74, the Queens Hotel is a convenient stopping-off point. The hotel offers trout fishing nearby and a 9-hole putting green. Other sports can be arranged near at hand. It has its own leisure complex and gymnasium and is well set up for functions and conferences. In addition to the Crystal Cocktail Bar for that quiet pre-meal drink, the oak-lined Queens Bar has an extensive menu of bar meals available throughout the day. Full Scottish breakfast and an extensive table d'hôte dinner is taken in the Princess Dining Room.
Dumfries 12, Gretna Green 16, Carlisle 23, Glasgow 72, Edinburgh 73.

Rates: Room & breakfast from £39.95 single, £55 dble
Weekend Breaks: 2 nights half board - £39.95 pppn
sharing twin. MC,Visa. Ⓥ ● *21 en suite bedrooms all with telephone, radio/TV+ satellite, hairdryer, laundry/ valet service, tea/coffee making facilities, trouser press.*
● *4-course table d'hôte £10.95.* ● *Snooker, gymnasium, jacuzzi/sauna, indoor sw'g pool.* ● *Open all year*

Corsemalzie House Hotel
Port William, Newton Stewart,
Wigtownshire DG8 9RL,
Dumfries & Galloway
Tel: (01988) 860254; Fax: (01988) 860213

Superb example of 19th century Scottish country mansion of classic proportions and character, the hotel is set in 47 acres of mature gardens and woodland, through which flows the Malzie burn, in an area of unspoilt natural beauty. Cuisine features 'Taste of Scotland' and 'Taste of Burns Country'cooking, both using fresh local produce. Salmon and brown trout fishing and game shooting packages are available and golfing arrangements can be made.

Rates: Single inc breakfast from £38; double from £76. Ⓥ *Visa, Mastercard, Amex accepted. Open 1st March-mid Jan. Spring & Autumn breaks available. Marquee receptions up to 200. Parking for 35*
● *14 en suite rooms with radio/TV, telephone, hairdryer, laundry, tea/coffee making, safe.*
● *Tdh til 9pm £22.* ● *Croquet, fishing, jogging, game shooting. Golf, riding, tennis nearby.*
Wigtown 6, Newton Stewart 13, Stranraer 20, Edinburgh 114.

Moffat House Hotel

High Street, Moffat, Dumfries and
Galloway DGl0 9HL
Tel: (01683)220039; Fax: (01683) 221288

Moffat is one of those delightful small towns
which lures travellers by its charm and environs. It has won both the *'Best Kept Village in
Scotland'* and the *'Scotland in Bloom'* awards and
is surrounded by some of the best hill walking
country and beautiful scenery in southern
Scotland. Set in the very heart of the town,
Moffat House is an Adam building which has
been skilfully converted into a most comfortable hotel in 2½ acres of landscaped gardens.
The public rooms are warm and inviting and
the bedrooms are immaculately decorated,
comfortably furnished, and have all the amenities that we now expect of a good modern
hotel. It is without doubt the best hotel for
miles around. It is only minutes from the A74
(M6), yet nestles in relatively unknown and
beautiful countryside. For anyone wishing to
take a holiday in this lovely area or breaking a
journey between England and Edinburgh or
Glasgow and beyond, Moffat House is the
ideal choice.

*Rates: Room and breakfast from £57.50 single,
£87.50 double. Dinner, room and breakfast from
£65 per person, including VAT.*
*Bargain Breaks: 3 days,d,b&b £165; 2 days £112;
Winter breaks Nov-March exc Xmas/New Year - 3
days d,b&b £140 pp; 2 days £95 pp.*

● *20 en suite bedrooms (including one deluxe
with four-poster bed and three rooms for the
partially disabled), all with telephone, TV and
hospitality tray; baby listening.*
● *Table d'hôte dinner £21. Last orders 9 p.m.; bar
meals, special diets available.*
● *Children wel-
come; dogs ac-
cepted in bed-
rooms only; con-
ferences max. 80.*
● *Good hill walk-
ing; leisure centre
nearby; golf one
mile; tennis ½
mile; riding two
miles.*
● *Open all year.
Major credit
cards accepted.*
**A74 (M6) 1,
Carlisle 40,
Edinburgh 55,
Perth 110, Oban
140, London 335.**

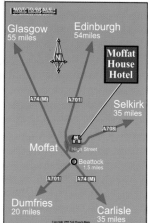

Scotland

Greywalls Hotel

Muirfield, Gullane, East Lothian EH31 2EG

Tel: (01620) 842144; Fax: (01620) 842241

This lovely hotel enjoys views over the Firth of Forth and Muirfield golf course. Its architecture, history, atmosphere and award-winning restaurant combine to make a stay at Greywalls a very pleasurable experience. The then holiday home was created by the Architect of New Delhi, Sir Edwin Lutyens, in 1901 and later the leading Scottish architect Sir Robert Lorimer added a wing, making Greywalls a unique co-operation between two eminent designers, as well as being the only complete Lutyens house in Scotland. The beautiful walled garden has been attributed to Gertrude Jekyll. One famous visitor was King Edward V11 and his outside lavatory is now transformed into a charming bedroom aptly named the *King's Loo*. Greywalls became a hotel in 1948 and the same family, which has now owned it for over seventy years, continue to impart the atmosphere of a private house to their guests. This shows in the bedrooms and the wood panelled library with its open fire - probably one of the finest rooms in this home from home. The bar is cosy and the sun room a delight. A new chef arrived to preside over the acclaimed restaurant in 1998. The kitchen produces modern British cuisine using the best of Scottish produce. The cool green dining-room overlooks Muirfield golf course. Greywalls is a perfectly enchanting place and the hotel's particular magic has few equals.

Rates: Single room including breakfast from ☑ *£95.00; double room with breakfast from £190.00. Leisure Breaks: Spring & autumn breaks available.*

- *23 en suite bedrooms with satellite TV, radio and direct-dial telephone, hairdryer, laundry service.*
- *Last orders for dinner 21.00. Meeting room with capacity for 20 guests; secretarial services.*
- *Golf, tennis (hard court & grass court), croquet. Airport pick-up. Ample car parking.*
- *Open April-October. Major credit cards accepted.*

Haddington 7¹/₂, Edinburgh 18, Berwick-upon-Tweed 45, Glasgow 62, London 377.

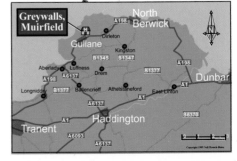

The Woodside Hotel

High Street, Aberdour, Fife KY3 0SW
Tel: (01383) 860328; Fax: (01383) 860920

The Woodside is an hotel which can claim
personality, from the first warm welcome by
Nancy and Peter Austen, the resident owners
and their friendly staff. I enjoyed its character,
exemplified by its history and its facilities. It
was built in 1873 by the Greig brothers, one of
whom became a Russian admiral, and original oil paintings of both brothers hang in the
foyer. As for the facilities: The Clipper Bar is
one of the most unusual in Scotland featuring
antique stained glass and panelling from the
famous Orient line vessel *Orontes*. The style of
the hotel persists into the elegant restaurant
where Nancy's expertly prepared à la carte or
table d'hôte menus range from Scottish through
French to Chinese. The lovely bedrooms have
been completely redecorated, each one individual in style and featuring a clan, and there
is a superb suite as well . The village, dominated by its 14th Century castle, is a gem
offering the freshness of the seaside, the tranquillity of the country, a picturesque old harbour and the prettiest railway station in Britain - and there are many other attractions in
the area. The personality of the Woodside, so
perfectly matched by the character of the
village, guarantees a most enjoyable stay.

Rates: Single room with breakfast from £55. **V**
Double room including breakfast from £70.
Leisure Breaks: Please 'phone for current offers.

● *20 en suite bedrooms with colour TV, direct-dial
telephone, hairdryer, trouser press, laundry service, non-smoker bedrooms, tea/coffee making facilities.*
● *Last orders for dinner 21.30 hrs. Special diets
available.*
● *Business services including meeting room with
25 guest capacity. Beauty salon adjacent.*
● *Car rental. Car parking 40 cars. Pets welcome.*
● *Open all year. Main credit cards accepted.*

**Dunfermline 7½, Edinburgh 17, Kincardine
17, Kinross 13, London 392 .**

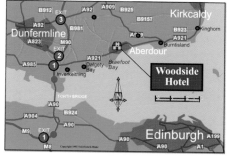

Balbirnie House

Balbirnie Park, Markinch, Glenrothes,
Fife KY7 6NE
Tel: (01592) 610066; Fax: (01592) 610529

A delightful Georgian house dating from 1777
now restored as a small luxury hotel, maintain-
ing the warmth and friendliness of its past, yet
providing top modern facilities. The hotel is
the centrepiece of a 416-acre park featuring
specimen trees and a rare collection of rhododendrons. There is a par 71 golf course in the
park (the hotel was named *Golf International
Hotel of the Year* in 1998) and other famous ones
nearby. Other recreations include fishing, clay
pigeon shooting, off-track driving and motor
racing. The Fife coast of quaint villages and castles
is near at hand; Edinburgh is one hour away.

*Rates: Single room inc. breakfast from £120; double
from £180. Credit cards accepted. Open all year.* Ⓥ
Pampered Weekend Break *dinner, b&b+tea £85
pppn sharing.* ***Golf Breaks*** *from £110 pppnight.*
● *30 en suite bedrooms with radio/TV, telephone, hairdryer, laundry, tea/coffee making, 24-hr room service, trouser press.* ● *Golf, billiards, croquet, jogging.
Squash, shooting, riding nearby.* ● *Conferences to 150.*

Kinkell House Hotel & Restaurant

Easter Kinkell, Conon Bridge, by
Dingwall, Ross-shire, Highland IV7 8HY
Tel: (01349) 861270; Fax: (01349) 865092

Situated on the Black Isle, just off the A9, 10 m
north of Inverness, Kinkell House overlooks
the Conon estuary, Dingwall and the Cromarty
Firth and has fine views to the Wester Ross
hills. Co-owner Marsha Fraser presides over
the cooking in the acclaimed restaurant, which
has won an AA rosette. The menu changes
daily and makes use of local produce. Kinkell
is well placed for day trips to Loch Ness, Skye,
Inverewe Gardens, local distilleries etc. Good
shopping is available in nearby Inverness and
most sporting activities can be arranged locally.

*Rates: Single room inc. breakfast from £45.50; dble
from £70. M'card & Visa accepted. Open all year.* Ⓥ
Bargain Breaks: *3 nights db&b for price of two.*
● *9 en suite bedrooms with TV, telephone, hairdryer,
laundry service, tea/coffee making. Facilities for disabled. Car parking 30.* ● *Last orders 2030.* ● *Fishing,
golf, bathing, shooting, tennis, riding, sw'g pool nearby.*

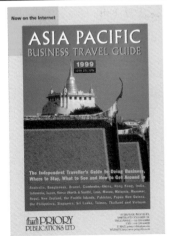

Travelling to Asia-Pacific?

Our guide, which has been published annually for ten years,
provides in 350 pages an introduction to the region and gives
a summary of the economic and political problems which have
brought harder times to this area hitherto accustomed only to
growth. It lists hotels, main tourist sites, exhibitions, useful
addresses, restaurants, airline connections and much more....

*"Not a word is wasted...any executive heading East for the
first time can be confident with this in his briefcase"*
                                -Executive Travel Magazine, London
*"The most comprehensive, yet compact Far East Travel Guide
on the market"*   - Lloyds List, London
"A fund of information"   - Check-in Magazine, Munich
*"Visually a delight to browse through...highly recommended,
and not just for the business visitor."*
                                - Academic Library Book Review, USA

ISBN 1 871985 30 7   350 pages, paperback   **£9.95**

Rosedale Hotel

Portree, Isle Of Skye, Highland IV51 9DB
Tel: (01478) 613131; Fax: (01478) 612531

The Rosedale was originally a row of William
IV cottages adjacent to the harbour in old
Portree. It now occupies nearly all of one side
of the waterfront and looks out across the
Sound of Raasay to the Isle beyond. An interesting feature is the first floor restaurant,
which gives a unique view of fishermen un-
loading the day's catch, some of which you
may find on the next day's menu! Tony
Parkyn supervises the cuisine, which uses as
much local produce as possible, and the restaurant maintains its AA Rosette Award, amid
other plaudits. A good selection of Highland
malt whiskies is available in the friendly bar,
including the locally distilled *Talisker.*
Two comfortable lounges help you relax and
plan the next day's sightseeing - maybe
Dunvegan Castle or the Museum of Island
Life. Rosedale is a few minutes' walk from the
centre of Portree with its shops and leisure
centre. There is a nine-hole golf course nearby.
You will be assured of a warm welcome by
the Andrew family at any time, but they recommend an early visit when the weather is at
its best and the island less busy.

*Rates: Room and breakfast from £35.00 per
person inclusive of VAT. Other terms on application.* **Bargain breaks:** *Skye Explorer holiday rates
available for stays of 3 days or more including accommodation, breakfast, dinner and free admission
to Dunvegan Castle, the Clan Donald Centre and
the Museum of Island Life. Prices from £50 per day.*

● *23 en suite bedrooms (7 ground floor) all with
television, telephone, radio, tea/coffee making facilities, also 3 attractive twin bedded rooms with
private bathrooms available in nearby Beaumont
House; full central heating.*
● *Boating; tennis, swimming pool, squash and golf
nearby; fishing by arrangement; open air parking.*
● *Closed October to mid-May, but office open for
enquiries and advance bookings*

**Kyle of Lochalsh 34, Invermoriston 90, Fort
Augustus 97, Edinburgh 237, London 650.**

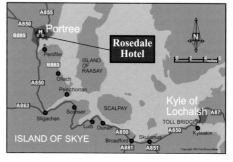

Eddrachilles Hotel

Badcall Bay, Scourie, Sutherland IV27 4TH
Tel: (01971) 502080; Fax: (01971) 502477

The Eddrachilles commands a fine position, overlooking the sea with mountains behind it. Inside, the hotel is clean, bright and comfortable, with many of the windows having a sea view, thanks to the foresight of Mr. and Mrs. Alasdair Wood, who have restored and extended this old building, and are kind and hospitable hosts. The logistics of providing food and drink in these remote parts makes the discovery of an à la carte and table d'hôte menu, together with an interesting wine list, a pleasant surprise. The emphasis is on home cooking, using fresh and seasonal ingredients. Hill lamb, venison and seafood are the local delicacies. The north of Scotland is unique; its remote and untouched beauty cannot be described in a few words. You can explore it from quiet, single-track roads, or, for the more energetic, there are numerous scenic walks and climbs. Nearby Handa Island is famous as a bird sanctuary, and boat trips across the short stretch of water can be made from Tarbet. When returning to Eddrachilles after a tiring day of exploration, you can always be assured of warmth, comfort and good food.

Rates: Room and breakfast from £37.00; dinner, room and breakfast from £48.00. Prices include VAT. **Bargain breaks** - reduced rates available on stays of 3, 6 or 10 days.

● *11 en suite bedrooms (4 on ground floor), all with direct dial telephone and TV.*
● *last orders for dinner 8. 00 p.m; bar lunches available; special diets by arrangement.*
● *Children of 3 years and over welcome.*
● *Sailing/boating; fishing.*
● *Hotel closed Nov.-Feb. inclusive. Mastercard and Visa credit cards accepted.*

Ullapool 40, Thurso 95, Inverness 98, Edinburgh 245, Glasgow 266, London 620.

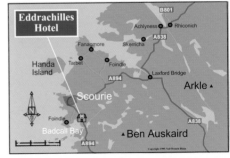

Craigellachie Hotel of Speyside

Speyside, Banffshire, Moray AB38 9SR
Tel: (01340) 881204; Fax: (01340) 881253
E-mail: sales@craigellachie.com.

A true haven of Highland hospitality at the centre of the world - for malt whisky! The fabulous new master rooms and mini suites all have a view over the river Spey. Award winning chef David Kinnes and his team produce daily changing menus using only the highest quality produce, purchased locally whenever possible. The internationally famous Quaich Bar, with one of the largest selections of drinking malt whiskies **in the world** is recognised as *the* place to drink *the drink*. Aberdeen & Inverness airports are each around an hour's drive away and Elgin train station is 12 miles. AA ◎◎ Food. STB ★★★★

Rates: Single inc breakfast from £77.50; double from £95. Major credit cards accepted. Open all year.
Special Breaks from £52.50 pppn,db&b. ● *16 standard rooms; 6 master rooms, 4 mini-suites, all en suite with radio/TV, telephone, hairdryer, laundry, tea/coffee making, trouser press.* ● *Fixed price dinner to 22h00 £27.50.* ● *Snooker, indoor games, gym, tennis. Walking, shooting (clay and game), cycling, fishing nearby.*

The Seafield Arms Hotel

Cullen, Banffshire, Moray AB56 2SG
Tel: (01542) 840791; Fax: (01542) 840763

"No superior between Aberdeen and Inverness". This quote from the 1845 statistical account of Scotland still aptly describes the Seafield Arms. As befits a member of the Taste of Scotland scheme, à la carte meals using the best of local produce are served in the elegant dining-room. Personal service is the hallmark of this hotel. Sit in the Findlater Lounge enjoying the roaring log fire in season and sample one of over 100 whiskies on display, as befits an hotel on the Whisky Trail. Cullen is a good centre for visiting North-east Scotland. Sea bathing and fishing, deer stalking, shooting and pony trekking can all be enjoyed near by.

Rates: Room inc. breakfast from £38 single, £60 Ⓥ *double. Major credit cards accepted. Open all year.*
Winter Weekend Breaks Oct-March 2 nights b&b from £70. ● *Tdh til 2130 £17. Lunch, àlc, diets avail.*
● *20 en suite bedrooms with radio/TV, telephone, hairdryer, laundry, tea/coffee making, trouser press.*
● *Fishing, golf, riding, shooting, tennis, swim'g locally*

Montgreenan Mansion House Hotel

Nr. Kilwinning, N. Ayrshire KA13 7QZ
Tel: (01294) 557733; Fax: (01294) 850397

Montgreenan Mansion was built by Dr Robert Glasgow in 1817 who, in the words of a contemporary "laying off the ground with much taste, rendered it a very desirable residence". And so it remains today - it has always been a family home, with a tranquil peaceful atmosphere. The hotel has a picturesque practice golf course, putting green, tennis court, billiard room and croquet. The cellar boasts over 200 bins and complements the tempting cuisine, which is inspired by a wealth of local produce.

Rates: Single room inc breakfast from £70; Ⓥ *double from £110. Visa, Access, Amex, Diners accepted. Open all year. Weekend rate: 2 nights, d,b&b £130 per person.* ● *Tdh til 9.30 £25.80.*
● *21 en suite bedrooms with TV, telephone, hairdryer, laundry, tea/coffee making, trouser press.*
● *Billiards, croquet, tennis, golf practice course*

Stakis Dunkeld House Resort Hotel

Dunkeld, Perthshire PH8 0HX
Tel: (01350) 727771; Fax: (01350) 728924

A small place in the country, built by the seventh Duke of Atholl as a wedding present for his wife and latterly to look after his weekend guests, Dunkeld House has always been one of my favourite hotels. Situated in 280 acres of moor and forest directly on the banks of the Tay, the hotel has all the elegance of an Edwardian country house with the comfort of a modern luxury resort hotel. All 97 bedrooms are furnished to the highest standard. The star room is *The Bothy* where the bed is a boat and the double shower is enormous. Enjoy the champagne and canapes which will appear at 6 pm on the first night of your stay. The elegant restaurant serves International and Scottish cuisine with the accent on *Taste of Scotland* dishes. Christian presides over the Cocktail Bar which has a fine selection of malts. You can burn off the calories in the *Living Well Health Club* and other Dunkeld Park Activities include 4x4 off road driving, grass karts, quad bikes, JCB driving, archery and championship clay pigeon shooting under the expert tuition of Ian Marsden, Commonwealth Games Medallist.

Rates: Single room with breakfast £125.75; **V** double with breakfast £151.50. Dinner, b & b from £75 per person sharing.
Bargain breaks - Various fun & themed weekends available throughout the year. Apply for details.
● *97 en suite bedrooms (inc. 3 family rooms & 3 suites), all with direct dial telephone, TV + satellite, hairdryer, laundry/valet service, most with minibar, tea/coffee making facilities, 24 hour room/meal service, music/radio/alarm clock, trouser press.*
● *Non-smoker and disabled bedrooms available.*
● *3-course table d'hôte £30; lunch, à la carte & diets available; last orders 2100.*
● *Executive centre inc. 5 meeting rooms to 100.*
● *Pool table, croquet, fishing, fitness centre, indoor games, jacuzzi/sauna, shooting, indoor swimming pool, tennis. Golf 2 miles; riding 14 miles.*
● *Open all year. Major credit cards accepted.*
Pitlochry 13, Perth 15, Glasgow 69, Edinburgh 57

Dalmunzie House Hotel

Spittal O'Glenshee, Blairgowrie,
Perthshire PH10 7QG
Tel: (01250) 885224; Fax: (01250) 885225
E-mail: dalmunzie@aol.com

If you are looking for perfect peace and quiet
or for a sporting holiday, this impressive
country house, hidden away in the hills, is an
excellent venue. Dalmunzie has been in the
Winton family for many years, and is now
looked after by Simon and Alexandra, whose
care and attention result in a well run house,
personal service, and a happy atmosphere.
The sitting rooms, cosy cocktail bar and spacious bedrooms are all in excellent decorative
order, well furnished and comfortable, and
log fires and central heating ensure warmth in
every season. In the dining room, the varied
table d'hôte dishes are well cooked and feature traditional Scottish fare, which is accompanied by a carefully chosen wine list. This
family owned sporting estate can organise
almost any shooting holiday, whilst other field
sports, trout fishing, walking and climbing also
await you here. Dalmunzie have their own 9
hole golf course available for guests. Nearby
Glenshee offers well organised skiing for all
abilities, and for those wishing to explore on
wheels, there are quiet roads and much to see.

*Rates: Room and breakfast from £41 per person,
weekly rates from £375 per person, full board.* **V**
*During the ski season, dinner, bed and breakfast
from £47-£57.*
***Bargain breaks**: From Jan-April 2 nights from
£94 & 5 nights from £210. From April-October 3
nights from £165.*

● *18 bedrooms (1 for the disabled, 16 en suite),
lift.*
● *Last dinner orders 8.30 p.m.; light bar lunches;
special diets on request. Restaurant AA rosette.*
● *Children welcome; dogs accepted; conferences
to 20.*
● *Games room; bar billiards; 9 hole golf course;
tennis; shooting/fishing (trout/salmon, own
rainbow trout stocked loch); skiing in Glenshee;
pony trekking; mountain bikes.*
● *Closed December. Mastercard & Visa accepted.*
**Perth 35, Dundee 37, Braemar 15, Blairgowrie
20, Edinburgh 78, London 453.**

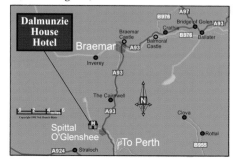

Scotland

Ardeonaig Hotel

South Loch Tay Side,
Perthshire FK21 8SU
Tel: (01567) 820400;
Fax: (01567) 820282
Internet:
http://www.ardeonaighotel.co.uk

The Ardeonaig Hotel is none other than a pure haven for the visitor and sportsman alike. It is situated amongst breathtaking scenery. Within a 25 minute drive, there are golf courses at Killin, Kenmore and Aberfeldy. This secluded 17th century inn has its own salmon fishing rights on the Loch, with its own boat and rod and drying room. Guests can also fish for salmon on the River Tay, and excellent stalking can be arranged. The tasty Scottish cuisine is created from the freshest of local produce, and is complemented by a good selection of international wines. The Ardeonaig boasts a cheery bar, which offers some of the best Scottish malts, a cosy sitting room, and a second floor library with wonderful views over Loch Tay and the hills of Ben Lawers. I can recommend a stay at the Ardeonaig either for the sporting facilities or purely for a spate of peace and relaxation.

Rates: Room & breakfast from £43.50; dinner, **V** *room and breakfast from £68.00. Prices inc. VAT.*

● *14 en suite bedrooms (5 ground floor), all with tea/coffee making facilities.*
● *Last orders for dinner 9.00 p.m; special diets; dogs accepted; conferences max. 16; public telephone box in hotel.*
● *Own harbour and boats; shooting/fishing; riding nearby; limited service in the winter.*
● *Switch, Delta, Access & Mastercard accepted.*
Perth 50, Stirling 50, Edinburgh 72, London 445.

Peebles Hotel Hydro

Peebles EH45 8LX
Tel: (01721) 720602;
Fax: (01721) 722999
E-mail:
hydro@scotborders.co.uk

Situated high above the east end of Peebles with superb views across to the river Tweed is the Hydro - the ultimate Scottish Borders experience. Dating from 1907 the magnificent Edwardian building has one of the most impressive staircases in Scotland. The accommodation is of a high standard and includes family rooms. There are two restaurants: the main dining room offering the best of Scottish traditional fare and international dishes and, new this year, *Lazels*, bistro-style, and open 0930-1800. There is also a new children's dining room. The Hydro is a destination in itself, with many sporting facilities under one roof. It is also well placed for exploring the whole gamut of Scottish history, with castles, abbeys, stately homes and battlefields nearby and Edinburgh only 30 minutes away.

Rates: Room & breakfast from £65 single, £100 double. All major credit cards accepted. **V**
Bargain Breaks: Many special breaks on application
● *137 en suite bedrooms, all with radio/TV, direct dial telephone, hairdryer, laundry service, minibar, tea/coffee making facilities, 24-hr room/meal service, trouser press. Bedrooms for disabled available. Open all year. 7 meeting rooms 28-450*
● *Tdh dinner £21.50. A la carte, lunch & special diets available. Last orders 9.00 p.m. Car parking 200.*
● *Business services inc 7 meeting rooms, 28-450.*
● *Billiards/snooker, fishing, gymnasium, indoor games jacuzzi, massage, sauna, solarium, squash, badminton, indoor pool, tennis, riding, beauty salon, hairdresser.*
Galashiels 18, Glasgow 49, Edinburgh 22.

Toftcombs Country House & Restaurant

Peebles Road, Biggar,
Lanarkshire ML12 6QX
Tel: (01899) 220142;
Fax: (01899) 221771

The magnificent red sandstone Toftcombs House was purchased in late 1997 by Charlie and Vivian Little. Situated directly on the A 702, the route between Edinburgh and the A74(M), the house has been refurbished and is now a fine small country house hotel with great views of the surrounding countryside. There has been a house on the site since the 16th century and at one time it was tenanted by the family of William Gladstone, Victorian prime minister. Public rooms and restaurant are impressive. For less formal dining there are the bar and coffee lounge. The small market town of Biggar is a good centre for touring the south of Scotland. Glasgow and Edinburgh are about one hour's drive. The superb New Lanark Historical Site, designated an Outstanding Conservation Area and nominated as a Unesco World Heritage Site, is nearby and well worth visiting.

Rates: Room & breakfast from £45 single; £60 **V** *dble. All major credit cards + Switch, Delta, acc'd.*

● *4 en suite bedrooms, all with colour TV, hairdryer, telephone, tea/coffee making facilities, laundry service, safety deposit box, trouser press. Non-smoker bedrooms available. Car parking for 50.*
● *Table d'hôte dinner £12. A la carte, lunch & special diets available. Last orders 9. 30 p.m.*
● *Golf, hill walking.* ● *Open all year.*
Abington 12, Lanark 13 ,Glasgow 36, Edinburgh 28

Forest Hills Hotel

Kinlochard, Aberfoyle,
Stirling FK8 3TL
Tel: (01877) 387277;
Fax: (01877) 387307

Dominated by the towering bulk of Ben Lomond to the Northwest and on the banks of Loch Ard at the edge of the Trossachs, Forest Hills offers everything for a memorable holiday. I was particularly attracted by the setting - 25 acres of landscaped gardens and woodland with rushing burns, winding pathways and breathtaking scenery. The original house dates from Edwardian times and boasts some fine wood panelling in the lobby. The Garden Restaurant features the best of local produce prepared in the traditional manner by award-winning chefs. For less formal dining there are grills in the Bonspiel Cafe/Bar. For that relaxing pre-dinner drink, there is the piano bar with log fires in winter and superb views in summer. Nearly every sporting activity is available in the purpose built Leisure Centre or in the immediate vicinity.

Rates: Room & breakfast from £63 single; £95 **V** *double. Open all year. Credit cards accepted.*
Bargain Breaks: Min. 2-night stay, dinner,b&b from £55 pppn.
● *56 en suite bedrooms, all with colour TV, telephone, hairdryer, laundry service, tea/coffee making facilities, trouser press.*
● *Table d'hôte 4-cse dinner £26.95. A la carte, lunch & special diets available, Car parking for 70*
● *Billiards/snooker, croquet, fishing, gymnasium, indoor games, jacuzzi, jogging track, massage, sauna, solarium, shooting, squash, indoor swimming pool, tennis. Golf 5 m, riding 2m.*
Stirling 23, Glasgow 26, Perth 40, Edinburgh 57.

Scotland

Inchyra Grange Hotel, Leisure Club & Restaurant

Grange Road, Polmont, Falkirk, Stirling FK2 OYB
Tel: (01324) 711011; Fax: (01324) 716134

Situated just off the M8 Motorway, Inchyra Grange was originally a period manor house which has been developed into a fine hotel meeting the demands of the most discerning leisure or business traveller. It stands ijn 44 acres of private grounds. The Priory restaurant has recently been extended to create a number of semi-private areas. The chef serves a daily changing menu, according to local availability. Light, less formal meals are available in the Pelican Leisure Club Restaurant. Most of the main attractions of Central Scotland are within a day's touring - St Andrews and East Lothian for golf, Loch Lomond and the Trossachs for scenery, Stirling Castle and Bannockburn for history, Glasgow and Edinburgh for culture and Glengoyne or Glen Turret to experience the Water of Life (whisky).

*Rates: Single (room only) from £80; double (room only) from £90. **Bargain Breaks:** 1.11.98-31.3.99 Min 2 nights stay £45 pppn b&b; £65 pppn d,b&b*

● *109 en suite bedrooms inc 2 suites, all with radio/TV+ satellite, telephone, hairdryer, laundry service, minibar, trouser press, tea/coffee making, 24-hr room service. Non-smoker & disabled bedrooms available.* ● *Tdh til 2130 £31. A la carte, lunch & diets available. AA ⊛ Restaurant.*
● *Gymnasium, jacuzzi, massage, sauna, indoor pool, tennis. Golf adjacent; riding locally.*
● *Business services inc 7 meeting rooms to 500.*
● *Open all year. All credit cards accepted.*

Houstoun House Hotel & Country Club

Uphall, West Lothian
EH52 6JS
Tel: (01506) 853831;
Fax: (01506) 854220

The old tower of Houstoun House, which forms its redoubt, dates from the 17th century. Today this tower, the adjacent manor house (*The Women House*) and the *Steading,* together with some new buildings, have all been sympathetically combined to form the 4-star Hotel & Country Club. For that pre-dinner drink or nightcap the *Vaulted Bar* has a selection of around 100 single malt whiskies, including some of 'cask strength'. The hotel has two restaurants: *Pelegrinos,* an Italian bistro situated in the Leisure Club and the main Dining Room which has been created from a combination of the Great Hall, Drawing Room and Library and which has two AA rosettes. Standing in 20 acres of parkland and close to Edinburgh Airport, Houstoun, with its many activities, is ideal for a business or leisure stay.

*Rates: Single inc. breakfast from £70; double from £110. **Bargain Breaks:** 1.11.98-31.3.99 Min 2 nights stay £55 pppn b&b; £78 pppn d,b&b.* ⓥ
● *74 en suite rooms inc 1 suite, all with radio/colour TV + satellite, direct-dial telephone, hairdryer, laundry service, tea/coffee making, 24-hr room service, bathrobe, iron, trouser press. Non-smoker and disabled rooms available. Open all year* ● *Table d'hôte dinner £32.50 ⊛⊛. A la carte, lunch & special diets available. Last orders 2130. Italian Bistro* ● *9 Conference rooms to 350 pax. Parking for 200.* ● *Croquet, gymnasium, massage, sauna, indoor pool, tennis, beauty salon, dance studio. Golf and riding adjacent.* ● *Major credit cards accepted.*

Moët & Chandon -Signpost exclusive champagne partner.

Guernsey

The Channel Island of Guernsey - a veritable haven for the holidaymaker. A modern airport, excellent harbour, hotels and guest houses with every amenity. A thriving tourist industry which encourages and welcomes visitors, and rewards them with all the comforts associated with up-to-date civilised living.

But existing alongside the evidence of today's lifestyle are customs and traditions that have resisted change. Large chunks of Guernsey's intricate and chequered history blend harmoniously with the present. This is all part of Guernsey's unique character; the present is built around the past rather than unceremoniously trampling upon it.

For the visitor who is ignorant of Guernsey's history, it would seem also that the island cannot decide whether it is French or British! In St. Peter Port, for example, street names are displayed in both English and French, and the town retains a definite air of an ancient Norman seaport. Now and again throughout the island, one can catch snatches of conversations spoken in Guernsey patois, which the uninitiated could forgivably mistake for French.

The French/British connection is in itself unusual. Geographically closer to France, but essentially a "British" Island, Guernsey was once under the domination of the Norman dukes, who in turn were vassals of the French king. William II of Normandy, crowned William I of England in 1066, established the connection with England and subsequent events have established the Channel Islands as part of the dominion of the Kings of England, but never part of their kingdom.

An air of the past, a French flavour - the visitor cannot ignore these influences. St. Peter Port, a flourishing commercial centre with its busy harbour, still preserves its past identity, with its buildings of traditional Guernsey granite and its unspoilt skyline. And from the castle ramparts throughout the summer season booms the noonday gun, after a ceremony that is fascinating to witness.

Guernsey has many unique attractions for the visitor. The Little Chapel is the smallest chapel in the world, and lavishly decorated with pottery and shells, has room for only five people inside. Victor Hugo, the famous French author, lived in exile for 15 years on Guernsey, and his house is an extravagant monument to his life and work. Guernsey has a host of museums, a butterfly centre, zoo, aquarium, craft centre and a variety of fascinating archaeological sites as well as a fine leisure centre which caters for all the main sports. Add to this Guernsey's spectacular cliff walks and beautiful countryside and the visitor will find that all tas-tes are catered for.

As is to be expected, Guernsey is famed for a number of traditional dishes and delicacies, not the least of which is the Guernsey Gache, a sort of fruit loaf still popular on the island. It can be purchased in a number of shops, and many people have their own, special recipes, but perhaps the most intriguing place to purchase it is in the Old Guernsey Market, held on Thursdays in St. Peter Port. Traditionally dressed stall holders sell all manner of island-produced wares from freesia corms, to the beautifully made, oiled-wool Guernseys for which the island is so famous.

St Peter Port

There is much to fascinate the holidaymaker in Guernsey; one could spend many return visits delving into traditions, customs and folklore alone. The islanders, proud of their heritage and keen to share it, afford the warmest of welcomes to every visitor.

Channel Islands

Historic Houses, Gardens & Parks

Candle Gardens, St Peter Port, G'y
Castle Cornet & Maritime Museum, Guernsey
Eric Young Orchid Foundation, Trinity, Jersey
Fantastic Tropical Gardens, St. Peter's Valley, Jersey
Grande Marais Koi Farm, Vale, G'y Howard David Park, St. Helier, Js'y
Jersey Flower Centre, St. Lawrence
Jersey Lavender Farm St. Brelade
La Mare Vineyards, St. Mary, Jsy
La Seigneurie, Island of Sark Samares Manor, St Clement, Jsy
St. Ouen's Manor Grounds, St Ouen, Jersey
Saumarez Manor, St Martin's, Guernsey
Specialist Gardens at Castle Cornet, Guernsey
Sunset Carnation Nurseries, St. Ouen's Bay, Jersey

Walks & Nature Trails

Grandes Rocques, Guernsey
Guided nature walks - Jersey's Coastal Walks:
  i) Grosnez to Sorel
  ii) Sorel to Bouley Bay
  iii) Bouley Bay to St. Catherine's
Le Catioroc Nature Trail & L'Eree
Port Soif Nature Trail, Guernsey
Shingle Bank Portinfer, Guernsey
The Saumarez Nature Trail& Park Walk, starting at Cobo Bay, Guernsey
St Peter Port to St Martin's Point Walk, Guernsey

Historical Sites & Museums

La Valette Underground Military Museum, St. Peter Port, Guernsey
German Occupation Museum, St. Peter Port, Guernsey
Guernsey Aquarium, Havelet Bay
Guernsey Museum & Art Gallery, St Peter Port
National Trust of Guernsey Folk Museum, Saumarez Park

Fort Grey Shipwreck Museurn, St. Saviours, Guernsey
Battle of Flowers Museum, St Ouen, Jersey
Elizabeth Castle, St Aubin's Bay, Jersey
Faldouet Dolmen, Gorey, Jsy
German Underground Hospital, St. Lawrence, Jersey

Grosnez Castle & La Pinacle, Les Landes, Jersey
Hamptonne Country Life Museunn, St. Lawrence, Jersey
The Hermitage St Helier, Jersey
La Hougue Bie, Grouville, Jersey
Island Fortree Occupation Museum, St. Helier, Jersey
Jersey Motor Museum
The Living Legend, St Peter, Jersey
Mont Orgueil Castle, Gorey, Jersey
The Pallot Heritage Steam Mu seum, Trinity, Jsersey
St. Peter's Bunker Museum, St. Peter, Jersey

Entertainment Venues

Fort Regent Leisure Centre, St Helier, Jersey
Guernsey Bird Sanctuary, St Andrew's
Jersey Butterfly Centre, St Mary
Jersey Shire Horse Farm & Mu seum, St Ouen
Jersey Pottery, Gorey Village
Jersey Zoo, Trinity
Le Friquet Butterfly Centre, Castel, Guernsey
Oatlands, Guernsey's craft Centre, St Sampson's

Channel Islands

DIARY OF EVENTS

February

14-22. **Jersey Chess Festival**
Feb-Mar. **Guernsey Eisteddfod Festival.** Beau Sejour Centre, St Peter Port

March

13-19*. **English Bridge Union Bridge Week.** Guernsey

April

April. **Guernsey Fesatival of Food and Wine** leading to....
26-28. **Guernsey Salon Culinaire.** Displays by visiting & local chefs; competitions.
2-4/5. **Guernsey Easter Runs.**
2-4/5. **Guernsey Easter Hockey Festival.**
29-May 2. **Jersey Jazz Festival.**

May

9. **Liberation Day.** Celebration of the liberation of Guernsey from German occupation.St PP
13-17.5. **100 Years of Motoring Festival.** Jersey.
15-23. **Good Food Festival,** Jersey .

June

3-5. **Floral Guernsey Show.** Cambridge Park, St Peter Port
9-10. **Early Summer Flower Show,** Howard Davis Park, St Helier, Jersey.
27*. **Guernsey Horse Driving Society Annual Show,** Sausmarez Manor, St Martins

July

July. **Guernsey International Folk Festival.**

12-18. **Jersey Floral Festival.**
24-Aug 1. **Guernsey St Peter Port Town Carnival.**

August

1*. **Rocquaine Regatta,** Rocquaine Bay, St Pierre du Bois, Guernsey
2-8. **Alderney Week.** Carnival Time in Alderney.
12-13. **Jersey Battle of Flowers.**
August. **9th Guernsey Custom & Classic Bike Show.** Mont Herault, St Pierre du Bois.
18-19*. **North Show/Battle of Flowers.** Saumarez Park, Gnsy.
18. **Jersey Summer Flower Show.**

September

2-5. **Jersey Film Festival.**
10-12. **Country Show 1998.** Howard Davis Farm, Trinity, Jersey
16. **International Air Display,** Jersey.
16*. **Battle of Britain Air Display.** St Peter Port, Guernsey
18-26*. **English Bridge Union Congress,** St Pr Port, Guernsey
30-Oct 3. **World Music Festival.** Jersey.

October

October. **Guernsey Jazz Festival.**
17-23*. **23rd Int'l Chess Festival** Peninsula Hotel, Vale, Guernsey

dates to be confirmed
For further details contact:

TOURIST BOARDS

States of Guernsey Department of Tourism and Recreation, PO Box 23, St. Peter Port, Guernsey, Channel Islands GY1 3AN. Tel: 01481 723552
Jersey Tourism
Liberation Square, St Helier, Jersey E1 1BB, Channel Islands. Tel: 01534 500700

Jersey

The island of Jersey has something to offer everyone, but there's a lot more for children than just the obvious attractions of sun, sea and sand. Its wealth of sporting facilities, historic sites and animal centres make it an ideal spot for family holidays, and even offer children and parents the chance to get away from each other once in a while.

If you really can't bear to tear yourself away from the sea, there are all kinds of watersports available around the island and Jersey Tourism can provide a comprehensive list of surfing, sailing and water-ski clubs.

But if the children want to go it alone, there's no need for parents to worry. *The Wind & Water Windsurfer School* at St. Aubin offers a 5-hour windsurfing course for beginners from the age of nine upwards, using a small lightweight rig for younger pupils. Tuition is by fully qualified instructors.

Youngsters who prefer riding a horse to a surfboard are well catered for by the island's numerous riding stables, several of whom are also pleased to welcome unaccompanied helpers. Prices average £9 an hour for a hack, £10-12 for a lesson and hard hats can usually be provided, so there's no need to squeeze one into the hand-luggage.

A number of sports centres and pleasure parks offer a variety of activities from weight-training to table tennis, go-karts to snooker, but perhaps the best known of them all is Fort Regent - the huge sports and leisure complex housed in the Napoleonic fortress overlooking St. Helier.

When the family is tired of having fun and fancies a little gentle education, there is no shortage of historical sites to interest visitors of all ages. Elizabeth Castle in St. Aubin's Bay was begun in the reign of Queen Elizabeth I and has been re-

fortified throughout the centuries right up until the First World War. Open only during the summer months, the castle is reached across the bay from St. Helier by an amphibious vehicle service using a World War II landing craft.

Even older - a mere 5,000 years - is the 40ft mound of the Neolithic tomb at La Hougue Baie in Grouville. Here you can walk right inside the ancient burial chamber, visit the railway exhibition and the agricultural museum, or just relax in the wooded park.

Those who like natural history will enjoy a visit to the Kempt Tower Interpretation Centre on the Five Mile Road at St. Ouen. A converted Martello tower, it contains displays and artefacts relating to the special characteristics of Jersey's "mini national park". Open every afternoon from June to September.

Animal lovers of all ages are well catered for on the island. Heatherbrae Farm in St. John offers visitors the chance to learn all about milk production and watch the 50-strong herd of pure bred Jersey cows during afternoon milking. There's also a fascinating Shire Horse Farm in St. Ouen and, for the very large to the very small, a butterfly farm at the Haute Tombette.

Finally, no animal lover can afford to miss the unique collection of endangered species at the Jersey Wildlife Preservation Trust established 33 years ago by naturalist Gerald Durrell in Trinity.

Jersey may measure a mere nine miles by five, but it is packed with interesting things to see and do - for the young in years and the young at heart!

Channel islands

Bella Luce Hotel & Restaurant

Moulin Huet, St. Martins, Guernsey
GY4 6EB
Tel: (01481) 38764; Fax: (01481) 39561

The Hotel Bella Luce is a former 12th century manor house that is attractive both inside and out. There is an abundance of flowers, from the sweet peas lining the swimming pool, to the wonderful hanging baskets on the walls. The Proprietor, Richard Cann, and his staff take great pride in running this hotel to ensure their guests' maximum contentment. All the public rooms are beautifully furnished and very comfortable. The lounge bar, with its oak beamed ceiling, has a warm and friendly atmosphere, and is the ideal place in which to enjoy either a drink or a dish chosen from the extensive bar lunch menu. The freshly prepared food served in the restaurant is excellent, with a delicious choice of dishes from either the table d'hôte or à la carte menus. To accompany these, there is a comprehensive wine list to suit all palates. During my recent visit, my overall impression was one of total peace and tranquillity, punctuated only by birdsong. The hotel is just two miles from the beautiful "capital" of Guernsey, St. Peter Port, and the island's magnificent cliffs and coastal scenery make breathtaking views.

Rates: Room and breakfast £27-£51; dinner, room and breakfast £41-£64.
Bargain breaks *available 1st November-1st April, £26 pppn for b & b.*

● *31 en suite bedrooms (3 ground floor), all with direct dial telephone and TV; room service; baby listening.*
● *Last orders for dinner 9.45p.m.; bar meals; special diets.*
● *Children welcome; dogs accepted at management's discretion.*
● *Outdoor heated swimming pool; sauna; solarium.*
● *Open all year; major credit cards accepted.*

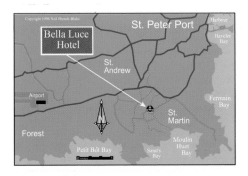

The Duke of Richmond Hotel

Cambridge Park, St Peter Port,
Guernsey GY1 1UY

Tel: (01481) 726221; Fax: (01481) 728945
E-mail: duke@guernsey.net;
Internet: http//accom.guernsey.net/duke

*Rates: Single room with breakfast from £55;
double room with breakfast from £75.*   **V**
*Bargain Breaks: Discounts of 10% for week-
ends. Terms inclusive of flights & ferries can be
arranged.*

Situated opposite Cambridge Park and overlooking the picturesque capital of St Peter
Port, the Duke of Richmond Hotel is well located for both holiday maker and business
visitor alike. It stands on the site of *Grovers*
Hotel, established in 1790, of which the third
Duke of Richmond, Master of Ordnance from
1781 to 1795, was a patron. This well run hotel
prides itself on courteous, attentive service
and standards throughout hold the keynote of
comfort. Seaview and penthouse rooms benefit from stunning views. The Saumarez
Cabin - with its unique ship's cabin motif, the
Victoriana Bar with its period atmosphere,
and the restaurant with its pastel decor are all
full of style. Presentation and service is first
class. Groups and private functions can be
well catered for in the ballroom and other
flexible rooms. An attractive sun terrace and
pool are set in the grounds with extra leisure
and sports facilities at Beau Séjour nearby. The
Duke of Richmond is an ideal base from which
to explore the enchanting island of Guernsey
and the cobbled streets of St Peter Port and its
shopping centre, which are within easy reach.

● *75 en suite bedrooms with satellite TV, direct-
dial telephone, hairdryer, laundry service, tea/cof-
fee making facilities, radio alarm clock, safety deposit box, 24-hour room service, trouser press;
non-smoker rooms available.*
● *Table d'hôte £15; à la carte, lunch & special diets available; last orders 9.30 pm.*
● *Business centre inc. meeting rooms to 36 people.*
● *Outdoor swimming pool.*
● *Open all year. All major credit cards accepted.*

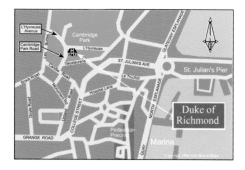

The St Pierre Park Hotel

Rohais, St Peter Port, Guernsey GY1 1FD
Tel: (01481) 728282; Fax: (01481) 712041.
E-mail: stppark@itl.net

Set in 45 acres, the St Pierre Park is an oasis of luxury and tranquillity in the heart of an island of historic and scenic beauty. Set beside a lake, it offers the very best in cuisine, comfort and service where time stands still. Rooms contain everything you are ever likely to require at arms' length, combining superb decor with wonderful scenic views. Two award winning restaurants and a brasserie with terraces and gardens and fountains cater for every taste - from gourmet to healthy options with wines to suit every dish and palate - and of course seafood at its very best. Recreational facilities include a 9-hole Tony Jacklin designed par 3 golf course, a beautiful indoor swimming pool with an adjoining Health Suite, sauna, steam room and spa bath. Cardio vascular and full beauty treatments are also on hand. Croquet, crazy golf, a jogging trail, driving range and tennis courts also help to keep you in trim. Outside the gates are the other delights Guernsey has to offer: history, shopping, spectacular views and some of the cleanest beaches in Europe.

*Rates: Single room inc. breakfast £125; double room inc. breakfast £165. **Bargain Breaks:** min 2 night break pp sharing inc b&b,dinner plus following: Relaxation Break - chocolates, champagne & fruit from £87.50; Golfing Break 18 holes per day - from £94.50. Health & Pamper Break inc ½ hour beauty treatment per day -from £94.50 Discover Guernsey Break inc. car hire from £87.50. 20% disc for Nov-Feb. 7 nights for 6 all year round.*

● *132 en suite bedrooms Inc. 9 suites with satellite TV, direct-dial telephone, hairdryer, laundry service, tea/coffee making facilities, radio alarm clock, safety deposit box, 24-hour room service, trouser press; non-smoker & disabled rooms available.*
● *Table d'hôte £16; à la carte, lunch & special diets available; last orders 10.30 pm.*
● *Business centre inc. 9 meeting rooms up to 200. people. Hair salon, car rental, car parking for 300*
● *Indoor swimming pool, snooker, croquet, fitness club, golf, indoor games, jacuzzi/sauna, jogging track, massage, crazy golf. Fishing, watersports, riding, shooting, outdoor pool nearby.*
● *Open all year. All major credit cards accepted.*

The Old Government House Hotel

Ann's Place, St. Peter Port, Guernsey
GY1 4AZ
Tel: (01481) 724921; Fax: (01481) 724429

Within the heart of St. Peter Port, enjoying
breathtaking views, the location of the OGH
(as it is affectionately known) is the perfect
setting for a holiday or business break on
Guernsey. Once the official residence of the
Island's Governors, the Hotel has served
visitors since 1858 and is today a gracious
blend of old and new, offering the highest
standard of accommodation and with all
bedrooms' colour schemes complementing
the character of the hotel. The Regency restaurant is one of the island's finest with à la carte,
table d'hôte and themed gourmet menus
being offered, accompanied by Chateau and
Estate bottled wines from an excellent list.
The Centenary is one of three bars - each with
their own personality - and light lunches can
be taken there, or at the relaxing poolside outdoors. If night life is on your agenda, the
Centenary Bar also hosts regular dancing as
does the No 10 night club. The OGH is quite
simply a very good hotel - to be recommended
whatever the reason for your stay.

*Rates: Single room including breakfast from
£57.00. Double room with breakfast from
£114.00.*   **V**

● *71 en suite bedrooms with satellite TV, direct-
dial telephone; hairdryer, trouser press, laundry
service, tea/coffee making facilities. Disabled access
to most rooms.*
● *Last orders for dinner 21.30 hrs. Special diets
available. A la carte restaurant.*
● *Fishing, fitness centre, massage, golf,
watersports, riding, sauna, squash, tennis all can
be arranged nearby.*
● *Three conference rooms to capacity of 225
guests. AV equipment and full secretarial service.
Car rental. Car parking for 25 cars.*
● *Open all year. All major credit cards accepted.*

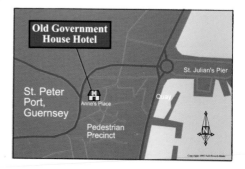

The White House Hotel

Herm Island, via Guernsey GY1 3HR
Tel: (01481) 722159; Fax: (01481) 710066

Herm is a 20-minute boat journey from
Guernsey and is the smallest of the Channel
Islands. There are no cars and Herm's magic
starts to work as soon as you are greeted on
the quayside: the pretty harbour houses the
island's three shops and the Ship Inn. Nearby
is the castellated manor, where the owners of
the island, the Heyworths, live and where you
will find the island's school and 10th century
chapel. There are bracing cliff walks and
beautiful unspoiled beaches, wild flowers and
clear landscapes for painting.

As the gentle chugging of a tractor heralds the
arrival of your luggage, you know the White
House Hotel is special. After all, how many
hotels can boast an island as their garden, a
harbourside setting and such spectacular sea
views? Where else could you enjoy shellfish
so fresh that the oyster beds can be seen from
your table in the award-winning restaurant?
Tradition is cherished at the White House
Hotel. In the 38 delightful bedrooms, you'll
find private bathrooms and baby listening but
no televisions, clocks or telephones. Children

have always been welcome, with a popular
high tea for junior diners. The hotel encourages you to unwind and the island is perfect
for that away-from-it-all break.

> **Rates:** *Single room dinner, bed& breakfast* Ⓥ
> *from £54.50. Double room d,b&b from   £62.50.*
> **Bargain Breaks:** *Bluebells in Bloom Spring
> Break to end-May (exc Easter) £118 pp two
> nights inc boat fare, 75cl of wine & flowers.*

● *38 en suite bedrooms with hairdryer, radio, baby
listening, tea/coffee making. Non-smoker bedrooms
available.*
● *Last orders
for dinner 9
pm. Special
diets and lunch
available.*
● *Croquet,
fishing, sea
bathing, sailing,
outdoor swim-
ming pool.*
● *Open April
2-Oct 10th.
Amex, Visa,
Master-, Euro
and Switch
accepted.*

The Moorings Hotel & Restaurant

Gorey Pier, Jersey JE3 6EW

Tel: (01534) 853633; Fax: (01534) 857618

E-mail: Casino@itl.net

Rates: Single room including breakfast from £35. Double room with breakfast from £70.00. **V**
Winter Breaks available 1st Nov-31st March. Full Christmas programme inc. travel and hire car from £215 demi-pension.

I have been wining and dining here for over 25 years and I share in the view of its popularity which causes it to be a frequent meeting place for local residents. Joyce McMinnies, the wife of the founder of SIGNPOST also spent several happy holidays here. Its position is unique and bridges time. Overlooked by an Elizabethan castle, floodlit at night, the Moorings provides a haven for those who enjoy good food and wine combined with an individual and sensitive service in homely and comfortable surroundings. The quayside outside is often thronged with shoppers plying its quaint arcade of shops. The pretty harbour, once the centre of Jersey's oyster industry, is alive with colour and movement throughout the day. Several times each day ferries arrive and depart for local French ports. This is a great centre not only for shopping but also for walking, cycling, golf, sailing and many other holiday pursuits. In many ways Gorey retains the relaxed and festive atmosphere of a seaside fishing port at the turn of the century. You will enjoy your holiday here - the ambience and location are unsurpassed.

● *17 en suite bedrooms with TV, direct-dial telephone; hairdryer, trouser press, muisc/radio/ alarm clock, tea/coffee making facilities.*

● *Restaurant, two bars + lounge; last orders for dinner 10.15 pm; A la carte, lunch & special*

● *Fishing, golf, watersports, riding, sailing/ boating, outdoor swimming pool, tennis nearby.*
● *Business services. Car rental.*
● *Open all year. Visa, Mastercard, Amex, Switch accepted.*

Channel Islands

The Atlantic Hotel

St. Brelade, Jersey JE3 8HE
Tel: (01534) 44101; Fax: (01534) 44102

With extensive refurbishments completed to the highest of standards and having been under private ownership since 1970, the Atlantic can now be recognised as a truly stylish and "international" hotel. From the imposing columned entrance, through to the reception hall and lounge areas, classic antique furniture, contemporary furnishings, and warm, inviting décor, all contribute towards a theme of understated luxury. Outstanding views across the gardens, the delightfully colourful, tropical outside pool area, and the coastline beyond, can be admired from both the lounge and the main restaurant. Innovative menus, a fine wine list, good presentation and attentive service in the elegant restaurant are all supervised by the most professional of restaurant managers. The Palm Club provides a romanesque indoor pool, jacuzzi, solaria, sauna and gymnasium, and there is an outside tennis court. Conferences can be catered for. With its many attractions and facilities, the Atlantic Hotel makes an ideal venue for any stay, be it for business or sheer self indulgence! The Atlantic is a first class hotel in a good location.

Rates: Single inc breakfast from £100; double £125
Bargain Breaks: Winter breaks (November, December, March) for a minimum of 2 nights in a golf view room - £75 per person per night to include room, breakfast, 4-course table d'hôte dinner, and car hire.

● *50 en suite bedrooms including Garden Studio Rooms, and two luxury suites, all with telephone, colour TV and radio, laundry service; lift; night service.*
● *Tdh dinner £24.50; last orders 9.30p.m.; lunch, à la carte and special diets available.*
● *Children welcome; conferences to 60 taken.*
● *Health & leisure centre, tennis, in- & outdoor swimming pools. Sea bathing, golf nearby.*
● *Open Mar-Dec. All major credit cards accepted.*

St. Helier 5, Airport 2.

Hotel de France

St. Saviour's Road, St Helier,
Jersey JE1 7XP
Tel: (01534) 614000; Fax: (01534) 614999
E-mail: enqgen@defrance.co.uk
Internet: http://www.defrance.co.uk

With a magnificent façade overlooking the town of St Helier, Hotel de France links history with a spacious and luxurious contemporary interior. Recently refurbished and raised to a new peak of modernity, a marble clad Otis lift will deliver you to the right floor with barely discernible movement. It is a hotel for the new millennium. Staff whose aims are friendliness, hospitality and service guide you to the hotel's dining rooms where superb cuisine and fine wine cater for every occasion. With both outdoor and indoor swimming pools to keep you in trim and a choice of sauna, steam bath or beauty salon to pamper and relax you, your every need and comfort is assured. Children are particularly welcomed in school holidays, one child under 12 sharing with parents getting free bed & breakfast, the second getting 50% off, plus supervised sports and pastimes from 4 to 11 pm at the Children's Club. Jersey is renowned for its sunshine, so here is the place to top up your tan and enjoy duty and VAT-free shopping, as well as some of the cleanest beaches in Europe close at hand.

Rates: Single room inc. breakfast from £47. Double room inc. breakfast from £94.
***Bargain Breaks:** Please enquire.*

● *320 en suite bedrooms with direct-dial telephone, colour TV+ satellite, hairdryer, laundry service, tea/coffee making facilities, trouser press*
● *Table d'hôte from £18.50; à l carte, lunch & special diets available. Last orders 2130.*
● *Business centre inc. 20 meeting rooms, capacity 6-1000. Hairdresser/beauty salon. Car parking & rental, newsagent/hotel shop*
● *Outdoor & indoor swimming pools, fitness centre, whirlpool/sauna, squash on premises. Golf, watersports, riding, sailing, tennis nearby.*
● *Open all year. All major credit cards accepted.*

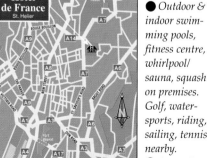

Channel islands

The Lobster Pot

L'Etacq, St Ouen, Jersey JE3 2FB
Tel: (01534) 482888; Fax: (01534) 485584

With a breathtaking vista over the unspoiled
sands of St Ouen's Bay, this 17th-century
granite farmhouse has long been a favourite
restaurant with locals and visitors alike.
Under the new owners, the Restaurant, Bar,
Kitchen and Residents' Lounge have been
tastefully refurbished to give a new feel.
Although known to specialise in seafood, the
restaurant also offers a wide variety on the à
la carte menu, under the new innovative chef,
Gerard Le Miere. The hotel and restaurant are
wonderfully light, fresh and airy, and provide
a relaxed and peaceful atmosphere all year
round. Mountain bikes can be arranged for
the more adventurous visitor. The hotel is
situated in the tranquil north-western corner
of the Island, and has winding cliff paths
leading from its door, while still only a
minute's walk from the beach. The area enjoys
fantastic sunsets and an abundance of wildlife
unique to this part of the island. The Lobster
Pot is a choice haven away from the crowds,
yet close enough to all Jersey's attractions and
only a twenty minute drive from St Helier.

Rates: *Double room with full Eng. breakfast from £60 per head; single person supplement £30.*

● *12 en suite bedrooms, with colour TV + video/satellite, direct-dial telephone, hairdryer, tea/coffee making facilities, trouser press, room service, CD/radio/alarm clock.*
● *Separate lunch and evening menus; à la carte and regular specials; average à la carte £50 per head including drinks.*
● *Beach and cliff paths adjacent. Golf, riding 2 miles; many other activities within 5 miles.*
● *Airport pickup; car parking for 50, car rental.*
● *Business services inc 2 meeting rooms to 100*
● *Open all year. Visa, Mastercard, Switch accepted.*

Hotel Petit Champ

Sark, Channel Islands GY9 0SF
Tel: (01481) 832046; Fax: (01481) 832469
E-mail: hpc@island-of-sark.co.uk
Internet: http://www.island-of-sark.co.uk

The island of Sark is truly unique. It retains a feudal constitution dating back to the reign of Elizabeth I, has its own government, no income tax and is home to just 550 residents. It is also a natural, car free and tranquil retreat for people who enjoy beautiful walks, breathtaking scenery and a refreshing break from the modern world. The Hotel Petit Champ is a reflection of all that with its secluded position and views to the sea. Here, under the expert supervision of the resident proprietors Chris and Caroline Robins, is a true gem of an hotel with a country house atmosphere and 16 cosy en suite bedrooms, some of which have balconies. There are three sun-lounges as well as a peaceful library lounge. Drinks before dinner are taken in the intimate bar and then guests repair to the candlelit restaurant renowned for its good cuisine with local lobster and crab dishes as specialities. A solar heated swimming pool nestles in the natural setting of an old quarry and forms a perfect sun trap. The

hotel Petit Champ, set in the island magic of Sark, is truly enchanting and the spell draws visitors back for holidays year after year.

Rates: Single room including breakfast and dinner from £46. Double room with breakfast and dinner from £44 per person. **V**

● *16 en suite bedrooms. Hairdryers available.*
● *5-course table d'hôte dinner £17.50; à la carte, lunch & special diets available. Last orders 20.30.*
● *Putting green and solar heated outdoor swimming pool, garden walks, boat trips. Nearby sea fishing, tennis, billiards, badminton.*
● *All-inclusive holidays with travel available.*
● *Open Easter to early October. Mastercard, Visa, Switch, Amex & Diners Card accepted.*

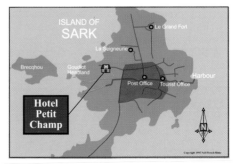

Signpost and Ireland

The founder of Signpost, W G McMinnies, travelled extensively in Ireland, and, although Ireland was not included in the first 1935 edition, he dedicated a special edition to the country in 1950 (see cover illustration on right). Thereafter Ireland was included until the early eighties, then there was a break until the 1996 edition. Now we are pleased to report that some 20% of all our pages are devoted to Hibernia. We thought readers would be interested to read the extracts below from the 1950 edition as well as to see entries from two hotels who have featured both in the first Irish edition and in this Diamond Jubilee Edition.

Top: Parknasilla Great Southern Hotel in 1950. See page 261 for today's hotel.
Below: Cover of the 1950 SIGNPOST to Ireland, featuring the editor.

In 1950 Great Britain was still in the throes of rationing, so that the grandfather of the present publisher wrote:

"*My three-week tour cost £10-12 a week, staying at the best hotels... Remember that food is not subsidised in Eire...A butcher I picked up told me that the country was overflowing with meat and bacon and he couldn't understand why Britain did not take more, and that the oat crop was so large that the surplus was fed to animals...this seems as strange as the fact that Eire has ample petrol and that such things as sweets, tobacco and drink are all easily obtainable.*"

As to finding his way around..." *Instructions on finding the way, generally with an airy wave of the hand 'keep switching off' or 'keep straight on to the left'. Often I was told to turn right, while my informant waved his left hand to make sure I understood.*" There are tales of Ireland's most unorthodox hotel-keeper, Major Dermot Freyer of the then Corrymore House Hotel on Achill Island, County Mayo, who charged guests a few shillings if he liked them or even nothing at all if they helped by chopping wood or doing a job in the house, or a guinea if he didn't like them! But then, as his successors are today, Mr McMinnies was everywhere made to feel most welcome and was bowled over by the charm of the country and its people. This he communicated to his readers and we hope we may emulate him today.

Right: Portmarnock Golf & Country Club in 1950. See page 252 for today's hotel.
Below: 'Obstacles to enforce a reduced speed limit at the bridge near Yougal, Co Cork' 1950

Co. Kerry (E), Parknasilla

ON THE NORTH BANK OF KENMARE RIVER ESTUARY.

THIS Great Southern Railway hotel is indeed fortunate in its setting for behind it are luxuriantly wooded hills, and great spreads of rhododendrons, eucalyptus, rose and pine trees and semi-tropical flowers of many kinds. In front sea and river merge, promontories, scores of islets accessible by bridge or boat and distant coastline bewildering the onlooker as to which is mainland and which is not. Out of this famous and lovely setting rises a fine 100 room stone-built hotel recently enlarged. Judging by the gaily coloured crowd and the buzz of conversation in the cocktail bar before lunch, a good time was being had by all. And there is no doubt that the place lays itself out to maintain the party spirit for they dance every night and people soon get together for expeditions, fishing, picnics, bathing, boating, walking and so on. Tennis and golf are available too on the spot. I enjoyed my lunch served by attractive maids in buff aprons and port coloured uniform. Bedroom equipment and detail work were entirely satisfactory. Daily from 35/-. Other Great Southern hotels at Killarney, Mallaranny, Galway, Sligo and Kenmare.

Co. Dublin (E), Nr. Dublin, Portmarnock Country Club.

ON THE COAST BETWEEN HOWTH AND MALAHIDE.

MR. J. P. GALVIN and his good wife, who incidentally at one time ran the best hotel in Vienna, were both wise and fortunate to take over this millionaire's home from the Irish Tourist Board. And being keen and competent hotelkeepers they have naturally endowed this beautifully appointed place with food, service and facilities to match its quality. Before looking round let me say that the house lies alongside the famous golf course and a wonderful stretch of sand and bathing beach. There is a longish view south towards Dublin and Ireland's Eye while at hand is a sheltered and semi-tropical garden where you can laze at your leisure. And now for the inside. Here there is the immediate appeal of spacious and well proportioned apartments, soft colour scheming and really comfortable detail work. There's a fine dining room where I enjoyed a first-class dinner. In my bedroom the lighting over bed and shaving mirror was excellent, the bed cosy and the appointments delightful and complete. The fresh cork carpeted bathroom provided almost boiling water and was a joy to use. All this inevitably produces a feeling of well-being, may even of opulence, in the heart of a visitor. In conclusion please note that you can use the place though it is called a Country Club and that there's no nonsense like there is in Britain about having to join before you get a drink. Weekly 10-15 gns. according to season.

Houses, Gardens & Parks
Andress House, Co Armagh
The Argory, Co Armagh
Castle Coole, Co Fermanagh
Castle Ward, Co Down
Cratlow Woods House, Co Down
Downhill, Londonderry
Florence Court, Co Fermanagh
Gray's Printing Press, Strabane, Co Tyrone
Hezlett House, Co Londonderry
Mount Stewart House, Garden & Temple
Rowallane Garden, Saintfield, Down
Springhill, Moneymore, Co Londonderry

Templetown Mausoleum, Co Antrim
Wellbrook Beetling Mill, Cookstown, Co Tyrone

Historical Sites & Museums
Carrickfergus Castle, Carrickfergus, Co Antrim
City Hall, Belfast
Devenish Island, Lough Erne
Giant's Causeway, Nr Coleraine, Co Antrim
Glen of Glenariff, NE of Ballymena
Slieve Gullion, Newry, Co Down
Stormont Castle, Belfast
Ulster Museum, Belfast

Northern Ireland

DIARY OF EVENTS

January
2-8. **New Year Viennese Concerts.** Ulster Orch Box Office, Bft
16-17. **Gillette Northern Ireland Open Fencing Championships.** Avoniel, Belfast.
29-31. **Holiday World.** Kings Hall, Belfast.

February
22-Mar 13*. **Belfast Musical Festival.** Balmoral, Belfast
27-Mar 6*. **Opera Northern Ireland Spring Season.** Grand Opera House, Belfast

March
17. **Horse Ploughing Match & heavy Horse Show.** Ballycastle.
17. **St Patrick's Day Celebrations.** Armagh, Newry, Ballymena, Downpatrick.
27-28. **World Cross-country Championships.** Barnett Park, Belfast.

April
1*. **North-West Storytelling Festival.** Verbal Arts Centre, Londonderry.
10-13. **Circuit of Ireland Motor Rally.**Start/finish Bangor, Down
23-May 2*. **F oyle Film Festival.** The Nerve Centre, Londonderry
17-18. **City of Belfast Spring Fair.** Barnett Park, Belfast.

May
May. **Festival of Light Opera.**

Bangor, Co Down
3*.**Belfast Marathon & Fun Run**
12-14*. **Royal Ulster Agricultural Society Show.** Balmoral, Belfast
18*. **Ballyclare Horse Fair.** Ballyclare (part of festival 16-23 May)
28-29*. **International Jazz & Blues Festival.** Londonderry
28-29* **County Antrim Agricultural Show.** Ballymena Showg'ds

June
1-4*. **Black Bush Causeway Coast Amateur Golf Tournament.** Causeway Coast.
4-6*. **Jazz & Blues Festival,** Holywood, Co Down.
4-26*. **Castleward Opera.** Strangford, Co Antrim
18-26*. **Proms '98.** Ulster Orchestra Symphony Concerts, Ulster Hall, Belfast
26-28. **Northern Ireland Game Fair.** Shane's Castle, Antrim

July
12-16*. **North of Ireland Amateur Open Golf Champ'ship.** Royal Portrush, Causeway Coast
19-25. **City of Belfast International Rose Week.** Dixon Park, Belfast.

August-November
30-31 Aug. **Oul' Lammas Fair.** Ireland's oldest traditional fair. Ballycastle.
7-18* Sept. **Ideal Home Exhibition.** Kings Hall, Belfast.
18-19 Sept. **City of Belfast Autumn Flower Show**. Botanic Gdns
3 Oct. **Rugby World Cup.** Pacific 1 v Europe 6. Windsor Park, Belfast
12-28* Nov. **Belfast Festival at Queens.** Queens University, Bft

For further information, contact:
The Northern Ireland Tourist Board
St Anne's Court, 59 North Street
Belfast BT1 1NB
Tel: (01232) 231221; Fax: (01232) 240960

Republic of Ireland

Annes Grove Gardens, Castletownroche
Ayesha Castle, Killiney, Co Dublin
Bantry House, Bantry, Co Cork
Birr Castle Demesne, Co Offaly
Blarney Castle & Blarney House, Blarney, Co Cork
Bunratty Castle & Folk Park, Bunratty, Co Clare
Carrigglass Manor, Longford, Co Longford
Castletown House, Cellbridge, Co Kildare
Cloghan Castle, Banagher, Co Clare
Colnalis House, Castlerea, Co Roscommon
Craggaunowen - The Living Past - Kilmurry, Co Clare
Dunguaire Castle, Kinvara, Co Galway
Dunloe Castle Hotel Gardens, Beaufort, Killarney, Co Kerry
Emo Court, Portlaoise, Co Leix
Fernhill Garden, Sandyford, Co Dublin
Fota Wildlife Park, Fota Island, Carrigtwohill, Co Cork
Glin Castle, Glin, Co Limerick
GPA Bolton Library, Cashel, Co Tipperary
Japanese Garden, Tully, Co Kildare
Johnstown Castle Demesne, Wexford, Co Wexford
The James Joyce Tower, Sandycove, Co Dublin
The John F Kennedy Arboretum, New Ross, Co Wexford
Knappogue Castle, Quin, Co Clare
Kylemore Abbey, Kylemore, Connemara, Co Galway
Lismore Castle, Lismore, Co Waterford
Lissadell, Sligo
Lough Gur Visitor Centre, Lough Gur, Co Limerick
Lough Rynn Estate & Gardens, Mohill, Co Leitrim
Malahide Castle, Malahide, Co Dublin
Mount Congreve Gardens, Nr. Waterford
Mount Usher Gardens, Ashford, Co Wicklow
Muckross House & Gardens, Killarney, Co Kerry
National Botanic Gardens, Glasnevin, Dublin 9
Newbridge House, Donabate, Co Dublin
Phoenix Park, Dublin
Powerscourt Gardens & Waterfall, Enniskerry, Co Wicklow
Powerscourt Townhouse Centre, 59 South William St, Dublin 2
Riverstown House, Glanmire, Co Cork
Royal Hospital, Kilmainham, Co Dublin
Russborough, Blessington, Co Wicklow

Slane Castle, Slane, Co Meath
Strokestown Park House, Strokestown, Co Roscommon
Swiss Cottage, Chir, Co Tipperary
Thoor Ballylee, Gort, Co Galway
Timoleague Castle Gardens, Bandon, Co Cork
Tullynally Castle, Castlepollard, Co Westmeath

Augustinian Priory (14thC), Kells, Co Kilkenny
Blarney Castle & Stone, Co Cork
Castle (State Apartments), Dublin
Christ Church Cathedral, Dublin
Cliffs of Moher & O'Brien's Tower, Lahinch, Co Clare
Glengarrif, 8m N of Bantry, Co Cork
Grianan of Eilach Fort, 18m NE of Letterkenny, Co Galway
Jerpoint Abbey ruins, 12m SE of Kilkenny, Co Kilkenny
Lough Corrib/Claregalway, Galway, Co Galway
Lough Gill/Lough Colgath, Sligo, Co Sligo
Lynch's Castle, Galway, Co Galway
Mellifont Abbey, Drogheda, Co Louth
Monasterboice, Drogheda, Co Louth
Monastic City/St Kervin's Church, Glendalough, Co Wicklow
Municipal Art Gallery/Hugh Lane Gallery, Dublin
Museum of Modern Art, Kilmainham, Dublin
National Gallery, Dublin
National Museum, Dublin
Ring of Kerry, Killarney, Co Kerry
St Ann's Shandon Church, Cork
St Canice's Cathedral, Kilkenny, Co Kilkenny
St Patrick's Rock (Rock of Cashel), Co Tipperary
Sheehans Pt, remains of Carhan House, Waterrville, Co Kerry
Timoleague Franciscan Abbey, Courtmacsherry, Co Cork
Trinity College Library, Dublin
Tulla Church, 10m E of Ennis, Co Clare
Writers' Museum, Dublin

DIARY OF EVENTS

Republic of Ireland

February

6. **Rugby International: Ireland v France.** Landsdowne Road, Ballsbridge, Dublin 4

March

2-11*. **Dublin Film Festival.** Various cinemas in Dublin.
15-17. **St Patrick's Festival.** Nationwide (Day = 17th)
26-28. **Galway International Set Dancing Festival.** Through the streets & shops of Killarney, Co Kerry.
27-April 4. **World Irish Dancing Championships.** West County Hotel, Ennis, Clare

April

10. **Rugby Football Union. Ireland v Italy.** Dublin.
15-25. **Dublin Film Festival.** Various cinemas throughout Dublin.
29-May 2. **Cork International Choral Festival.** City Hall, UCC, Triskel Arts Centre.

May

1-5. **West of Ireland Amataur Open Golf Championship.** Inniscrone, Co Sligo.
6-9. **Murphy's International Mussel Fair.** Bantry, Co Cork.
7-10. **Kinsale Vintage Classic International Rally.** Co Cork.
14-July 11. **Co Wicklow Gardens Festival.** Throughout Co Wicklow, south Co Dublin, Co Carlow & North Co Wexford.
23-24. **A.I.M.S Choral Festival.** New Ross, Co Wexford.
28-June 6. **Dundalk International Maytime Festival.** Dundalk, Co Louth.

June

3-4. **Irish Seniors Amateur Open Golf Championship.** Tullamore, Co Offaly.
19-27. **Dublin Int'l Organ & Ch oral Festival.** Var. venues, Dublin
24-27. **Dublin Garden Festival.** RDS, Simonscourt Pav. Dublin 4
24/27. **Heineken Athlone River Festival/Peoples Regatta.** River Shannon, Athlone, Co Westmeath.

July

1-4. **Murphy's Irish Open.** Druids Glen, Co Wicklow.
10-17. **Ballina Street Festival & Arts Week.** Ballina, Co Mayo.
12-25. **Galway Arts Festival.** Various Venues, Galway City.

August

5*. **Dublin Horse Show.** Ros Showg'd, Ballsbridge, Dublin
12-15. **Powers Irish Coffee Festival.** Foynes, Co Limerick
20-26.**Rose of Tralee Int'l Fest -ival.** Brandon Hotel, Tralee.

September

15-Nov 1. **Waterford Int'l Festival of Light Opera.** Theatre Royal, Waterford.

October

4-16. **Dublin Theatre Festival.** Major theatres, Dublin
2/9/10/15/24. **Rugby World Cup 1999.** Ireland v America 3/America 3 v Europe 6/Ireland v Pacific 1/Ireland v Europe 6/4th Quarter Final. Lansdowne Rd, Ballsbr, Dublin 4.
10-17. **Cork Int'l Film Festival.** Cork Opera House etc, Cork.
15-31. **Wexford Festival Opera** Theatre Royal etc, Wexford.
22-25. **Guinness Cork Jazz Festival.** Various venues, Cork

*Provisional dates.
For further information, contact:
Bord Fáilte (Irish Tourist Board), Baggot Street Bridge, Dublin 2.
Telephone: 1 676 5871/6024000
Fax: 1 475 8046

Ireland

Circuit of Ireland

Ireland is roughly 300 miles long from the north coast of Donegal to the south coast of County Cork and about 170 miles wide from Dublin on the east coast to the west coast of County Mayo. Dublin and Belfast have fine airports. Car ferries run from Holyhead to Dun Laoghaire, Fishguard to Rosslare, Swansea to Cork, and Stranraer in Scotland to Larne in Northern Ireland. In recent years they have all been modernised. Efficient and helpful car hire firms operate in the principal cities and even in a small town one may well alight on an efficient service station if your own car needs attention.

One of the most attractive reasons for choosing Ireland as a country for scenery, sport and ports of call, is the freedom of its roads. They are not infested by monster juggernauts, exasperating queues and long delays at junctions. So the driver proceeds in peace enjoying the view of the country without wondering if he's likely to be mown down by some rushing madman. Be warned, 'though, that road surfaces are not always as smooth as in Britain, so cars tend not to live to a ripe old age.

Ireland, North or South, has a huge choice for people of varied interests. Fishing, of course, the Dublin Horse Show, racing, splendid golf courses, unpolluted sands, ancient relics, and all sorts of magnificent coastal scenery like the tremendous Cliffs of Moher on the west coast, Blarney Castle near Cork where you can kiss the stone and supposedly be rewarded with exceptional eloquence. The Giant's Causeway, easily reached from Portrush in County Antrim, and its thousands of basalt columns which are certainly one of the most curious geological formations in the world. As a similar formation is found in the Scottish Island of Staffa on the west coast of Scotland, it has been suggested that these formations may extend and meet under the Irish Sea. These wonders are only a tiny list of the strange collection of objects, some of which were in existence thousands of years ago.

Now a few hints on how to see the West of Ireland. Whether you start from Dublin, Rosslare or Cork, from a viewing point it's better to follow the sun round, in other words left handed keeping to the coast. Starting at Rosslare you can visit the famous crystal glass factory at Waterford; in nearby Middleton, the home of Irish whisky, you can tour a distillery. Wexford has a famous Opera Festival and Heritage Park, bringing Irish history to life. County Cork and County Kerry are generally reckoned to provide the finest and most varied scenery. Cork is Ireland's second city, home of *Murphy's* stout and the famous jazz festival. The road from Cork gives one a taste of the mountains ahead, Killarney follows, a veritable wonderland of mountains and lakes many with odd names like the *MacGillicuddy Reeks* 3,414' which include the highest peaks in Ireland. There are first class hotels in the town and several most excellent ones a few miles west. One could spend a fortnight exploring this wonderful and beautiful area alone.

From Killarney to Waterville, a noted fishing town with several first class and friendly hotels. Limerick and Galway are the main cities of Ireland's West Coast; the latter famous for its annual Race Meeting and Oyster Festival. In nearby Connemara you will find the world famous marble, and see the equally famous wild Connemara ponies. Next to County Mayo where the soft pastel shades of the mountains and clouds appeal to the artist and photographer. In the Oughterard, Clifden, Newport and Westport area have some charming family run hotels of special merit.

Southwest of Westport the 2,510' high hump of *Croagh Patrick* (near Knock) attracts yearly pilgrimages up its stony flanks and unfortunately now is apt to be trippery with tourists sometimes outnumbering pilgrims. County Donegal is famed for its Atlantic Drive and has one of the least polluted coasts in Europe.

From here one turns east into Londonderry and then to Portrush and its golf courses and the Giant's Causeway near Bushmills. The Antrim coast road south to Belfast affords sea and land views while a more exciting hilly road from Bally Castle takes in Carrick-a-Rede whose cliffs and suspension bridge are well worth a visit. In Dungannon you can visit and purchase the famous Tyrone Crystal.

Kincora Hall

Killaloe, Co Clare
Tel: (061) 376000; Fax: (061) 376665

Killaloe, on the southern tip of Lough Derg and the upper end of the Shannon, is one of Ireland's most popular cruising and fishing centres. Nearby is a well known Irish music location. It is a beautiful spot where mountain and lake come together. There are a wealth of activities available locally. Kincora Hall has its own private marina and you can watch the comings and goings from the acclaimed *Thomond Room* restaurant. The food has a fine local reputation and good use is made of local produce. The town is of deep historical interest, reflected in the 'history lesson' scrolls on the walls of the hotel. Killaloe has traces of prehistoric settlements, megalithic tombs and early Christian churches. Kincora Hall Hotel is a great place to relax after a day's sightseeing, walking, fishing, riding, golf, or sailing.

*Rates: Single room with breakfast from IR£45; double from IR£80. **Bargain Breaks:** Midweek Special - 2 nights b&b + one dinner £85 pp. Weekend Special - 2 nights b&b + one dinner £89 pp.*

● *30 en suite bedrooms with satellite TV, direct-dial telephone, hairdryer, laundry/valet service, 24 hour room/meal service, trouser press.*
● *Fishing, boating (own marina). Golf, riding, watersports, sailing, shooting locally.*
● *Business services inc. conference rooms 150.*
● *Open all year. Major credit cards accepted.*
Limerick 13, Nenagh 16, Ennis 32, Dublin 109.

Seaview House Hotel

Ballylickey, Bantry, Co Cork
Tel: (027) 50073/50462;
Fax: (027) 51555

This delightful country house hotel stands in its own wooded grounds close to the Ballylickey Bridge over the river Ouvane, commanding views of Bantry Bay and the distant mountains. Locally and further afield, Seaview is renowned for its comfort and cuisine. Owner Kathleen O'Sullivan has doubled the hotel in size without forgoing the friendly welcome and personal service for which the house is so well known. She is an accomplished cook and the cuisine has been recognised by several awards including two AA rosettes. Bedrooms are furnished with antiques and there is a cottage and a small lodge in the grounds for family occupation if required. Ballylickey is an ideal centre for touring the peninsulas of West Cork and Kerry. There are two golf courses nearby as well as other activities in the vicinity.

*Rates: Single room with breakfast from IR£60; double from IR£100. **Bargain Breaks:** on request.* Ⅴ

● *17 en suite bedrooms with satellite TV, hairdryer, tea/coffee making facilities. Facilities for disabled.*
● *Table d'hôte dinner £25. A la carte & special diets available. Last orders 9 pm.*
● *Open 15 March-15 November. All major credit cards accepted.*

Bantry 5, Killarney 45, Cork 55, Dublin 216.

Ireland

Emmet Hotel

Emmet Square, Clonakilty, West Cork
Tel: (023) 33394; Fax: (023) 35058

The new Emmet Hotel is situated in a very picturesque Georgian square in the bustling West Cork town of Clonakilty. The central location just off the main street makes the new Emmet hotel the ideal base for touring, sightseeing, holidaying or for business purposes. The hotel has recently been refurbished to a very high standard. The decor is tasteful and fits the relaxed atmosphere of this very homely hotel. All food is cooked to order using the best local fresh produce, organically farmed where possible. The bistro and bar menus offer a variety of enticing ideas and flavour. Emmet Square itself has an interesting background. It was laid out between 1785 and 1810 and called originally Shannon Square. It has housed a classical school, a meeting house for Plymouth Brethren, a constabulary barracks, a glebe and a gentleman's club. Its most famous resident was Michael Collins, who lived at No 7. Clonakilty is a good centre for touring Cork and Kerry. Local attractions include beach fishing, pony trekking, golf and a model railway village opened in 1997.

Rates: Single room inc. breakfast from IR£35; double room inc. breakfast from £65.   **V**
Bargain Breaks: Midweek packages available low season; weekends in low season. Details on application.

● *20 en suite bedrooms, all with air-conditioning, colour TV+ satellite, direct dial telephone, hairdryer, laundry/valet service, tea/coffee making facilities, safety deposit box.*
● *Table d'hôte dinner £18.20; à la carte, lunch & special diets available.*
● *Two meeting rooms, capacity 120. Airport pickup*
● *Indoor swimming pool, fitness centre 500 metres; fishing, golf, sea/river bathing, watersports, sailing, riding nearby.*
● *Open all year. All major credit cards accepted.*

Cork Airport 31, Cork 32, Dublin 193.

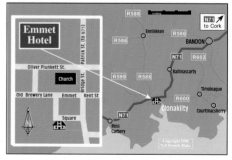

Maryborough House Hotel

Maryborough Hill, Douglas, Cork
Tel: (021) 365555; Fax: (021) 365662
E-mail: maryboro@indigo.ie

The Maryborough is a charming old world
mansion at the centre of natural parkland with
majestic oaks, rhododendrons and an outstanding collection of shrubs and plants. Every
room has views of these outstanding gardens.
The 18th century core building has been restored to preserve all the original Georgian features: high stuccoed ceilings, gracious curved
staircases with antique furniture to match. The
Garden Room connects the old mansion with
the new wing and leads to the 21st century
amenities - banqueting and conference areas,
state-of-the-art leisure club, swimming pool,
and to the contemporary restaurant which
serves an exciting mixture of modern flavours
and styles, created where possible from fresh
local produce. Douglas is a pleasant suburb of
Cork, handy for the airport and ferry port ,
close to the city centre and road network, yet
Maryborough provides an oasis of old world
elegance, mixed with new world efficiency. A
good business or holiday hotel for those embarking on a tour of southwest Ireland.

Rates: Single room inc. breakfast IR£99-150;
double room inc. breakfast from £110-220.   **V**
Bargain Breaks: Weekend breaks - 2 nights b&b
+ 1 dinner from £110 per person sharing.

● *57 en suite bedrooms, all with colour TV+
satellite, direct dial telephone, hairdryer, laundry/
service, tea/coffee making facilities, 24-hr room
service, trouser press. Non-smoker and disabled
bedrooms available*
● *Table d'hôte dinner £21; à la carte, lunch &
special diets available. Last orders 10 pm.*
● *Six meeting rooms, capacity 5-500. Airport
pickup. Car parking 300. Car rental.*
● *Billiards/snooker, croquet, gymnasium, jacuzzi,
massage, sauna, indoor swimming pool, tennis.
Fishing, golf, watersports, sailing, riding nearby.*
● *Closed 24-26 Dec. All major credit cards accepted*
Cork 3, Airport 5, Killarney 51, Dublin 157.

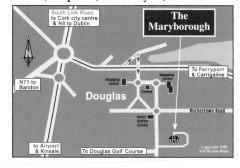

Innishannon House Hotel

Innishannon, Co. Cork
Tel: (021) 775121; Fax: (021) 775609
E-mail: innishannonhotel@tinet.ie

Back in 1720, when a wealthy farmer had his home built half a mile from the village of Innishannon, he could hardly have imagined that over 250 years later it would be a delightful country house hotel offering world class hospitality. Innishannon House Hotel is only 15 minutes from Cork airport but the setting is as romantic as you could wish, with gardens running down to the river Bandon where salmon and trout fishing as well as boating are available free to guests. All the bedrooms overlook this rural idyll and they in turn are full of personality, being individually decorated and furnished with antiques. They vary in size, from smaller attic rooms to spacious ones on the first floor and the vast suite with its period bathroom. My walk round the public rooms was also an experience. A pleasant sunny drawing-room with a corner bar gives on to a separate 'snug' and the whole is decorated with verve using idiosyncratic modern paintings juxtaposed with traditional Irish landscapes. The new chef de cuisine is Pearse O'Sullivan, the son of the house, and the restaurant has won several awrds including two AA rosettes for "culinary excellence"1993 through 1998. In 1998 the hotel was the only Irish hotel in 50 worldwide to win the *Insider Award* from Holiday/Travel Magazine USA. The Innishannon is a hotel to be savoured for its character and the quality of its hospitality.

Rates: *Single room including breakfast from IR£75; double room with breakfast from IR£99; Garden Suite £250.* **Ⅴ**
Leisure Breaks: *Any two nights b&b plus one table d'hôte dinner from £95 pp sharing; Jan-Mar, November and sometimes April, May, Oct. Dec.*

● *14 en suite bedrooms with radio and colour TV; direct-dial telephone, hairdryer, laundry service; non-smoker rooms; disabled facilities.*
● *Last dinner orders 21.30.*
● *Fishing & boating from the hotel's grounds. Golf, riding, shooting, squash and tennis all nearby.*
● *Meeting room with 150 capacity; AV equipment & secretarial services. Safe deposit box. Car parking 100 cars.*
● *Open all year. All major credit cards accepted.*

Cork 14, Killarney 46, Bandon 4½, Dublin 175.

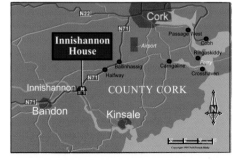

Castle Grove Country House & Restaurant

Ballymaleel, (off Ramelton Road), Letterkenny, Co Donegal.
Tel: (074) 51118; Fax: (074) 51384

Castle Grove is a fine Georgian house, set in its own estate and approached by a mile long drive through parkland. It overlooks Lough Swilly and boasts a quietness and quality of life that is rare in most parts of the world today. Bedrooms are individually decorated and the restaurant specialises in seafood and the best of Irish food, accompanied by an excellent cellar. The house exudes the warmth and comfortable informality of a private home. Nearby is Glenveagh National Park, whose magnificent park and castle are open to the public, and Churchill Art Gallery. There are 3 local 18-hole golf courses and fishing, shooting and riding are all available in the area.

Rates: Single room inc. breakfast IR£45-55; double room IR£80-100; suites IR£150-200. **V**
Leisure Breaks: Midweek 2nights b&b + 1 dinner £95 pp sharing; weekend £105 pp. Exc July/Aug.

● *14 en suite bedrooms with direct-dial telephone, hairdryer, laundry service, radio/alarm, trouser press. Colour TV & minibar on request. Non-smoker rooms available.*
● *Tdh dinner til 2130 £20; à la carte, lunch & diets available. Car parking for 25. Meeting room for 20.*
● *Golf, fishing, tennis, riding nearby. Watersports 12 m*
● *Open Jan-22 Dec. Major credit cards accepted.*
Letterkenny 2½, Londonderry 22, Donegal 30, Dublin 159

Streeve Hill

25 Dowland Road, Limavady, Co Londonderry BT49 OHP
Tel: [+44] (0)15047 66563
Fax: [+44] (0) 15047 68285

A visit to Northern Ireland should include a spell at Streeve Hill, a small and elegant early Georgian country house within the Drenagh estate. The house has been lovingly restored and furnished with fine antiques, blending its 18th-century charm with contemporary comforts. Peter and June Welsh will welcome you to cosy evenings by the fire and delicious dinners with lovely china and fine linen. There are flowers everywhere - June Welsh is a keen gardener as well as an excellent cook. Each bedroom is different and one would like to spend a night in each! This is a good centre for exploring the counties of Antrim and Londonderry. Royal Portrush golf course is nearby and the Giant's Causeway is 30 minutes away. But if you do go out, make sure to be back in time for a superb dinner.

Rates: Single room inc. breakfast £50; Double room inc. breakfast £90. **V**

● *3 en suite non-smoking bedrooms with colour TV, direct-dial telephone, hairdryer, trouser press.*
● *4-course table d'hôte dinner £30 at 8pm. Special diets available. Car parking for 10.*
● *Golf, fishing, tennis, riding, squash, nearby; 2nd golf course, sailing 10 miles.*
● *Open all year exc. Xmas. Visa, Mastercard, Amex cards accepted.*
Coleraine 13, Londonderry 17, Ballymena 39, Belfast 62

Beaufort House and Serviced Apartments

25 Pembroke Park. Ballsbridge, Dublin 4
Tel: (00353-1) 6689080;
Fax: (00353-1) 6609963

Beaufort House will most probably become your 'home away from home' whilst in Dublin. Its owner Kate Mullally has created a lovely relaxed atmosphere - the rooms are individually and thoughtfully furnished, the decor sympathetic, bright, cosy and comfortable. All guestrooms have PC modem points, yet are graced with original fireplaces and old world elegance. Breakfasts are a house speciality, offering crêpes suzette and home-made bread. Afternoon tea is available and light meals are served until 10.30 pm in the conservatory. The house is only minutes' walk to Dublin's busy financial and entertainment centre and all guests have access to private leisure facilities. As an alternative to the hotel, try one of the elegant serviced apartments. All have personal phone/fax & answering service, housekeeping, dry cleaning and reception facilities. Beaufort Performance Car Rental is also available from the same premises, so you can treat yourself to another bit of escapism!

Rates: Single inc. 4-course breakfast IR£45-85; double with breakfast IR£55-160.   **V***
Leisure Breaks: Winter 2-night breaks from £50 per person. Also luxury weekends incorporating sports car rental or chauffeur driven, theatre, restaurant and private table reservations.
(*Please state at time of booking)

● *9 en suite bedrooms with colour TV, direct-dial telephone, hairdryer, laundry service, tea/coffee making, music/radio/alarm clock, safety deposit box, trouser press & iron. Non-smoker & disabled bedrooms available. Modem points in bedrooms.*
● *Car parking 5. Car rental. Airport pickup.*
● *Leisure Centre available nearby. Golf one mile.*
● *Open all year. Visa, Mastercard, Diners, Amex credit cards accepted.*

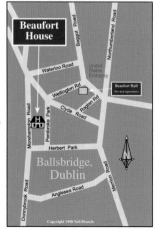

Conrad International Dublin

Earlsfo5t Terrace, Dublin 2
Tel: (00353-1) 676 5555;
Fax: (00353-1) 676 5424;
E-mail: info@conrad-international.ie

Stay at the Conrad International right in the heart of Dublin just off St Stephens Green and opposite the National Concert Hall and you will find yourself in a truly cosmopolitan atmosphere. You will also be throughly spoiled. There are some most attractive suites in this hotel and you will feel that all the little extras have been thought of. The Conrad International is home to two of Dublin's finest restaurants - the gourmet *Alexandra* which offers a range of Irish and continental cuisine or you can enjoy the bright, airy atmosphere of the *Plurabelle*, a brasserie, which serves breakfast, lunch and dinner at popular prices. Traditional afternoon tea is served in the *Lobby Lounge* or you can sit back with a Guinness, an Irish coffee or your favourite cocktail in the *Alfie Byrne's* Pub - as popular with Dubliners as it is with visitors. Business visitors are particularly well catered for, with personal faxes in each bedroom, a business centre and four state-of-the-art conference and meeting rooms. There is also a fully equipped fitness centre. The Conrad is a truly international hotel for an international city.

Rates: Single room inc. breakfast from IR£195; double room inc. breakfast from IR£220.

● *191 en suite bedrooms (inc 9 suites) all with colour TV+ satellite, AC, direct-dial telephone, hairdryer, laundry/valet service, minibar, music/radio/alarm clock, trouser press. Non-smoker & disabled bedrooms available.*
● *Table d'hôte dinner £18.50. A la carte, lunch & special diets available. Brasserie. Irish Pub.*
● *Business centre and four meeting rooms, max cap. 350 theatre-style. Car parking for 80.*
● *Fitness centre/gym. Barber shop/hairdresser. Golf 25 minutes,(see Portmarnock Hotel page 252)*
● *Open all year. Visa, Mastercard, Diners, Amex credit cards accepted.*

Merrion Hall

54/56 Merrion Road, Ballsbridge, Dublin 4
Tel: (01) 668 1426/1825; Fax: (01) 668 4280

When awards are given there is always a lurking danger of complacency setting in - but in so far as Merrion Hall, the 1994 Guest House of the Year, is concerned, the reverse applies. This impeccably maintained family-run guest-house is situated south of the city centre on the main ferry road, and specialises in providing an exceptionally warm and welcoming ambience where nothing is too much trouble for the proprietress Mrs. Sheeran. Here too you have all the facilities of a superbly run hotel: the place is spotless, the en suite bedrooms attractive and well equipped, and the dining room overlooking a pretty garden is bright and airy. Yet my favourite room was the larger of the two sitting rooms which is naturally homely and nicely furnished with the family harp providing an original centrepiece. At Merrion Hall you start your day fully refreshed for it has won awards for its breakfasts too. The menu is a full page of fresh and home-made fare and, to do full justice to it

and to this charming guest house, you will need to stay for quite a few days, which would be a very happy experience. Total refurbishment was undertaken in 1997 and a further 10 bedrooms added.

Rates: *Single room including breakfast from IR£50; double room with breakfast from IR£60.* **V**
Leisure Breaks: *Winter weekends - 2 nights from IR£55.00 pp with breakfast.*

● *24 en suite bedrooms with satellite TV; direct-dial telephone, fax & modem facilities, hairdryer, laundry service; tea/coffee making facilities.*
● *Breakfast only, but several good restaurants nearby.*
● *Car parking 12 cars.*
● *Closed 20 Dec - 3 January.*
● *Credit cards accepted.*

Merrion Hotel

Upper Merrion Street, Dublin 2
Tel: (00353-1) 6030600; Fax: (00353-1)
6030700. E-mail: info@merrionhotel.com

The Merrion, Dublin's newest five-star luxury
hotel, opened in October 1997 and after just
one month, won Fortune Magazine (USA)'s
Best Hotel Room in Dublin award. It is situated
in the centre of Dublin, opposite the Irish
Parliament. Created from four Grade 1 listed
Georgian townhouses and a specially commissioned contemporary wing, the hotel is
arranged around two 18th Century style gardens. Stunningly restored Georgian interiors
provide the perfect backdrop for one of Ireland's most impressive contemporary art
displays, some on loan from private collections. There are two restaurants and two bars:
Mornington's Brasserie offers exciting contemporary cuisine with an Irish flair and *Restaurant Patrick Guilbaud* offers gourmet dining.
Lord Mornington's former wine vault has
become the *Cellar Bar* and there is *No 23* for
that more intimate drink. The Tethra Spa
offers an 18-metre swimming pool and state
of the art Leisure Club. The Merrion is a member of Leading Hotels of the World.

*Rates: Single room including breakfast from
IR£215; double room with breakfast from IR£250.*
*Leisure Breaks: The Merrion Getaway - one night
in a luxurious double room, full Irish breakfast + a
bottle of champagne on arrival- IR£180 per couple.*

● *145 en suite bedrooms (inc 20 suites) with AC,
colour TV+satellite, telephone/fax/ISDN lines, hairdryer, laundry/valet service, minibar, 24-hr room/meal
service, radio/alarm clock, safety deposit box, trouser
press. Non-smoking & disabled bedrooms available.*
● *Table d'hôte dinner £23. A la carte, lunch &
special diets available. Last orders 10.30 pm.*
● *Business services inc. 6 meeting rooms, cap. 60.*
● *Indoor swimming pool, steam room, gymnasium
& spa treatment rooms. Fishing, golf, watersports,
sailing, shooting, squash, tennis, riding nearby.
Beauty salon. Car rental. Car parking for 60.*
● *Open all year. Visa, Amex, Diners cards accepted*

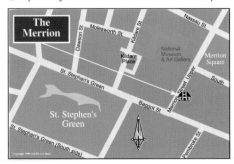

Ireland

Portmarnock Hotel & Golf Links

Strand Road, Portmarnock, Co Dublin
Tel: (00353-1) 8460611;
Fax: (00353-1) 8462442;
Internet: http://www.portmarnock.com

You can only be surprised, as I was, to discover that a location so close to Dublin, eleven
miles to the city centre and four to the airport,
seems so peaceful and quiet. A bracing salty
wind from the ocean, together with clear
views of the Lombay Islands, the green of the
golf links and the sandy dunes all conspired
to envelop me as I arrived at the hotel. There
are miles of sandy beaches on which to walk
or ride. The orginal owners of the house were
the Jameson family, of whisky fame. Now it
has become an international hotel with an 18-
hole golf course designed by Bernhard Langer
and covering 180 acres. Other sports like archery or quad bikes are equally on offer near
the hotel. All bedrooms overlook either the sea
or the golf course. The *Osborne* restaurant has
an excellent choice of international cuisine and
a good selection of wines. The less formal *Links*
restaurant caters for golfers and locals alike.
Portmarnock is the ideal place to stay if you
are visiting Dublin for business or pleasure,
but prefer the quiet of the countryside.

*Rates: Single room inc. breakfast from IR£135.
Double room with breakfast from IR£195.*
*Bargain breaks: 2 nights b&b, one round of golf,
one dinner £225 per person (subj. to availability).*

● *103 en suite bedrooms with radio, colour TV+
satellite, direct-dial telephone, hairdryer, laundry
service, minibar (exec rooms), non-smoker bedrooms, 24-hour room service, safety deposit box,
trouser press. Facilities for the disabled.*
● *2 restaurants. Special diets available. Last
orders 10 pm. Ample car parking.*
● *Own 18-hole golf course. Archery, quad bikes,
sailing, riding, clay pigeon shooting nearby.*
● *Full business services including 5 meeting
rooms to total capacity 350.*
● *Open all year. Mastercard, Visa, Amex, Diners credit cards accepted.*

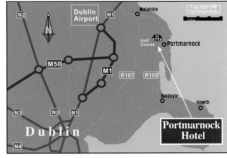

The Shelbourne Dublin

A Meridien Hotel

27 St. Stephens Green, Dublin 2.
Tel: (01) 676 6471; Fax (01) 661 6006
E-mail: egoold@shelbourne.ie
Internet: http://www.shelbourne.ie

The Shelbourne has probably the most distinguished address in Ireland, for it is part of the country's history synonymous with Dublin, and is located in the heart of the city with superb views of St. Stephens Green - Europe's largest garden square. The Irish Constitution was drafted here and both Thackeray and James Joyce wrote of its grandeur as still expressed in its marbled hall and spacious lounge where people gather to gossip over tea or coffee. Hence its other reputation as a fashionable place to meet and measure the business of the world, in the famous Horseshoe Bar of the Shelbourne. For this elegant Georgian hotel has been at the centre of Dublin life since 1824. Another tradition which remains is its standing as a superbly comfortable hotel with a welcoming demeanour. The bedrooms are generally large and stylish in their décor with the suites having lovely more traditional furniture, and all rooms being well appointed. Following refurbishment, The Shelbourne is an even finer hotel than it was, yet it has lost nothing of the charm and personality which has given it such a distinctive place in history. I would stay there as much for those characteristics as for the sheer enjoyment of experiencing the qualities of a first class hotel.

Rates:Single room inc. breakfast from IR£193.50; Double room with breakfast from IR£242.

● *190 en suite bedrooms with radio, colour TV, direct-dial telephone, hairdryer, laundry service, mini-bar; non-smoker bedrooms; 24-hour room service. Safety deposit box, trouser press available*
● *Choice of fine dining restaurant,* No 27 The Green *or upbeat, bistro-style Italian/Californian* Side Door Restaurant.
● *Full health & fitness centre with 18m pool.*
● *Full business services including 11 meeting rooms to total capacity 400; AV equipment available; barber shop; beauty salon; news stand.*
● *Open all year. Major credit cards accepted.*

Ardagh Hotel & Restaurant

Ballyconneely Road, Clifden, Co.
Galway
Tel: (095) 21384; Fax (095) 21314
E-mail: ardaghhotel@tinet.ie
Internet: http://www.commerce.ie/ardaghhotel

Stephane and Monique Bauvet add gallic flair
to this simple family run hotel which is situated beside the road, close to lovely, sandy
beaches and the excellent Connemara Golf
Club. It is a quiet place and unpretentious but
with two features of remarkable quality in its
restaurant and the bedrooms. The first floor
dining room enjoys beautiful views over
Ardbear Bay and Monique creates the most
delicious fare from local produce with lobster
and seafood generally being a speciality,
complemented by locally grown vegetables.
The wine list is good as well. In addition
there's a comfortable bar downstairs where
pub lunches are served and the home-made
soup is lovely. The Ardagh has two pleasant
lounge areas for relaxation but it was the
family rooms which impressed me as being
amongst the best I have ever seen. Twin beds
for the children are set aside in an alcove
slightly separated from the rest of the room.

There is plenty of space for them to play too -
and colour TV and sea views. The rooms
reflect the whole ambience of the Ardagh as
being clean, comfortable and friendly. It is a
charming hotel for a leisurely holiday.

Rates: Double room for 2 persons from IR£95

● *21 en suite bedrooms with TV.*
● *Billiards/ snooker. Squash one mile. Water-
sports three miles. Riding five miles. Golf (10
miles) by arrangement with hotel.*
● *Open end March - November.*
● *All major credit cards accepted.*

**Ballyconneely 5, Oughterard 32, Westport
43, Galway 49, Dublin 168.**

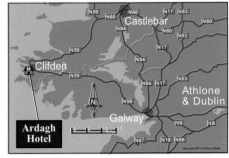

Dingle Skellig Hotel

Dingle Peninsula, Co. Kerry
Tel: (00353) [0] 66 915 1144; Fax: (00353)
[0] 66 915 1501; E-mail: dsk@iol.ie

Dingle Skellig Hotel overlooks Dingle Bay and, wherever you look, you can see the sea - either at first hand or in the numerous seascapes or murals in the hotel! The hotel has a magic feeling of space, tranquillity and friendliness. During my stay, the staff were, without exception, polite, cheerful and welcoming. The food was delicious - there was a choice of six main courses, three of them seafood, my steamed John Dory on a bed of spinach being memorable. The hotel is built on three floors with families on the middle floor and couples and individuals on the third floor where all rooms have personal videos and CD players. All rooms have views of either the sea or mountains and gardens. The hotel has first class conference and leisure facilities. The Dingle Peninsula offers all sorts of activities: hill walking, trips to the Blasket Islands, climbing, fishing, abseiling, shopping in Dingle and much more. There is golf at Ceann Sibeal - the most westerly course in Europe. You will enjoy this complete 'hotel experience' as much as I did. Watch out for *Fungi* - Dingle's friendly dolphin - you may well glimpse him from a window!

Rates: *Single room inc. breakfast from IR£55;*
double inc. breakfast from IR£90. **Ⅴ**
Bargain Breaks: *Winter Specials from £85 pp for*
2 nts b&b + one dinner. Golden Breaks available.
Winter midweek specials from £115 pp - 3 nts
b&b + 2 dinners. Midweek Golf Specials from
£135 pp - 3 nts b&b, 2 dinners + 2 rounds golf.

● *115 en suite bedrooms, all with radio, colour TV+ satellite, telephone, hairdryer, laundry, tea/coffee making, 24-hr room service, safe. Non-smoker and disabled bedrooms available.*
● *Fitness centre/gym, indoor games, jacuzzi, sea bathing, massage, solarium/steam room, indoor swimming pool, boat trips. Sailing, riding, fishing 1m; golf 10m. Car parking - 200.*
● *Business services inc 3 meeting rooms to 250*
● *Open Feb-Dec. All major credit cards accepted*

Tralee 30, Killarney 40, Limerick 95, Dublin 216.

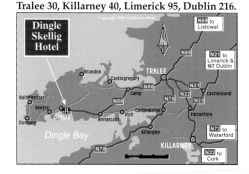

Ireland

The Rosegarden Guesthouse & Restaurant

Kenmare, Co Kerry
Tel: (00353) 64 42288;
Fax: (00353) 64 42305

The Rosegarden is within walking distance of Kenmare - a busy market town full of interesting little shops - on the Ring of Kerry. Peter and Ingrid Ringlever have custom built a charming guesthouse and surrounded it with a lovely rosegarden. The interior is bright and spotlessly clean with cheerful blue and yellow curtains and table mats. The rooms are all en suite with showers and have all modern facilities. Peter's restaurant cum bistro was packed on the evening I stayed there with both tourists and locals - always a good sign! They had fresh fish, shellfish, lamb and a dish of the day on the menu and very good it was too. Peter and Ingrid run their guesthouse with cheerful, welcoming, calm efficiency. An excellent budget choice.

Rates: Single room inc. breakfast from IR£32.50; double room inc breakfast from IR£45. **Bargain Breaks:** *3-day special: 3 x b&b + dinner £120 per person. 7-day special: 7 x b&b + dinner £250.*

● *8 en suite bedrooms with power showers, telephone, colour TV+satellite, hairdryer, tea/coffee making, radio, safety deposit box. Car parking 25.*
● *A la carte restaurant. Last orders 9 pm*
● *Fishing, golf, watersports, sailing, swimming pool, tennis, riding, seafari (seals & birds) nearby.*
● *Open 1 April-Oct 31. Credit cards accepted.*
Killarney 20, Bantry 25, Cork 58, Dublin 210

Richmond House

Cappoquin, Co Waterford
Tel: (058) 54278; Fax: (058) 54988

This elegant 18th century Georgian house, Waterford's only four star Country House Hotel, stands in timbered parkland in the undiscovered Blackwater Valley close to the picturesque town of Cappoquin. Managed personally by Jean Deevey, Richmond House has all the old world charm and character of the family home and is extensively furnished with beautiful furniture and antiques throughout. The public rooms are as cosy and warm as the attention given to guests. The main drawing room leads to a conservatory overlooking the garden where you can have a quiet drink before dinner. Pride of place should be given to the spacious restaurant with one of its three rooms set aside as 'honeymooners' corner'. The son of the house, Swiss-trained Paul and his wife Claire preside over a menu which is not only popular locally but enjoys international recognition, being featured in many guide books.

Rates: Single room with breakfast from IR£50; double from IR£80

● *9 en suite bedrooms with colour TV, direct-dial telephone, hairdryer, trouser press, tea/coffee making facilities.*
● *Table d'hôte dinner £28. A la carte & diets available. Last dinner orders 9 pm.*
● *Fishing, golf & riding within 3 miles.*
● *Open March-20th December.*
● *Visa, Amex, Diners & Mastercard accepted.*

Cork 31, Waterford 40, Rosslare 90, Dublin 136

Hotel Dunloe Castle

Killarney, Co. Kerry
Tel: (064) 44111; Fax: (064) 44583
E-mail: khl@iol.ie

Like its sister hotel, the Europe, Dunloe Castle is a modern hotel set in the most fabulous gardens leading to the ruins of the old castle itself. This park is host to a remarkable award-winning botanical collection of rare flowers and plants as well to grazing Hafflinger horses. Inside the hotel, the furnishings and décor are faultless, inviting and comfortable and, whilst every facility is provided for meetings and conferences, the keynote is an atmosphere in which to relax and unwind. The restaurant serves the most delicious food with the accent on local specialities. The surrounding countryside is famous for walking, fishing and riding, with tennis and swimming on the premises. What could be more rewarding than to dine here after, let us say, a day playing golf opposite the hotel or on one of the numerous famous courses nearby, fishing or perhaps walking up the Gap of Dunloe? This is the outdoor sportsman's paradise, the gourmet's heaven and the holiday maker's *Shangri-La*, all packaged into one superb venue.

Rates: Single room with breakfast from IR£94; double room with breakfast from IR£116. Ⓥ
Bargain Breaks: Any two nights, b & b + one dinner IR£129 per person sharing, exc July/Aug.

● *110 en suite bedrooms, one suite, all with satellite TV, direct-dial telephone, hairdryer, laundry service, 24-hour room service.*
● *Table d'hôte dinner £24; à la carte, lunch & special diets available; last orders 9.30 pm.*
● *Free river fishing, golf adjacent, jogging track, riding, indoor swimming pool, indoor tennis. Historical gardens, sailing, squash nearby. Shooting by arrangement.*
● *Open May - October. All credit cards accepted except JAC.*
Tralee 25, Kenmare 27, Cork 57, Limerick 69, Shannon 84, Rosslare 172, Dublin 189.

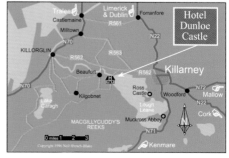

Ireland

Hotel Europe

Killarney, Co. Kerry
Tel: (064) 31900; Fax: (064) 32118
E-mail: khl@iol.ie

Space, grace and elegance are but few of the words which would describe this modern hotel set overlooking Killarney's lakes and mountains. All the rooms are bright and airy, beautifully furnished with a perfect blend of antique and modern and the elegance is enhanced by the quiet efficiency of the staff. There are superb views from the restaurant where the most delicious Irish and international cuisine can be enjoyed, with local fish, lobster and smoked salmon as specialities. The 5-star Hotel Europe is the right choice for an active holiday. Some of Ireland's most beautiful and famous golf courses are within easy reach of the hotel. The spectacular surrounding countryside also provides opportunities for tennis, swimming, pony trekking, cycling and hiking. The hotel itself has an excellent fitness centre and children can entertain themselves in the playroom or ride the hotel's own Hafflinger ponies. Hotel Europe is the ideal place to relax after an invigorating day exploring some of Ireland's finest countryside.

Rates: Single room with breakfast from IR£94; double room with breakfast from IR£116. **V**
Bargain Breaks: Details on application.

● *199 en suite bedrooms, 6 suites, all with satellite TV, direct-dial telephone, hairdryer, laundry service, 24-hour room service.*
● *Table d'hôte dinner £27; à la carte, lunch & special diets available; last orders 9.30 pm.*
● *Billiards/snooker, fishing, golf adjacent, indoor swimming pool, fitness centre, free riding, boating, indoor tennis. Watersports & squash nearby. Shooting by arrangement.*
● *Open March - November. All credit cards accepted except JAC.*

Tralee 22, Kenmare 24, Cork 54, Limerick 69, Shannon 84, Rosslare 172, Dublin 189.

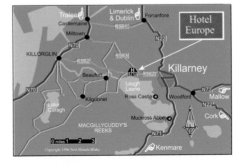

Hotel Ard Na Sidhe

Caragh Lake, Killorglin, Co. Kerry
Tel: (066) 69105; Fax: (066) 69282
E-mail: khl@iol.ie

It is a pity to call this an hotel, for at Ard Na
Sidhe (*The House of the Fairies*), one is a guest in
an elegant country house. Warmly furnished
with antiques, it has that welcoming atmosphere that so many hotels try to emulate but
few seem to achieve. Built in 1880 with fabulous award-winning gardens sloping down to
the lake, the house offers a tranquillity rarely
found today. It has valuable antiques, open
fires and a magnificent, mature garden which
has twice won first prize in the Irish National
Gardens Competition. You can read, go for
walks, paint, dream or simply 'switch off' in
this idyllic setting. For those seeking a more
active holiday, the environs provide more
sporting activities than almost any comparable
area in Europe: golf (nine courses within a 30-
mile radius) fishing and hill trekking to name a
few. Whilst Ireland is a relaxing country, even a
leisurely tour is tiring. Any visit to the south
west and the Ring of Kerry would be incom-
plete without staying here for at least a couple
of days to recharge the batteries.

Rates: *Single room with breakfast from IR£70;
double room with breakfast from IR£116.* **V**

● *17 en suite bedrooms, 2 suites, all with direct
dial telephone, hairdryer.*
● *Table d'hôte dinner IR£27. Special diets available; last orders 9.00 pm*
● *Leisure facilities available at sister hotels
Dunloe Castle and Hotel Europe (see previous
pages).*
● *Open May - October. All credit cards accepted
except JAC.*

Killarney 12, Tralee 16, Dublin 207.

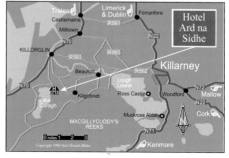

Ireland

Carrig House
Country House & Restaurant

Caragh Lake, Killorglin, Ring of Kerry
Tel: 00353 (0) 66 69100;
Fax: 00353 (0) 66 69166

Once you leave the main road, you know you are heading somewhere special. You are about to discover one of the best kept secrets in Ireland. This charming and meticulously restored Victorian residence has a sense of timelessness about it. It is perched on the shores of Lake Caragh in Kerry with some of the cleanest air in Europe, beautiful gardens and spectacular views across the still waters to the Kerry mountains. The restaurant overlooks the lake and serves the freshest Irish food with salmon and trout from the lake, succulent Kerry lamb from the hill, wild game and organic vegetables from the hotel's own garden. Frank Slattery is a most welcoming host and Mary has done a wonderful job with the decor and with fresh flowers in all public rooms. This area of Kerry has sailing, climbing, golf, archaeological sites and some of the best walks in the southwest within easy reach. Carrig only opened in 1997 but has already established a considerable reputation. Be sure to reserve well in advance as its popularity can only grow.

*Rates: Single room with breakfast from IR£63;
double from IR£86.*   **V**
Bargain Breaks: On application.

● *9 en suite bedrooms (one suite) with colour TV, direct-dial telephone, radio/alarm clock, hairdryer, tea/coffee making facilities.*
● *3-course table d'hôte dinner £30. A la carte and special diets available. Last dinner orders 21.00 hrs*
● *Rock climbing, sailing, golf, cycling, canoeing, walking all nearby.*
● *Open all year exc. 24-26 Dec. Car parking for 20*
● *Visa, Mastercard, Diners credit cards accepted.*

Killorglin 3, Killarney 12, Limerick 16, Cork 66, Dublin 207

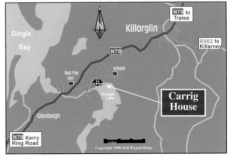

Parknasilla Great Southern Hotel

Sneem, Co. Kerry
Tel: (064) 45122; Fax: (064) 45323

When I last stayed in this remote hotel it was a good experience, so I was pleased to find it even more inviting under new owners. It is the view that makes it really special. The luxurious Victorian Great Southern Hotel overlooks Kenmare Bay and stands in 300 acres of sub-tropical gardens. The setting is majestic and it blends easily with its parkland surroundings which offer a nine-hole golf course, horse riding and much more. The interior is impressive: - lots of public rooms and an especially fine upper conservatory corridor in glass with comfortable seats and splendid views over the bay. The stylish Pygmalion Restaurant, which George Bernard Shaw patronised, enjoys the same outlook whilst the library, the billiard room and the Doolittle bar are in quiet contrast to the bustling main lounge. The roomy bedrooms have sparkling bathrooms and all modern facilities. The hotel has recently celebrated its centenary and is an ideal jumping off point from which to explore the beauties of south-west Ireland: the villages of West Cork, the Ring of Kerry and the Killarney National Park.

Rates: Single room with breakfast from IR£116; Double room from IR£96 per person. **V**
Bargain breaks: 2 nights, one dinner low season from IR£120 per person.

● *83 en suite bedrooms with satellite TV, telephone, hairdryer, trouser press, laundry service, 24-hour room service. Non-smoker rooms available.*
● *Last orders for dinner 20.45 hrs. Special diets.*
● *Billiards/snooker; indoor games room; jacuzzi, sauna; indoor swimming pool; jogging track; watersports, riding, fishing, shooting, tennis, 9-hole golf course, clay pigeon shooting, archery, pétanque.*
● *Full business services and 2 conference rooms with capacity for 50 guests; AV equipment.*
● *Airport pick-up. Car parking for 75 cars.*
● *Closed Jan/Feb; Major credit cards accepted.*

Kenmare 16, Cork 80, Limerick 100, Dublin 216.

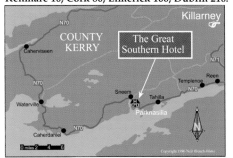

Ireland

The Kildare Hotel & Country Club

Straffan, Co. Kildare
Tel: (353-1) 601 7200; Fax: (353-1) 601 7299
E-mail: hotel@KClub.ie; Web: http://www.kclub.ie

Opulent is the word often used to describe The Kildare Hotel & Country Club and it lives up to its reputation as a superlative country house hotel. The elegant 19th Century manor house is set in 330 acres of landscaped countryside, with a mile of the river Liffey offering trout and salmon fishing to guests. The public areas are stylish with hand-painted drawing room and cocktail bar, period antiques and sumptuous furnishings set among the marble fireplaces and a marvellous fine art collection. The spacious bedrooms are luxurious, individually designed and richly furnished offering every indulgence - and with palatial bathrooms. The K Club also has self-contained garden courtyard suites. The Byerley Turk restaurant delivers a superb standard of table d'hôte and à la carte cuisine; and finally the sporting fac-ilities, including the Arnold Palmer designed golf course (home to The Smurfit European Open), are totally comprehensive. The K Club is one of the most complete places I have visited and it is an experience in itself to stay there.

Rates: Double room from IR£280.
Leisure Breaks: *Nov 1st - March 31st 1999. 2 nights' accommodation, 2 full breakfasts, 1 dinner and a choice of one leisure activity - at IR£300 pp sharing; also available for 2 guests, one night midweek, subject to availability. Chrismas & New Year packages available for 3-7 nights.*

● *45 en suite bedrooms with radio, satellite TV, direct-dial telephone; hairdryer, laundry service; minibar, 24 hour room service.*
● *Facilities for disabled. Last dinner orders 9.45 pm.*
● *Full business services provided including 3 conference rooms for 10-120 guests. AV equipment.*
● *Hairdresser; beauty salon; safety deposit box.*
● *Car rental. Transfers arranged.*
● *Open all year. Credit cards accepted.*
Naas 7, Dublin City Centre 17.

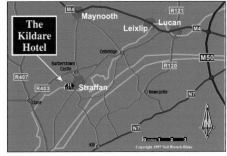

Knockranny House Hotel

Westport, Co Mayo
Tel: (098) 28600; Fax: (098) 28611

Knockranny House Hotel was built in classic Victorian style and opened in 1997. It is in a commanding position looking over the town of Westport to the majestic mountain of Croagh Patrick (famous for its pilgrimages). The public rooms give a feeling of space and comfort. The reception foyer and gallery are large and airy, whilst the conservatory, library and drawing room offer quiet havens from which to admire the views, have tea or just relax in front of an open turf fire. Westport itself is well worth visiting, full of life and exuberance with little streets and gaily painted shops, cosy restaurants and cheerful pubs. There is a country market once a week, one of the best in Ireland. Staff at Knockranny are always friendly and helpful, each being a mine of local information. All Suites and Deluxe bedrooms have jacuzzis, cable TV and voicemail. *La Fougère* AA Rosette Restaurant offers gourmet dining in a beautifully appointed room overlooking Croagh Patrick. The Brechon Bar has just been awarded the *Black & White Provincial Hotel Bar of the Year* title. The hotel has extensive banqueting and conference facilities. County Mayo has its own special beauty which takes a few days to explore.

Rates: *Single room inc. breakfast from IR£85; double room inc. breakfast from IR£130.*   **V**
Bargain breaks: *2 nights b & b + one dinner from IR£100 per person.*

● *50 en suite bedrooms (inc 3 suites) with satellite TV, direct-dial telephone, hairdryer, trouser press, laundry service, 24-hr room service, tea/coffee making facilities (on request), disabled and hypo allergenic bedrooms available.*
● *Tdh dinner £25; last orders 9.30 pm; lunch & special diets available.*
● *Golf, watersports, sailing, tennis & riding nearby. Ample car parking. Car rental.*
● *Full business services inc. 4 meeting rooms to 700*
● *Closed 24-26 December. Amex, Mastercard, Visa accepted.*

Knock Airport 40, Galway 55, Dublin 160.

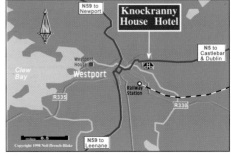

Ireland

Tullamore Court Hotel

Tullamore, Co. Offaly
Tel: (506) 46666; Fax: (506) 46677

Tullamore Court is a new hotel in the heart of
the Irish Midlands, which has already proved
itself very popular with young Dubliners taking weekend breaks and locals using it as a
wedding and conference/meeting centre. The
hotel is close to a range of amenities that include lakes, rivers, the Slieve Bloom mountains, golf courses, equestrian activities and the
heritage town of Birr with its medieval castle
and gardens. Hotel staff are most knowledge-
able about local attractions and I was provided
with a small touring map of Tullamore. In the
best traditions of Irish hospitality, the hotel bar
is the centre of activity and is the perfect place
to while away an evening listening to the music, the *craic* and the chat. The restaurant, under
executive chef Philip O'Brien, serves à la carte
and table d'hôte menus complemented by a
comprehensive wine list. The hotel's conference facilities include state-of-the-art audio-
visual equipment and the banqueting service
can accommodate up to 550 people. The health
and leisure centre is now open for burning off
those excess calories! Tullamore Court is a
good centre for business or pleasure in an area
of Ireland previously short of good hotels.

Rates: *Single room inc. breakfast from IR£70;
double room with breakfast IR£110.* **V**

● *72 en suite bedrooms (inc 3 suites) with radio/
TV+satellite, AC, direct-dial telephone, hairdryer,
trouser press, laundry/valet service, safety deposit
box, tea/coffee making facilities. Non-smoker and
disabled bedrooms available.*
● *4-course table d'hôte dinner £25. A la carte,
lunch & special diets available. Last orders 9.45 pm.*
● *Business centre inc 8 meeting rooms, cap. 5-700.*
● *Fitness centre/gym, jacuzzi, massage, indoor
swimming pool, crèche. Tennis ¹/₂ mile; golf 2 m,
riding 5m, sailing 12 miles.*
● *Closed 25 Dec. All major credit cards accepted.*

**Birr 23, Athlone 25, Kilkenny 52, Limerick
80, Dublin 65.**   *Birr Gardens*

Coolbawn Quay Holiday & Conference Village

Coolbawn, Nr. Nenagh, Co Tipperary
Tel: (via) 00353-1 660 3755;
Fax: (via) 00353 1 660 3872

This entire village is the brainchild of Kevin and Jay Brophy. This Dublin business couple - not satisfied with just building a cottage in the country, decided to construct an entire village right on the shores of Lough Derg in one of the most peaceful and rural parts of Ireland. Each individual house has been beautifully finished, cleverly combining a feeling of maturity and charm with clean cut contemporary design and with all modern facilities. You can stroll down the village street to the restaurant, bar and fitness centre or simply walk along the quayside. Like any village, it will develop with time. From early 1999 the visiting business traveller can rent office space in *The Old Schoolhouse* which has full conference, internet and office facilities. Medium sized banquets and functions can be accommodated. For those more interested in a leisure break, every variety of sport can be arranged, with the emphasis on the lakeside activities of sailing or fishing. *The Harbour Pub & Restaurant* is a popular rendezvous for music, *craic* and good eating. With its stone walled streets and village squares Coolbawn is reminiscent of a lough-side Portmeirion or Port Grimaud, only with a business element. A most enterprising development for Central Ireland.

Rates: Guesthouse from IR£35 pppn single/IR£50 pppn double. Self-catering from IR£375 for 3/4 night breaks. Sleeps 6-8 people.

● *The Harbour Pub & Restaurant. Last orders 11pm.*
● *Harbour Fitness Club, comprising two indoor training pools, fitness centre & sauna. Sports equipment for hire. Fishing, bathing, sailing, watersports. Riding, golf & tennis nearby. Private marina - berthing available.* ● *Full business services and conferencing.*
● *Closed 4 Jan-6 Feb '99. Major credit cards accepted*

Nenagh 6, Limerick 30, Galway 65, Dublin 100

Ireland

Gurthalougha House

Ballinderry, Nenagh, Co Tipperary
Tel: (067) 22080; Fax: (067) 22154

Lough Derg is Ireland's largest lake and Gurthalouga House, originally a 19th century hunting lodge, nestles on its eastern shore. It has recently changed hands. In the grounds there is a little private pier where two fishing boats were tied up and on the day I stayed there were two little boys armed with rods, jam jars and broad grins, dangling their legs into the clear water and waiting to catch their first trout or pike. Pigeons were cooing in the trees and two enormous St Bernard dogs were basking in the sunshine. There are many delightful walks in the grounds and you will see a great variety of flora and wildlife. Gurthalouga is first and foremost a country house without the formality of an hotel. Breakfast is served till lunchtime and there is a dear little cobbled stone courtyard full of flowers - an ideal place to sit and relax. Snack lunches are available but most people prefer to explore the surrounding countryside, many attractions being within easy reach - Yeats' Tower, The Rock of Cashel, the Cliffs of Moher to name but a few. Four golf courses, a

sailing school and pony trekking are all nearby. Local people come here especially for the relaxed and informal dinners. Menus change daily to reflect the changing seasons. It is a lovely place in which to come and relax and has won many deserved plaudits.

> **Rates:** *Single room inc. breakfast from IR£35; double inc. breakfast from IR£90.* Ⓥ

● *8 en suite rooms with direct-dial telephone.*
● *Table d'hôte £17.50. Last orders 9.30 pm.*
● *Fishing, tennis, croquet. Golf, riding, pony trekking, sailing nearby.*
● *Open March-October; weekends only Nov-Jan; closed February. Major credit cards accepted.*

Nenagh 6, Limerick 41, Galway 53, Dublin 111.

Ireland

Crookedwood & Clonkhill House

Crookedwood, Mullingar,
Co. Westmeath
Tel: (044) 72165; Fax: (044) 72166

Noel and Julie Kenny started Crookedwood as a restaurant, which,through necessity, blossomed into a restaurant *and* guesthouse. This year a second guesthouse (Clonkhill) has been opened and a minibus runs between the two buildings. Bedrooms are generous in size and provide every hotel convenience. The restaurant is cosy and intimate in what used to be the old wine cellars and Noel is a fine chef, having won several awards including the *Egon Ronay Irish Beef Award* in 1996. He makes skilled use of local meat, game and venison, accompanied by home-grown fresh vegetables and an extensive wine list.

Crookedwood used to be the Taghmon Parish Rectory and stands next door to the 15th-century Taghmon Church overlooking Lough Derravaragh. Other historic sites in the vicinity include Tullynally Castle, Multyfarnhan Franciscan Friary and Fore Abbey.

Otherwise fishing, golf and horse riding are available nearby and the staff will be pleased to advise visitors on the best local walks, golf courses, fishing rivers and lakes to help them to work up a good appetite for dinner!

Double Room Rates - Crookedwood: *IR£45-55 per person; single supplement £10.* **Clonkhill:** *IR£32.50-35 per person; single supplement £5.* Ⓥ

● *16 rooms, all non-smoking & en suite, with colour TV, direct-dial telephone, hairdryer.*
● *Table d'hôte dinner £25. A la carte, lunch & special diets available. Last orders 10 pm.*
● *Private dining room 10-30 persons. House open Tuesday-Saturday and Sunday lunch.*
● *Golf, riding, fishing, tennis, croquet nearby.*
● *Open all year. Major credit cards accepted.*
● *Directions: Coming from Dublin, take 3rd exit on Mullingar bypass (signed Castlepollard) - drive to Crookedwood Village. Turn right at the Wood Pub, 2 km further on you will see the house.*

Clonkhill House

Ireland

Humewood Castle

Rates: *Single room inc. breakfast from IR£140; double from IR£200.*

Kiltegan, Co. Wicklow
Tel: (+353) 508 73215; Fax: (+353) 508 73382; E-mail: Humewood@iol.ie

Humewood is indeed a fairytale castle with battlements and granite towers. It is not an hotel but a private house and sporting estate. Guests are invited to bring guns, jodhpurs, fishing tackle and hiking boots for an exceptional sporting stay. Shooting is allowed in Ireland on Sundays and the pheasant and duck shooting season can be extended till February 15th. Trail riding is on the doorstep and a day's hunting with the Kildare can be arranged. Trout and pike fishing is from four lakes on the estate. Any feeling one might have on entering of an austere or intimidating castle is immediately banished by the warm, welcoming, family atmosphere inside. Humewood was completed in 1870 for Hume Dick, MP for Co Wicklow. Each piece of furniture fits the period. I particularly admired the four-poster beds. Each bedroom has its own theme. Food is delicious and served in one of the two dining rooms. Humewood has been awarded the American Five Star Diamond Award twice - in 1997 and 1998. The castle can accommodate small conferences and banquets for up to 80.

● *13 en suite bedrooms, all with colour TV+ satellite, direct-dial telephone, hairdryer, laundry service. All bedrooms non-smoking.*
● *Table d'hôte dinner £39. Lunch & special diets available. Last orders 10 pm.*
● *Business services inc. meeting room to 20. Receptions up to 80 seated/120 cocktail. Car parking.*
● *Billiards/snooker, croquet, fishing, jogging track, massage, clay (20+ traps) and game shooting, polo, riding, 3-day event course, trail riding, hunting, bike riding, hill walking. Golf 20 miles.*
● *Open all year. Mastercard, Visa, Amex accepted.*

Baltinglass 6, Carlow 20, Wicklow 30, Dublin 40.

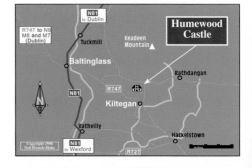

Rathsallagh Country House & Golf Club

Dunlavin, Co. Wicklow
Tel: (+353) 45 403112;
Fax: (+353) 45 403343

The approach to Rathsallagh is a long drive bisecting the golf course. Happily there are cattle grids whose rattle reminds golfers to give way to cars when making their swings! Rathsallagh was converted from a Queen Anne stable block into a comfortable country house with bags of charm and character. It sits in 530 acres of mature parkland. Joe and Kay O'Flynn will make you feel at ease with all home comforts and excellent food prepared from local ingredients, where possible. Breakfast is special at the house - there are big enticing silver domes on the sideboard and bread is home made. Indeed Rathsallagh has won the National Breakfast Award three times. The golf course was designed by Peter McEvoy and Irish professional Christy O'Connor and is laid out to 252 acres of lush parkland, with mature trees, natural water hazards, USGA-specification greens and a gently rolling landscape, belying its age. Rathsallagh is only an hour's drive from Dublin. It makes the perfect spot for a peaceful holiday for golfer and non-golfer alike.

Rates: *Single room inc. breakfast IR£95-110; double inc. breakfast IR£110-190.* **V**
Bargain Breaks: *Two nights dinner, b&b from IR£199 pp sharing. Same with 2 rounds of golf from IR£249. Midweek from IR£170 pp sharing.*

● *17 en suite bedrooms all with colour TV, direct-dial telephone, hairdryer, laundry service, tea/coffee making. Non-smoker & disabled rooms available.*
● *Table d'hôte dinner from £30; lunch & special diets available. Last orders 9 pm.*
● *Business services inc 3 meeting rooms, cap. up to 100. Airport pickup; car rental by arr't. Car parking*
● *Billiards/snooker, croquet, golf, indoor games, massage, sauna, clay shooting, indoor pool, tennis, archery. Fishing, riding locally.*
● *Open all year exc. 23-27 Dec.*
● *All major credit cards accepted.*

Heritage
HOTELS

What's your idea of the perfect getaway?

Rambling walks through rolling countryside, days splashing about by the seaside, or a shopping and culture trip - whatever you're looking for in a hotel break, you

can plan your ideal escape with Heritage. There are over 40 Heritage Hotels to choose from in a range of country, city and coastal locations throughout Britain.

The Bear, Woodstock

The Swan, Grasmere

The Berystede, Ascot

The Castle Hotel, Windsor

The Shakespeare, Stratford-upon-Avon

The Upper Reaches, Abingdon

From historic coaching inns, steeped in history, and attractive rural retreats surrounded by glorious scenery, to smart city-centre establishments - there is a Heritage Hotel to suit every taste. Each Heritage Hotel has its own unique charm and character, style and setting. All offer traditional hospitality and service tailor-made to your needs, leaving you free to unwind in the knowledge that everyday life has been left far behind.

Individual hotels for every Individual

Breaks from £29
Bed & Breakfast per person per night

To book or request a brochure, please call

0345 40 40 40

quoting 'Signpost 1'

www.heritage-hotels.com
Heritage is a division of Forte Hotels

The Luttrell Arms, Dunster, Somerset

ON THE ROAD
FROM BRIDGWATER TO MINEHEAD AND PORLOCK
24 Miles from Bridgwater, 2 miles from Minehead and 8 miles from Porlock.
(*For position see map on page* 17, *square G.4*).

An Inn of great historic interest in one of England's loveliest villages—Famous polo and staghunting centre—Modern comforts.

THE village of Dunster is renowned for the rambling beauty of its street, centred about its XVII century yarn market, its polo ground and the great family which has dwelt in the castle on the hill since 1499 and given its name to this grand old inn. The place from its stone porch with its arrow slits on either side to its elaborately carved oak, wonderfully moulded plaster effects, yawning fireplaces and fine beams is crammed with many hundred years' of local history, through which it has ever maintained a great reputation for its hospitality. And so we come to-day and find it still a famous port of call appealing to those of many different tastes. Here come year after year polo players, stag hunters, film stars, judges, playwrites and men of letters knowing full well that they will be made comfortable after their day's work or play. Here they can rest in peace and quiet enjoying in an atmosphere of the past the attention and accessories that make life pleasant in 1936. There's a comfortable lounge upstairs and pleasant bar below. Bedrooms with modern conveniences and plenty of hot water are other points. And for these creature comforts you have to thank Trust Houses.

SPORTING AND CONFERENCE FACILITIES

Sporting and conference facilities to be found at *Signpost* hotels are tabulated on the following pages. This section is arranged by regions within England, Wales, Scotland, the Channel Islands and Ireland and by counties within each country.

KEY

● Facilities available at hotel

❍ Facilities available within five miles of the hotel

✪ Special arrangements can be made by the hotel

TRADE DESCRIPTIONS ACT 1968
The facilities in italics in each hotel entry are submitted each year to us by hotels but the comments on each hotel are the personal opinion of a member of the Signpost team as he or she found it. Due to a number of factors such as changes in management or chefs, we are unable to guarantee that the visitor will find any particular hotel in the exact state that our inspectors found it or will have the same opinion of it. We are therefore not responsible for eventual disappointment but we try to include in the book a wide range of hotels and we sincerely hope that guests will agree with our inspectors' choice. Please use the Report Forms on the following page if you would like to make any particular comments.

PRICES. Please note that the prices quoted to us by establishments listed in this book date, in most cases, from mid-1998 and are liable to amendment by the hotels without prior notice.

Other column sub-labels (left to right): Beautician. Night club · Gliding. Power-flying · Health & beauty salon · Putting green · Boules · Bowls · Private moorings · Putting

Facility	7	8	9	10	11	12	13	14	15	16	17	18	19	21	22	23	24	25	27	28	29	30	31	32	33	35	36	37	39	41
Other											Beautician. Night club	Gliding. Power-flying	Health & beauty salon	Putting green							Boules							Bowls	Private moorings	Putting
Watersports	○		○		●	○	○	○	○	●	●			○	○		○											●	●	✪
Tennis	○	●	○	●	●			○	○				○	○	○			○	○	○			○				○	○	○	● ●
Swimming pool	●	●	●	●	●	○		●			○			●	○	●		○	○	●							●	●	●	● ●
Squash/badminton	○		●	○		○							●		○	○			○	○					●		○	●	●	○
Shooting	○	○		○					○	○				○		○			○	✪										●
Sea/river bathing	●	○		●		○	○		○	○	○	●	●	○			○			●			●	●			●	●	●	●
Sauna/solarium	●	●			●			●			●	●		●		●	●										●	●	●	●
Sailing/boating	○	○		○		○	○	○						○	○		○			○	○				●	○ ✪	●	●	●	● ●
Riding	○	○			○	○	○	○	○	○	○	○	○		○	○			○	○	○	✪			✪			○	○	● ○
Massage					○				●	●	●																		●	
Jogging track					●																									
Jacuzzi/whirlpool		●			●				●		●	●																	●	●
Indoor games		●			●				●	●			●								●							●		
Golf	○ ✪	●		○	○	○	✪	✪	○	○	○	○	○	●	○	○			○	○		✪ ●	○ ○				○	○	○	
Gym/fitness centre		●		●				○				●			●											○		●		
Fishing	○	○	○		○			○	○	○			○	○	●	○					○			●	●		●	●	●	● ✪
Croquet					●				●				●				●				●		●	●			●			
Conferences	●	●		●	●				●	●	●											●	●	●					●	●
Billiards/snooker	●	○		●	● ●					●	●		●									●							●	● ●

ENGLAND - The West Country

CORNWALL

7 Tredethy Country Hotel, Bodmin
8 Royal Duchy Hotel, Falmouth
9 Green Lawns, Falmouth
10 Cormorant Hotel, Golant
11 Polurrian Hotel, Lizard Peninsula
12 Coombe Farm, Nr. Looe
13 Nansidwell Country House, Mawnan
14 Crantock Bay Hotel, Newquay
15 Cross House Hotel
16 Beachfield Hotel, Penzance
17 Penventon Hotel, Redruth
18 Rose-in-Vale Hotel, St Agnes
19 Trevaunance Point Hotel, St Agnes
21 Carlyon Bay Hotel, St Austell
22 Boskerris Hotel, St Ives
23 The Garrack Hotel, St Ives
24 Talland Bay Hotel, by Looe

DEVON

25 Bovey House, Beer
27 The Berry Head Hotel, Brixham
28 Wigham, Nr. Crediton
29 Lord Haldon Hotel, Nr. Exeter
30 Combe House Hotel, Nr. Honiton
31 The Cottage Hotel, Hope Cove
32 Ernewood House, Ivybridge
33 Collavon Manor, Okehampton
35 Bolt Head Hotel, Salcombe
36 South Sands Hotel, Salcombe
37 Tides Reach Hotel, Salcombe
39 Saunton Sands Hotel, Saunton Sands
41 The Victoria Hotel, Sidmouth

Page

42 Royal Glen Hotel, Sidmouth						○								●			●	○		Surfing
43 Thurlestone Hotel	●	●	●	✪	●	○	●	●		●	○	○	●		✪	●	●	●	✪	
44 The Osborne Hotel, Torquay	●	●		○		○							●	○			●	●	○	+Indoor pool. Putting lawn
45 Watersmeet Hotel, Woolacombe				○		○					○	○		●	○		●	●		Surfing
46 Woolacombe Bay Hotel, Woolacombe	●	●		○	●	●		●			○	●	●	●	○		●	●		Short mat bowls, yacht
SOMERSET																				
48 Bindon Country House Hotel, Wellington		●	●	○		○					○				○		●	●		
49 Walnut Tree Hotel, Bridgwater		●											●							
WILTSHIRE																				
50 Crudwell Court, Nr Malmesbury		●	●	○	○	○					○	○			○	○	●	○		
51 Beechfield House, Melksham		●	●	●		○					○				○	○	●	○		
Central Southern England																				
BERKSHIRE																				
55 The Swan Diplomat, Streatley-on-Thames		●		○	●	○		●			○	✪	●		○		●	○		Bike hire, beautician
BUCKINGHAMSHIRE																				
56 Grovefield Hotel, Burnham		●	●	●																
DORSET																				
57 Queen's Hotel, Bournemouth	●	●		○	●	○		●		●	○	○	●	●	○		●			
58 Manor Hotel, Dorchester		●				○					○			●						
59 Manor House Hotel, Studland Bay						○					●	○		○				●		
60 Knoll House Hotel, Studland Bay				○	●	●	●	●			○	○	●	●			●	●		Windsurfing
63 Plumber Manor, Sturminster Newton		●	○	○		○				○	○				○			○		
HAMPSHIRE																				
64 Tylney Hall, Hook	●	●	●		●	○	●	●	●		○	●		●		●	●	○		+ Indoor pool.
65 Passford House Hotel,Nr. Lymington			●		●	○	●					○	○	●	○			●	●	Pétanque
66 Stanwell House Hotel, Lymington	○				○		○	○				○	○			○	○	○		
OXFORDSHIRE																				
67 Fallowfields, Kingston Bagpuize		●	●	○	○	○		●			○	○			●	○	●	●		
London & the South-East																				
KENT																				
83 Thanington Hotel, Canterbury	●																●			
84 Walletts Court, Nr. Dover			●	●		○								○				●		

Facility	85 Stade Court, Hythe	86 Hotel du Vin et du Bistro, Tunbridge Wells	87 Coulsdon Manor, Coulsdon	88 Bishop's Table, Farnham	89 Chase Lodge, Kingston-upon-Thames	90 Oatlands Park Hotel, Weybridge	83 Little Hemingfold Hotel, Battle	91 Grand Hotel, Eastbourne	92 Lansdowne Hotel, Eastbourne	93 Ashdown Park Hotel, Forest Row	94 Beauport Park, Hastings	95 Flackley Ash Hotel, Peasmarsh	103 Redcoats Farmhouse Hotel, Hitchin	104 The Swan, Southwold	114 The Peacock Hotel, Rowsley	115 The Swan Hotel, Bibury	116 Hotel on the Park, Cheltenham	118 Washbourne Court, Lower Slaughter
Other							Boules	+ Indoor pool	Putting, bridge		Putting green							
Watersports						○		○										
Tennis	○		●	○	○		●	●		●	●		○	○			○	●
Swimming pool						○	●	●	○	●	●							
Squash/badminton	○		●	○			○	○										
Shooting								○								○		
Sea/river bathing	●							●										
Sauna/solarium	○		●					●		●	●							
Sailing/boating	●				○		●	○						○				
Riding				○			○	○		●				○		○	○	○
Massage	○							●	●									
Jogging track								●										
Jacuzzi/whirlpool	○							●	●									
Indoor games	○	○			○			●										
Golf	○		●	○	○		○	○	○	●	●			○		○	○	○
Gym/fitness centre	○		●	○		●	●	●	●					○				
Fishing				○			●	○						○	●		●	
Croquet	○	●		●	●		●							●				
Conferences	●	●	●			●	●	●	●	●	●		●				●	●
Billiards/snooker	○						●	●	●									

SURREY (87 Coulsdon Manor, Coulsdon; 88 Bishop's Table, Farnham; 89 Chase Lodge, Kingston-upon-Thames; 90 Oatlands Park Hotel, Weybridge)

EAST SUSSEX (83 Little Hemingfold Hotel, Battle; 91 Grand Hotel, Eastbourne; 92 Lansdowne Hotel, Eastbourne; 93 Ashdown Park Hotel, Forest Row; 94 Beauport Park, Hastings; 95 Flackley Ash Hotel, Peasmarsh)

East of England
HERTFORDSHIRE (103 Redcoats Farmhouse Hotel, Hitchin)
SUFFOLK (104 The Swan, Southwold)

The Heart of England
DERBYSHIRE (114 The Peacock Hotel, Rowsley)
GLOUCESTERSHIRE (115 The Swan Hotel, Bibury; 116 Hotel on the Park, Cheltenham; 118 Washbourne Court, Lower Slaughter)

Page

Column headings (where labelled): **Putting green**, **Ballooning**, **Falconry**, ... **Falconry**

119 Burliegh Court, Minchinhampton
120 The Grapevine, Stow-om-the-Wold
121 Hare & Hounds, Westonbirt

HEREFORDSHIRE
115 The Swan at Hay Hotel, Hay-on-Wye

LEICESTERSHIRE
124 Stapleford Park, Nr. Melton Mowbray

NORTHAMPTONSHIRE
125 Fawsley Hall, Nr Daventry

NOTTINGHAMSHIRE
127 Langar Hall, Langar
128 The Old England. Nr. Newark

WARWICKSHIRE
130 Stratford Victoria, Stratford-upon-Avon

WORCESTERSHIRE
131 The Dormy House, Broadway

The North West
CHESHIRE
136 Sutton Hall Hotel, Macclesfield
137 Higher Huxley Hall, Chester

CUMBRIA
138 Rothay Manor Hotel, Ambleside
139 Wateredge Hotel, Ambleside
140 Appleby Manor Country House Hotel
142 Armathwaite Hall, Bassenthwaite Lake
144 Wild Boar Inn, Crook
146 Graythwaite Manor Hotel, Grange-o-Sands
147 Netherwood Hotel, Grange-over-Sands
148 Michael's Nook, Grasmere
149 The Wordsworth Hotel, Grasmere
150 Dale Head Hall Lakeside Hotel, Keswick
151 Stakis Keswick Lodore Hotel, Keswick

Top sub-headings (vertical): **Marina**, **Putting green**, **Golf practice hole, par 3**

Other	152	153	154	156	157	159	160	161	162	163	165	166	173	174	175	177	176	179	180	186
Watersports				○	○	○	○						●							
Tennis	✪				○	●	●	●		○			○	✪	●	●				●
Swimming pool					○						●	○			○	●				●
Squash/badminton						○						○								●
Shooting					✪					○			✪							
Sea/river bathing	○	●	●			○							●							
Sauna/solarium					○	○	●				●	●			●					●
Sailing/boating	○	●	●	○		●	○	○	●	○	○							○		
Riding	●	○	○	○	○	○	○	○	○	○	○		○	✪	○	○	○	○		
Massage					○															●
Jogging track																				
Jacuzzi/whirlpool											●									●
Indoor games											●							●		
Golf	✪		○		✪	✪	○	○	○	○	○		○	●	○	○		○	○	○
Gym/fitness centre				○	○	●					●	●			○					●
Fishing	○	●	●	●	○	●	●	●	●	○	●			✪			○			
Croquet					●	●												●		
Conferences	●	●			●	●			●	●	●	●	●	●	●	●			●	●
Billiards/snooker											●							●		

Page No / Hotels:

152 Scafelll Hotel, Nr. Keswick
153 The Swan Hotel, Newby Bridge
154 Sharrow Bay Contry House Hotel, Ullswater
156 Old Church Hotel, watermillock
157 Cedar Manor Hotel, Windermere
159 Langdale Chase Hotel, Windermere
160 Lindeth Fell Hoel, Bowness-on-Windermere
161 Linthwaite House Hotel, Windermere
162 Miller Howe, Windermere
163 Old Vicarage Country House Hotel, Witherslack

LANCASHIRE
165 Chadwick Hotel, Lytham St Annes

GREATER MANCHESTER
166 Meridien Victoria & Albert Hotel, Manchester

Yorkshire & the North East
NORTHUMBERLAND
173 Waren House, Bambergh

NORTH YORKSHIRE
174 Aldwark Manor Golf Hotel, Nr. York
175 Balmoral Hotel, Harrogate
177 Feversham Arms Hotel, Helmsley
176 Stone House, Hawes
179 Lastingham Grange Hotel, Kirkbymoorside
180 Judges Lodging Hotel, York

WALES
GWENT
186 St Mellons Hotel, Castleton

(Hotels not listed have not informed us of sporting/conference facilities)

Column headings:
- Pitch n putt. Play area
- Art gallery
- Gliding, grass ski-ing
- Hang gliding nearby
- Stalking by arrangement
- Bicycles, beautician

GWYNEDD
188 Trefeddian Hotel, Aberdovey
189 Bontddu Hall Hotel, Nr. Dolgellau
190 Borthwnog Hall, Nr. Dolgellau

MONMOUTHSHIRE
192 Glen-Yr-Afon House, Usk

PEMBROKESHIRE
185 Stone Hall, Haverfordwest
193 St Brides Hotel, Saundersfoot
194 Warpool Court Hotel, St David's

POWYS
195 Gliffaes Country House Hotel, Nr. Crickhowell

SCOTLAND
ABERDEENSHIRE
203a Ardoe House, Aberdeen
203b Maryculter House, Aberdeen
204a Balgonie Country House Hotel, Ballater
204b Thainstone House, Inverurie

ARGYLL & BUTE
205 Killiechronan House, Isle of Mull
206 Stonefield Castle Hotel, Tarbert
207 The Manor House, Oban
208a Dungallon House Hotel, Oban

DUMFRIES & GALLOWAY
209 Cairndale Hotel & Leisure Club, Dumfries
210b Queen's Hotel, Lockerbie
211 Moffat House Hotel, Moffat
210c Corsemalzie House Hotel, Newton Stewart

EAST LOTHIAN
212 Greywalls Hotel, Gullane

FIFE
213 The Woodside Hotel, Aberdour

Page No.	Other	Watersports	Tennis	Swimming pool	Squash/badminton	Shooting	Sea/river bathing	Sauna/solarium	Sailing/boating	Riding	Massage	Jogging track	Jacuzzi/whirlpool	Indoor games	Golf	Gym/fitness centre	Fishing	Croquet	Conferences	Billiards/snooker
214a Balbirnie House, Glenrothes					○	○				○					●			●	●	●
HIGHLAND																				
215 Rosedale Hotel, Isle of Skye			○				●		●						○		✪			
216 Eddrachilles Hotel, Scourie									●								●			
NORTH AYRSHIRE																				
217c Montgreenan Mansion House, Kilwinning	Putting green. Golf practice		●															●		●
PERTH & KINROSS																				
218 Stakis Dunkeld House, Dunkeld			●	●		●		●		✪			●	●	○	●	●	●	●	●
220a Ardeonaig Hotel, South Loch Tay					●			●	○					●		●		●		
219 Dalmunzie House Hotel, Spittal of Glenshee	Ski-ing nearby		●			●									●		●		●	
SCOTTISH BORDERS																				
220b Peebles Hydro Hotel, Peebles			●	○	●			●		●	●	●	●	●	○	●	●		●	●
STIRLINGSHIRE																			●	
221b Forest Hills Hotel, Aberfoyle		●	●	○	●	●	●	●	●	○	●	●	●	●	○	●	●	●	●	●
222a Inchyra Grange, Falkirk			●	○				●		○	●				○	●			●	
WEST LOTHIAN																				
222b Houstoun House Hotel, Uphall	Beautician. Dance studio		●	○				●		○	●				○	●		●	●	
CHANNEL ISLANDS																				
228 Hotel Bella Luce, Guernsey				●				●											●	
229 Duke of Richmond Hotel, Guernsey				●																
230 St Pierre Park Hotel, Guernsey	Crazy golf	●	●	●	○	○		●	○	○	●	●	●	●	●	●	○	●	●	●
231 Old Government House Hotel, Guernsey		○	○	●	○			○		○	○				○	○	○	○	●	○
232 The White House, Herm			●	●			●		●								●	●		
233 The Moorings Hotel & Restaurant, Jersey		●	●	●					●	●					●		●			
234 The Atlantic Hotel, Jersey			●	●			○	●							○	●			●	
235 Hotel de France, Jersey		○	○	●	●			●	○	○	●		○		○	●			●	
236 The Lobster Pot, Jersey	Mountain bikes							○		○					○					
237 Hotel Petit Champ, Sark	Putting green		○	●										○			○			○

(Hotels not listed have not informed us of their sporting/conference facilities)

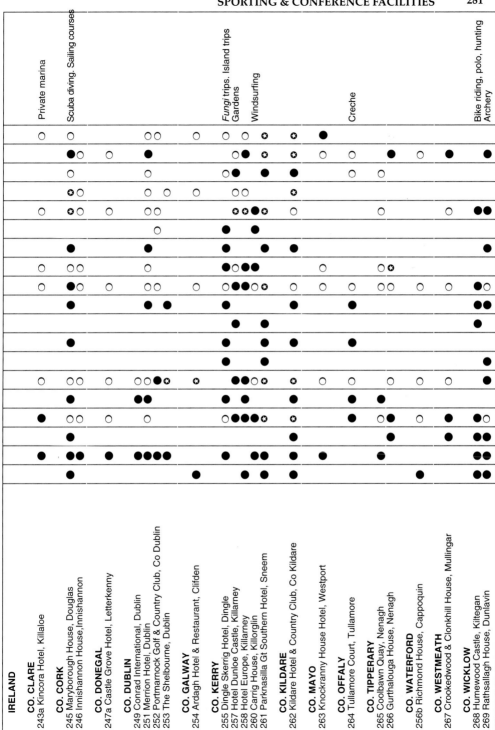

Facility columns (left to right): Private marina · Scuba diving. Sailing courses · *Fungi* trips. Island trips · Gardens · Windsurfing · Creche · Bike riding, polo, hunting · Archery

IRELAND

CO. CLARE
243a Kincora Hotel, Killaloe

CO. CORK
245 Maryborough House, Douglas
246 Innishannon House, Innishannon

CO. DONEGAL
247a Castle Grove Hotel, Letterkenny

CO. DUBLIN
249 Conrad International, Dublin
251 Merrion Hotel, Dublin
252 Portmarnock Golf & Country Club, Co Dublin
253 The Shelbourne, Dublin

CO. GALWAY
254 Ardagh Hotel & Restaurant, Clifden

CO. KERRY
255 Dingle Skerrig Hotel, Dingle
257 Hotel Dunloe Castle, Killarney
258 Hotel Europe, Killarney
260 Carrig House, Killorglin
261 Parknasilla Gt Southern Hotel, Sneem

CO. KILDARE
262 Kildare Hotel & Country Club, Co Kildare

CO. MAYO
263 Knockranny House Hotel, Westport

CO. OFFALY
264 Tullamore Court, Tullamore

CO. TIPPERARY
265 Coolbawn Quay, Nenagh
266 Gurthalouga House, Nenagh

CO. WATERFORD
256b Richmond House, Cappoquin

CO. WESTMEATH
267 Crookedwood & Clonkhill House, Mullingar

CO. WICKLOW
268 Humewood Castle, Kiltegan
269 Rathsallagh House, Dunlavin

LOCATION INDEX
ENGLAND

THE WEST COUNTRY

CHANNEL ISLANDS

IRELAND

Co. Clare
Killaloe   Kincora Hall   243a

Co. Cork
Bantry   Seaview House   243b
Clonakilty   Emmet Hotel   244
Douglas   Maryborough House   245
Innishannon   Innishannon House Hotel   246

Co. Donegal
Letterkenny   Castle Grove Hotel   247a

Co. Londonderry
Limavady   Streeve Hill   247b

Co. Dublin
Dublin   Beaufort House   248
Dublin   Conrad International   249
Dublin   Merrion Hall   250
Dublin   Merrion Hotel   251
Co Dublin   Portmarnock Golf & Country Club   252
Dublin   The Shelbourne Hotel   253

Co. Galway
Clifden   Ardagh Hotel & Restaurant   254

Co. Kerry
Dingle   Dingle Skellig Hotel   255
Kenmare   The Rosegarden   256a
Killarney   Hotel Dunloe Castle   257
Killarney   Hotel Europe   258
Killorglin   Ard-na-Sithe Hotel   259
Killorglin   Carrig House   260
Sneem   Parknasilla Great Southern Hotel   261

Co. Kildare
Straffan   The Kildare Hotel & Country Club   262

Co. Mayo
Westport   Knockranny House Hotel   263

Co Offaly
Tullamore   Tullamore Court   264

Co. Tipperary
Nenagh   Coolbawn Quay   265
Nenagh   Gurthalouga House   266

Co. Waterford
Cappoquin   Richmond House   256b

Co. Westmeath
Mullingar   Crookedwood & Clonkhill House   268

Co. Wicklow
Kiltegan   Humewood Castle   268
Dunlavin   Rathsallagh House   269

Signpost Approved Partners/Other Advertisers

Win a weekend* in a luxury SIGNPOST Country House Hotel!

*Two nights for two people, Bed and Breakfast

For a chance of winning a FREE weekend in a luxury SIGNPOST Country House Hotel for two people, just send us in your review of a hotel which you consider to be suitable for inclusion in SIGNPOST - the 2000 Millennium edition - and, if the hotel is inspected, meets our criteria and appears in our next edition, you will have a chance of winning a free weekend. 20 runners up will receive a second copy of SIGNPOST free of charge. Remember that it is unusual for us to include a chain hotel and that most Signpost hotels are privately owned and run. The hotel can be anywhere in the British Isles. *Use the space below for your review, which should not exceed 200 words, and continue on a separate sheet if necessary.*

I have stayed in the following hotel which I consider suitable for inclusion in the next edition of SIGNPOST:

Name of Hotel

Address

My review

Please see overleaf for conditions, tie-breaker and address panel.

Conditions

1. This competition is not open to employees of hotels reviewed
in this book, nor to employees or agents of Priory Publications Ltd,
W Foulsham & Co Ltd, Pelican Publishing Co, USA, nor to travel agents.

2. This form must be returned to Priory Publications Ltd
by 30th June 1999.

3. Priory Publications Ltd reserve the right to choose the hotel
at which the weekend is to be spent. The month of August is excluded.
The prize will not have a value of less than £200 but money
may not be claimed in lieu. The weekend must be taken during 1999.

4. The first twenty runners-up
will receive a FREE second copy of this guidebook.

5. The publisher's decision is final.
It is regretted that no correspondence concerning
returned forms can be entered into.

Cut out and send to SIGNPOST/Premier Hotels Competition Dept at Priory Publications Ltd.,
FREEPOST NH0504, Brackley, Northamptonshire NN13 5BR, UK *(No stamp required within UK)*

Name   Signature

Address

                                         Date

Tie breaker: *I prefer SIGNPOST/Premier Hotels of Great Britain and Ireland to other hotel guides because* . .

(20 words max.)

£5 VOUCHER

£5 off accommodation when this voucher is presented at establishments with V printed by their prices in Signpost 1999 *(see over for conditions)*

GUIDE TO PREMIER HOTELS AND ACCOMMODATION IN GREAT BRITAIN AND IRELAND

Signpost

SELECTED PREMIER ESTABLISHMENT 1999

£5 VOUCHER

£5 off accommodation when this voucher is presented at establishments with V printed by their prices in Signpost 1999 *(see over for conditions)*

GUIDE TO PREMIER HOTELS AND ACCOMMODATION IN GREAT BRITAIN AND IRELAND

Signpost

SELECTED PREMIER ESTABLISHMENT 1999

£5 VOUCHER

£5 off accommodation when this voucher is presented at establishments with V printed by their prices in Signpost 1999 *(see over for conditions)*

GUIDE TO PREMIER HOTELS AND ACCOMMODATION IN GREAT BRITAIN AND IRELAND

Signpost

SELECTED PREMIER ESTABLISHMENT 1999

£5 VOUCHER

£5 off accommodation when this voucher is presented at establishments with V printed by their prices in Signpost 1999 *(see over for conditions)*

GUIDE TO PREMIER HOTELS AND ACCOMMODATION IN GREAT BRITAIN AND IRELAND

Signpost

SELECTED PREMIER ESTABLISHMENT 1999

£5 VOUCHER

£5 off accommodation when this voucher is presented at establishments with V printed by their prices in Signpost 1999 *(see over for conditions)*

GUIDE TO PREMIER HOTELS AND ACCOMMODATION IN GREAT BRITAIN AND IRELAND

Signpost

SELECTED PREMIER ESTABLISHMENT 1999

£5 VOUCHER

£5 off accommodation when this voucher is presented at establishments with V printed by their prices in Signpost 1999 *(see over for conditions)*

GUIDE TO PREMIER HOTELS AND ACCOMMODATION IN GREAT BRITAIN AND IRELAND

Signpost

SELECTED PREMIER ESTABLISHMENT 1999

£5 VOUCHER

£5 off accommodation when this voucher is presented at establishments with V printed by their prices in Signpost 1999 *(see over for conditions)*

GUIDE TO PREMIER HOTELS AND ACCOMMODATION IN GREAT BRITAIN AND IRELAND

Signpost

SELECTED PREMIER ESTABLISHMENT 1999

£5 VOUCHER

£5 off accommodation when this voucher is presented at establishments with V printed by their prices in Signpost 1999 *(see over for conditions)*

GUIDE TO PREMIER HOTELS AND ACCOMMODATION IN GREAT BRITAIN AND IRELAND

Signpost

SELECTED PREMIER ESTABLISHMENT 1999

CONDITIONS

1. £5 off vouchers are only accepted for hotel accommodation at full tariff rate for the room and season, not against already discounted tariffs such as *Bargain Breaks*.
2. Only one voucher per person or party per stay can be presented.
3. Hotels should be informed when a booking is made that a Signpost £5 discount voucher will be presented in part payment.
4. Only Signpost hotels with Ⓥ printed by their prices will accept these vouchers.
5. A copy of Signpost 1999 must be produced when this voucher is used.
6. This voucher may not be accepted at Christmas, Easter or other times of peak occupancy in individual hotels.
7. This voucher is valid until 31st December 1999.

CONDITIONS

1. £5 off vouchers are only accepted for hotel accommodation at full tariff rate for the room and season, not against already discounted tariffs such as *Bargain Breaks*.
2. Only one voucher per person or party per stay can be presented.
3. Hotels should be informed when a booking is made that a Signpost £5 discount voucher will be presented in part payment.
4. Only Signpost hotels with Ⓥ printed by their prices will accept these vouchers.
5. A copy of Signpost 1999 must be produced when this voucher is used.
6. This voucher may not be accepted at Christmas, Easter or other times of peak occupancy in individual hotels.
7. This voucher is valid until 31st December 1999.

CONDITIONS

1. £5 off vouchers are only accepted for hotel accommodation at full tariff rate for the room and season, not against already discounted tariffs such as *Bargain Breaks*.
2. Only one voucher per person or party per stay can be presented.
3. Hotels should be informed when a booking is made that a Signpost £5 discount voucher will be presented in part payment.
4. Only Signpost hotels with Ⓥ printed by their prices will accept these vouchers.
5. A copy of Signpost 1999 must be produced when this voucher is used.
6. This voucher may not be accepted at Christmas, Easter or other times of peak occupancy in individual hotels.
7. This voucher is valid until 31st December 1999.

CONDITIONS

1. £5 off vouchers are only accepted for hotel accommodation at full tariff rate for the room and season, not against already discounted tariffs such as *Bargain Breaks*.
2. Only one voucher per person or party per stay can be presented.
3. Hotels should be informed when a booking is made that a Signpost £5 discount voucher will be presented in part payment.
4. Only Signpost hotels with Ⓥ printed by their prices will accept these vouchers.
5. A copy of Signpost 1999 must be produced when this voucher is used.
6. This voucher may not be accepted at Christmas, Easter or other times of peak occupancy in individual hotels.
7. This voucher is valid until 31st December 1999.

CONDITIONS

1. £5 off vouchers are only accepted for hotel accommodation at full tariff rate for the room and season, not against already discounted tariffs such as *Bargain Breaks*.
2. Only one voucher per person or party per stay can be presented.
3. Hotels should be informed when a booking is made that a Signpost £5 discount voucher will be presented in part payment.
4. Only Signpost hotels with Ⓥ printed by their prices will accept these vouchers.
5. A copy of Signpost 1999 must be produced when this voucher is used.
6. This voucher may not be accepted at Christmas, Easter or other times of peak occupancy in individual hotels.
7. This voucher is valid until 31st December 1999.

CONDITIONS

1. £5 off vouchers are only accepted for hotel accommodation at full tariff rate for the room and season, not against already discounted tariffs such as *Bargain Breaks*.
2. Only one voucher per person or party per stay can be presented.
3. Hotels should be informed when a booking is made that a Signpost £5 discount voucher will be presented in part payment.
4. Only Signpost hotels with Ⓥ printed by their prices will accept these vouchers.
5. A copy of Signpost 1999 must be produced when this voucher is used.
6. This voucher may not be accepted at Christmas, Easter or other times of peak occupancy in individual hotels.
7. This voucher is valid until 31st December 1999.

CONDITIONS

1. £5 off vouchers are only accepted for hotel accommodation at full tariff rate for the room and season, not against already discounted tariffs such as *Bargain Breaks*.
2. Only one voucher per person or party per stay can be presented.
3. Hotels should be informed when a booking is made that a Signpost £5 discount voucher will be presented in part payment.
4. Only Signpost hotels with Ⓥ printed by their prices will accept these vouchers.
5. A copy of Signpost 1999 must be produced when this voucher is used.
6. This voucher may not be accepted at Christmas, Easter or other times of peak occupancy in individual hotels.
7. This voucher is valid until 31st December 1999.

CONDITIONS

1. £5 off vouchers are only accepted for hotel accommodation at full tariff rate for the room and season, not against already discounted tariffs such as *Bargain Breaks*.
2. Only one voucher per person or party per stay can be presented.
3. Hotels should be informed when a booking is made that a Signpost £5 discount voucher will be presented in part payment.
4. Only Signpost hotels with Ⓥ printed by their prices will accept these vouchers.
5. A copy of Signpost 1999 must be produced when this voucher is used.
6. This voucher may not be accepted at Christmas, Easter or other times of peak occupancy in individual hotels.
7. This voucher is valid until 31st December 1999.

If you have stayed in an hotel which is not yet featured in SIGNPOST and you think it merits an inspection for possible future inclusion, please send one of the forms below in confidence (no stamp necessary) to Signpost, Priory Publications Ltd, FREEPOST NH0504, Brackley, Northamptonshire NN13 5BR

I would like to recommend the under-mentioned hotel for possible inclusion in the next edition of SIGNPOST - the premier hotel guide to the British Isles.

My name_____

My address_____

_____

Name of hotel_____

_____

_____

City/Town_____

_____

I certify that I have no connection of any sort with the management or owners of the above hotel

Signed_____Date_____

✂ —

GUEST RECOMMENDATION FORM

I would like to recommend the under-mentioned hotel for possible inclusion in the next edition of SIGNPOST - the premier hotel guide to the British Isles.

My name_____

My address_____

_____

Name of hotel_____

_____

_____

City/Town_____

_____

I certify that I have no connection of any sort with the management or owners of the above hotel

Signed_____Date_____

✂ —

GUEST RECOMMENDATION FORM

I would like to recommend the under-mentioned hotel for possible inclusion in the next edition of SIGNPOST - the premier hotel guide to the British Isles.

My name_____

My address_____

_____

Name of hotel_____

_____

_____

City/Town_____

_____

I certify that I have no connection of any sort with the management or owners of the above hotel

Signed_____Date_____

GUEST REPORT FORM

Cut out and send the enclosed form (no stamp necessary) to Signpost, Priory Publications Ltd, FREEPOST NH0504, Brackley, Northamptonshire NN13 5BR

I have stayed in the below mentioned hotel, recommended by SIGNPOST, and would make the following comments: *(Continue overleaf if necessary)*

NAME OF HOTEL _____ TOWN _____

REPORT _____

_____

_____

_____

_____

I certify that I have no connection with the management or owners of the hotel and I understand that my report will be treated in the strictest condidence.

Name:...Date.......................................

Address:.. SIG

--------------------✂--

GUEST REPORT FORM

Cut out and send the enclosed form (no stamp necessary) to Signpost, Priory Publications Ltd, FREEPOST NH0504, Brackley, Northamptonshire NN13 5BR

I have stayed in the below mentioned hotel, recommended by SIGNPOST, and would make the following comments: *(Continue overleaf if necessary)*

NAME OF HOTEL _____ TOWN _____

REPORT _____

_____

_____

_____

I certify that I have no connection with the management or owners of the hotel and I understand that my report will be treated in the strictest condidence.

Name:...Date.......................................

Address:.. SIG96/2

MAPS

The following section contains road maps of the British Isles and a plan of Central London.

Numbers in black ovals denote page numbers of SIGNPOST hotels. Turn to these pages for full details of hotels in areas where you are looking for accommodation.

Only major roads are shown and we therefore recommend that travellers also use a comprehensive road atlas when travelling "off the beaten track". Of course we hope that our individual hotel location maps will help.

298

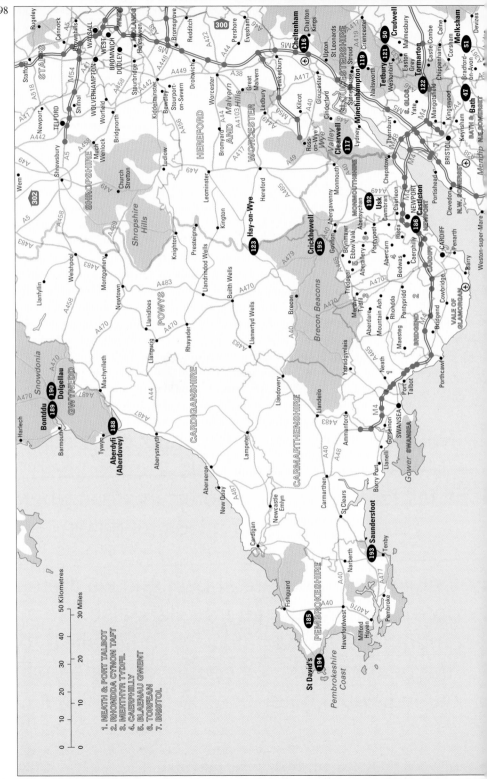

1. NEATH & PORT TALBOT
2. RHONDDA CYNON TAFF
3. MERTHYR TYDFIL
4. CAERPHILLY
5. BLAENAU GWENT
6. TORFAEN
7. BRISTOL

299

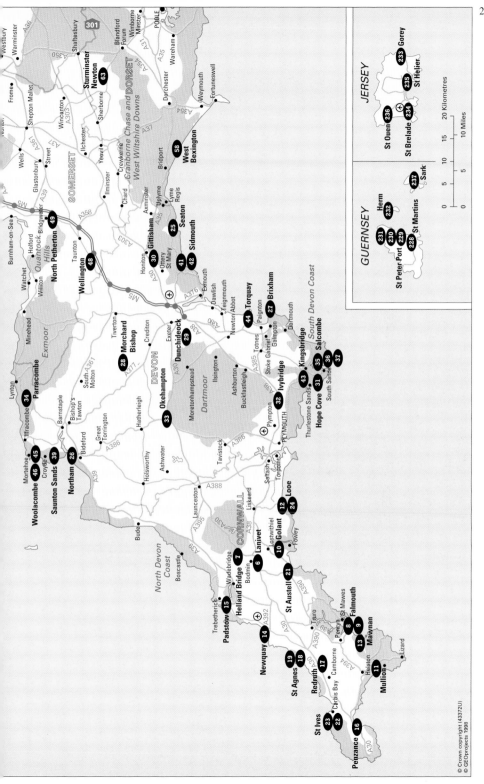

301

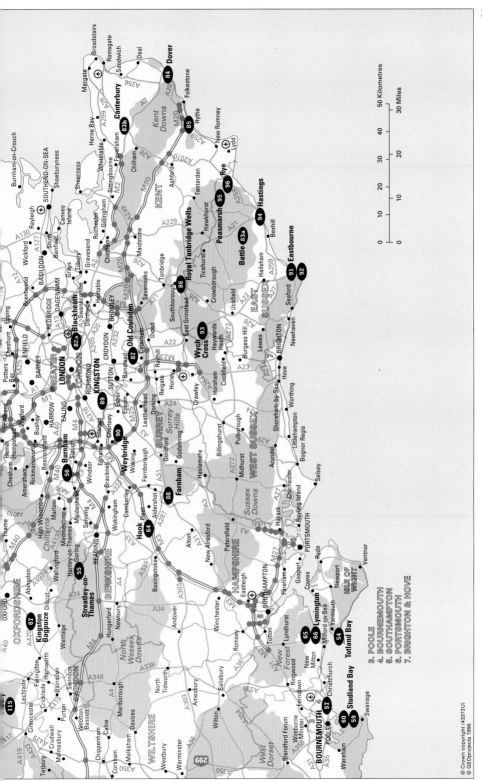

© Crown copyright (43372U)
© GEOprojects 1998

3. POOLE
4. BOURNEMOUTH
5. SOUTHAMPTON
6. PORTSMOUTH
7. BRIGHTON & HOVE

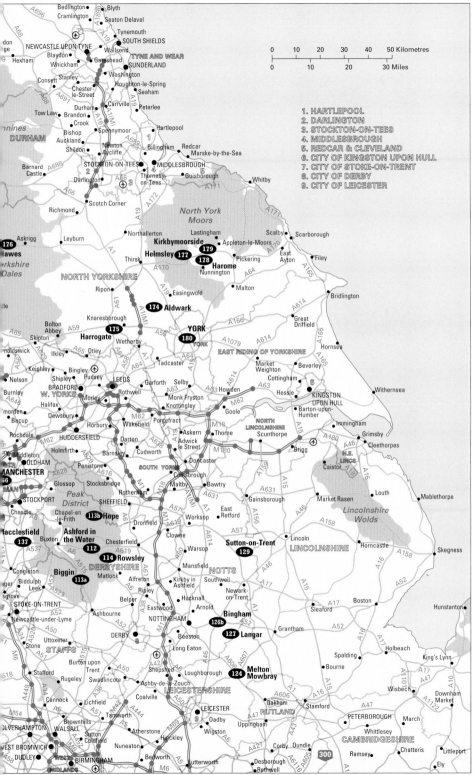

Scale: 0 10 20 30 40 50 Kilometres
0 10 20 30 Miles

1. HARTLEPOOL
2. DARLINGTON
3. STOCKTON-ON-TEES
4. MIDDLESBROUGH
5. REDCAR & CLEVELAND
6. CITY OF KINGSTON UPON HULL
7. CITY OF STOKE-ON-TRENT
8. CITY OF DERBY
9. CITY OF LEICESTER

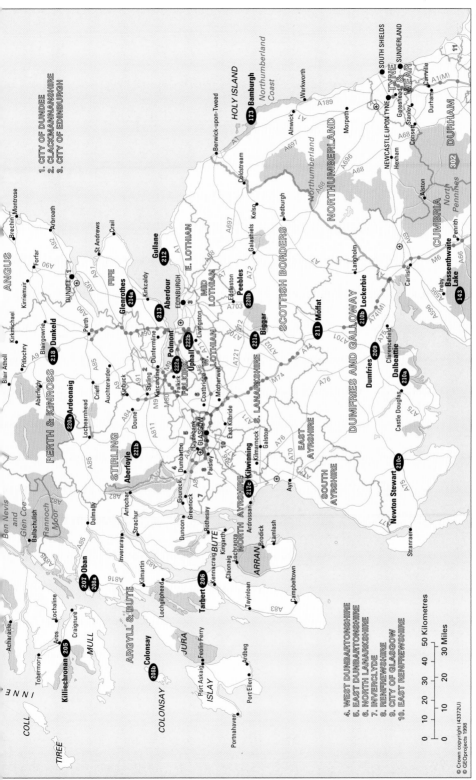

305

1. CITY OF DUNDEE
2. CLACKMANNANSHIRE
3. CITY OF EDINBURGH

4. WEST DUNBARTONSHIRE
5. EAST DUNBARTONSHIRE
6. NORTH LANARKSHIRE
7. INVERCLYDE
8. RENFREWSHIRE
9. CITY OF GLASGOW
10. EAST RENFREWSHIRE

0   10   20   30   40   50 Kilometres
0   10   20   30 Miles

© Crown copyright (43372U)
© GEOprojects 1998

CALEDONIAN ROAD

PENTONVILLE ROAD

ROSEBERY AVE

FARRINGTON RD

KINGS CROSS ROAD

GRAY'S INN ROAD

HIGH HOLBORN

The Howard Hotel

STRAND

VICTORIA EMBANKMENT

Somerset House

78

YORK WAY

A5200

YORK WAY

GRAY'S INN ROAD

THEOBALD'S ROAD

HIGH HOLBORN

Kingsway Hall Hotel

79

KINGSWAY

King's Cross Station

PANCRAS ROAD

EUSTON ROAD

SOUTHAMPTON ROW

RUSSELL SQUARE

Covent Garden

ST PANCRAS WAY

St Pancras Station

EVERSHOT ROAD

Euston Station

GOWER STREET

WOBURN PLACE

British Museum

OXFORD ST

CHARING CROSS RD

National Gallery

ROYAL COLLEGE STREET

CAMDEN ST

HAMPSTEAD ROAD

TOTTENHAM COURT RD

CAMDEN HIGH ST

ALBANY STREET

PORTLAND PLACE

REGENT ST

PARKWAY

REGENT ST

OXFORD STREET

Regent's Park

PORTLAND PLACE

WIGMORE STREET

OXFORD STREET

Primrose Hill

Boating Lake

BAKER STREET

The Montcalm

80

PARK

PRINCE ALBERT ROAD

PARK ROAD

MARYLEBONE ROAD

GLOUCESTER PLACE

SEYMOUR STREET

EDGWARE ROAD

The Langorf Hotel 1.75 km

82b

EDGWARE ROAD

SUSSEX GARDENS

BAYSWATER ROAD

WELLINGTON ROAD

ST JOHN'S WOOD ROAD

EDGWARE ROAD

Paddington Station

PRAED STREET

FINCHLEY ROAD

MAIDA VALE

BISHOP'S BRIDGE ROAD

EASTBOURNE TERR

Pembridge Court Hotel 600m

81

MAIDA VALE

HARROW ROAD

KENNINGTON ROAD

BRIXTON ROAD

A4

WATERLOO RD

WESTMINSTER BRIDGE RD

Waterloo Station

WATERLOO ROAD

YORK ROAD

LAMBETH ROAD

LAMBETH PALACE ROAD

CLAPHAM ROAD

KENNINGTON ROAD

HARLEYFORD ROAD

RIVER

Royal Festival Hall

VICTORIA EMBANKMENT

WESTMINSTER BRIDGE

ALBERT EMBANKMENT

SOUTH LAMBETH ROAD

WANDSWORTH ROAD

A3036

Charing Cross Station

WHITEHALL

Horse Guards Parade

Houses of Parliament

LAMBETH BRIDGE

MILLBANK

MILLBANK

VAUXHALL BRIDGE

VAUXHALL ROAD

GROSVENOR ROAD

NINE ELMS LANE

BATTERSEA PARK ROAD

St James's Palace

St James's Park

Westminster Abbey

VICTORIA STREET

BRIDGE ROAD

BELGRAVE ROAD

GROSVENOR ROAD

PALL MALL

Green Park

Buckingham Palace

The Royal Mews

GROSVENOR PL

Buckingham Palace Gardens

VAUXHALL BRIDGE ROAD

Victoria Station

ECCLESTON ST

PIMLICO ROAD

BUCKINGHAM PALACE ROAD

CHELSEA BRIDGE ROAD

CHELSEA BR

QUEENSTOWN RD

PICCADILLY

HOBART PL

Victoria Coach Station

KINGS ROAD

LOWER SLOANE STREET

CHELSEA EMBANKMENT

RIVER THAMES

Battersea Park

Boating Lake

KNIGHTSBRIDGE

SLOANE STREET

ALBERT BRIDGE

ALBERT BRIDGE ROAD

The Serpentine

KNIGHTSBRIDGE

BROMPTON ROAD

KINGS ROAD

BATTERSEA BRIDGE RD

Kensington Gardens

Round Pond

Kensington Palace

Royal Albert Hall

Science Museum

KENSINGTON ROAD

CROMWELL ROAD

FULHAM ROAD

OLD BROMPTON ROAD

KINGS ROAD

The Gallery Hotel

76 75 — The Gainsborough Hotel

77 Harrington Hall Hotel

74 The Cranley Hotel

REDCLIFFE GDNS

EDITH GROVE

FINBOROUGH ROAD

FULHAM RD

KINGS RD

800 Metres
880 Yards

400

440

© GEOprojects (UK) Ltd